THE STONE AGES

IN NORTH BRITAIN AND IRELAND

THE STONE AGES

IN NORTH BRITAIN AND IRELAND

BY

THE REV. FREDERICK SMITH

WITH AN INTRODUCTION BY

AUGUSTUS H. KEANE LL.D. F.R.G.S.

LATE VICE-PRESIDENT OF THE ROYAL ANTHROPOLOGICAL INSTITUTE

ILLUSTRATED BY OVER FIVE HUNDRED
DRAWINGS OF TYPICAL SPECIMENS

"Contempt, prior to examination, keeps men in ignorance."—PALEY

"Ἄγει δὲ πρὸς φῶς τὴν ἀλήθειαν χρόνος."—MENANDER

BLACKIE & SON LIMITED LONDON
GLASGOW DUBLIN AND BOMBAY
MCMIX

Dedication

DURING forty years many friends come and go. Many have come to the Author, have bidden him God speed in this work and have passed away. He would, with great affection, dedicate this volume to the memory of several of his lost friends, and to several who still are happily within possible sight and touch :

TO

The late Sir THOMAS MONCREIFFE, Bart., sometime President of the P.S.N.S., Perth.

,,   Colonel H. M. DRUMMOND HAY, C.M.Z.S., M.B.O.U., etc.

,,   F. BUCHANAN WHITE, M.D., F.L.S., etc., Founder and Editor of *The Scottish Naturalist*, Author of *Flora of Perthshire*, etc.

,,   Mr. JOHN YOUNG, C.E., Perth.

Friends in many a Scientific Excursion and Members with himself of the Perthshire " Alpine Club."

TO

The late Captain the Hon. ARTHUR HAY DRUMMOND, R.N., to whom the Author was privileged for some years to be Chaplain at Cromlix.

,,   The Rev. A. CORNELIUS HALLEN, M.A. (Cantab.), F.S.A.Scot., Founder and Editor of *The Scottish Antiquary*.

,,   Mr. ANDREW COATES, Pitcullen, Perth.

,,   Mr. JOHN PULLAR, Bridge-of-Allan.

AND TO

The Rev. OSMOND FISHER, M.A. (Cantab.), F.G.S., etc., who encouraged the Author in his research work while yet a lad, and, after forty years, has in the same matter been of great service.

Professor J. R. AINSWORTH DAVIS, M.A. (Cantab.), Principal of Royal Agricultural College, Cirencester.

The Rev. (Ex-Moderator) WILLIAM BLAIR, M.A., D.D., Dunblane.

ERSKINE BEVERIDGE, LL.D., F.R.S.E., Author of *Coll and Tiree*, etc.

Mr. HENRY COATES, F.R.S.E., President of Perthshire Soc. Nat. Science.

AND TO

AUGUSTUS H. KEANE, LL.D., etc., to whom the Author, in the preparation and issue of this volume, will ever be deeply indebted.

Synopsis of Contents

CHAPTER I

THE ORIGIN AND SCOPE OF THIS WORK

CHAPTER II

ON THE TRAIL IN NORTH BRITAIN

CHAPTER III

A COMPARATIVE STUDY OF RELICS

CHAPTER IV

A COMPARATIVE STUDY OF RELICS (*continued*)

CHAPTER V

A GREAT HUNTER IN CALEDON

CHAPTER VI

OUT OF THE PAST

CHAPTER VII

OUT FROM THE GLACIERS

CHAPTER VIII

OUT FROM THE GLACIERS (*continued*)

CHAPTER IX

THE GLACIAL STORY OF SOUTHERN ENGLAND

CHAPTER X

DOMESTIC FORMS (*Scotland*)

"Domestic" forms alone warrant of Palæo man in Scotland—Domestic implements hitherto scarcely recognised—Penalty paid for vicarious "collecting"—Scottish domestic forms suggest renewal of search in English gravels—Contents of English gravels complement of Scottish finds—Features peculiar to both areas—Suggestive of same people—Yet Scottish forms have characteristic features—Of better form and style than those of the South—*Raison d'être* of certain Scottish attributes—"Limitations" of flint elaborator—The author learned in Scotland what to expect in the English gravels—False views of what planes of cleavage, bedding, etc., are responsible for—Apologists of natural origin of these forms—Certain common yet unrecognised forms—Of simple but unmistakable elaboration—"Mullers," "rubbers," "grinders"—Occur in all Pleistocene and some more modern deposits—They are ubiquitous—Illustrations and discussion of "mullers"—From ancient river or delta deposits—From the boulder-clay—From present river-bed and seashore—Glaciated examples—Flint examples from S. E. coast of Scotland . . . .

CHAPTER XI

DOMESTIC FORMS (*England*)

Anticipation of the Scottish "mullers" in English deposits thirty-six years ago—A seeker of "organisms" in flints—Renewed search in English gravels—Unlooked-for corroboration of the Scottish relics—Proof that Scottish finds are Palæolithic—Examples from "coarse gravel of the hills"—From Colchester—Glaciated items—From Mitcham, Streatham, Norbury, Croydon—Much evidence for brief period of search ?—Where and how search made—"Gravelled" roads in England *versus* "metalled" roads in Scotland—Investigation more easy in England than in Scotland—Further examples from Mitcham and Croydon, etc.—Contrived *natural* handles—Small "scrapers" from Palæo deposits—English theory of "muller" forms—Concave facets and mullers—Possible bone-crushers—If "skin-curers," there must have been skins—Next group of implements prove to be skin-providers, "flayers"—Further specimens from Farnham, Ashe, and other places in Surrey . . . .

CHAPTER XII

PALÆOLITHIC MAN'S COMMON TASK

Effect of manual labour upon implements—"Simplest form of domestic (?) implements—These forms imply existence and use of other domestic forms—Skin-curers imply use of knives and flayers and offensive weapons—Where *mullers* are found *weapons* occur—Palæo man's "hall-mark"—Why mullers more common than knives—Mullers, knives, and boulder-clays—*Weapons* alone convey limited aspect of the man—*Domestic* forms vouchers of humanising traits—A "daily round and common task"—A never-ending occupation—An appreciable state of civilisation before last glacial inception—Early "puzzling" Scottish fabrications—Descriptions of same—FLAYERS !—knives and flayers—Modern instance of knife-making and knife-using—Picture of ancient man's procedure—A "flake"—When *flayers* were needed, sharp (knife) edges were chipped away—Fate of *such* knives in Scotland—Simplest forms of flayers—Examples of flayers and knives from Dalmuir "workshop"—A *section* from a pebble, study of—

CHAPTER XIII

SOME PALÆOLITHIC PUZZLES

CHAPTER XIV

HANDLES

CHAPTER XVIII

NEOLITHIC FORMS IN PALÆOLITHIC TIMES

CHAPTER XIX

NEOLITHIC FORMS IN PALÆOLITHIC TIMES (*continued*)

CHAPTER XX

GLACIAL MAN IN HIBERNIA

APPENDIX TO CHAPTER XX

"Survivals from the Palæolithic Age among Irish Neolithic Implements"

CHAPTER XXI

MISCELLANEA

APPENDIX

NOTE I.—"THE GREAT MAMMALIA" IN SCOTLAND

NOTE II.—FURTHER RESULTS FROM IRELAND

Introduction

It is a singular fact that in the early records of anthropological studies some of the most distinguished names have been Anglican and Roman Catholic clergymen, who appear not merely as enlightened followers in the wake of science, but as pioneers in this obscure field of research, and as zealous champions of the most advanced views regarding the antiquity of man. In England Dean Buckland startled the thinking public by announcing the discovery in 1821 of human relics in association with the remains of over seventy hyænas in the Kirkdale Cavern, Yorkshire, so that it was asked whether some antediluvian menagerie had broken loose in those parts. He was followed by the Rev. Mr. M'Enery, who in 1825 first drew attention to the "storehouse of antiquity" preserved beneath the stalagmite beds of Kent's Cave, and by the Rev. J. M. Mello, who led the way in the exploration of the no less famous Creswell caves, Derbyshire.

In France the Abbé Bourgeois is still remembered as one of the foremost champions of Tertiary man in Europe, and the first to recognise as human the still somewhat doubted eolithic flints extracted by him from the Miocene beds. of Thenay, near Pontleroy.

So now the Rev. Frederick Smith opens a new and wider chapter in the history of early man by extending the inquiry to the whole of the British Isles, and producing for the first time convincing evidence that both Scotland and Ireland were inhabited during the old Stone Age. His claim to have established this fact, against the inveterate prejudice and incredulity even of the most advanced British specialists, lies open before us, and demands a hearing. The time is past when his lifelong searches amid the boulder-clays, the river-drifts, the fluvial and marine deposits of North Britain could be disposed of with a smile or a sneer, and now that he has come forward with a frank appeal to the intelligence of all unprejudiced readers the least he is entitled to is that the appeal be taken into serious consideration and judged on its merits.

In order properly to estimate the full value of the results here set forth and amply illustrated by the deft hand of the author, it should be stated that he was in every way thoroughly equipped for his work : an expert palæontologist and stratigraphical geologist perfectly familiar with the lie of the land, and well acquainted with the various aspects of pre- and post-glacial formations, that is, of those deposits where the relics of ancient man might be expected to be found. And that it was no amateurish or arm-chair work, but everywhere carried on in the open air with an unflagging zeal and energy beyond all praise, the reader will readily infer from his own account of his *modus operandi*. Speaking of the ubiquitous presence of certain rude Palæoliths, he tells us (Chap. IX.) that "they occur in all Pleistocene deposits which I have had opportunity to examine ; they occur conspicuously in certain of the boulder-clays. They occur in the soils, but not everywhere ; they are found among the stones of the brook, in the pebble-beds of river-courses, and upon the seashores. I have followed the plough and picked them up. I have seen them thrown out from deep cuttings in the streets of cities ; I have gathered them from heaps which have been culled from the paths of mowers and reapers ; I have picked them up from what must have been a fireplace and work-shop of these ancient peoples, even in Scotland."

The plea of a man who can write thus is irresistible, and in my opinion his arguments will likewise be found irresistible. They tear up root and branch the narrow con-servative tree under which the leaders of the "orthodox" party—Cuvier, Owen, Virchow, and Evans, the "doubting

Thomas," as he was called by his foreign compeers—have hitherto taken shelter. And what a useless shelter these leafless trees have become, since the barriers of conservatism have now almost everywhere been broken down, and indubitable proofs of the presence of primitive man brought from the ends of the earth, not only from Caledonia and Hibernia, as here, but also from Somaliland, South Africa, Irania, East Asia, and South America. One or two recent instances may be mentioned to show that Mr. Smith is after all no great "innovator." At the Royal Society's Conversazione of May 1908, Mr. Henry Balfour exhibited a great number of Palæolithic finds collected by him all over the Zambesi basin, where relics of the Stone Ages had not hitherto been certified. "They were mostly of chalcedony, quartzite, and other minerals of the same kind [just as in Scotland], and present the same form as those found in the river-drifts of western Europe. Some of them bore a high polish, which the exhibitor thinks may be due to the action of sand containing silica,[1] and most were much water-worn; while he is able, from the geological formation of the strata in which they were found, to attribute to them an antiquity equalling anything previously assigned to human handiwork" (*Athenæum*, May 16, 1908).

In his "Recent Survey and Exploration in Seistan," on the Perso-Afghan frontier, in the very heart of Irania, Sir H. M'Mahon found not only some black pottery, which is the oldest known and "one of the first indications of dawning civilisation in primitive man," but also numerous "stone implements of the Palæolithic type," the presence of which had not previously been suspected in this part of the world. Some were of black volcanic rock, others of obsidian and agate, as in Scotland, and all seemed to have been chipped and otherwise manipulated

---

[1] This is quite in accordance with Mr. Smith's view that Neolithic *forms* were common in Palæo times, but were never intentionally polished, or only in so far as use may have given them a pseudo-polished aspect.

by the users, as if attempts had been made to fashion them to some useful purpose. Amongst them were spear-heads, knives, and rudely shaped axes, dating back to "many tens of thousands of years." The whole description, which may be seen in the *Geographical Journal* for September 1906, reads like an extract from one of Mr. Smith's graphic pages. The mention of the rude stone axes, which are here so fully dealt with, reminds us of the fact pointed out by Leo Frobenius, that this implement, of which there are three types, was "the characteristic tool of the Stone Age." See Figs. 340-42 in p. 436 of my English edition of *The Childhood of Man* (1908).

In far-off Korea are found, besides Palæolithic relics, numerous ancient monuments which look like duplicates of the European dolmens and cromlechs, as well as descendants of their Eurafrican builders, still characterised by their Caucasic features—white skin, light eyes, brown hair, full beard, and tall stature. Lastly, the range of Palæolithic man is now extended to South America, where Señor F. P. Outes has lately described no less than eight undoubted Palæolithic stations spread over a wide area in Patagonia (*La Edad de la Piedra en Patagonia*, Buenos Ayres, 1905).

Now, it may be asked, if primitive man could invade the New World, and penetrate to its utmost Austral extremity, what was to prevent him from crossing the border and ranging over North Britain? Here the *ipse dixit* of any number of shining lights cannot avail against hard facts, such as the abundant evidence of ancient relics and of now extinct Pliocene fauna, as described in this work. I have myself elsewhere shown that early man (*Homo Eurafricanus*) passed with this very fauna from North Africa into southern Europe, and spread thence over most if not all of the mainland. We have seen that he was found in association with the "hyæna beds" of Yorkshire and Derbyshire. Why not also with the elephant, the rhinoceros, and the other members of the same fauna in the Lothians? Two objections are advanced : first, that this fauna is not African, but Indian, having been specialised in the Siwalik uplands, whence it passed into Africa in comparatively late times ; second, that the great ice-cap of the glacial period opposed an insurmountable obstacle to the advance of the Eurafricans into North Britain. Both objections are groundless. Mr. Rudolf Martin has recently shown that the Indian origin of the African fauna, as hitherto assumed, is most probably a mistake, and that on the contrary these forms were specialised, not in the Siwalik Hills, but in Africa, as we now know was the case, for instance, with the ostrich (*Struthio karatheo-doris*), whose remains have been found in the Upper Miocene deposits of the island of Samos. Hence "the existence of such forms in India and southern Europe was due to a secondary immigration *from* Africa" (Meeting, Zoological Society, March 3, 1903).

The objection based on the great ice-sheet is constantly urged, yet has no weight at all once it is pointed out that there were not one but several successive glaciations separated one from the other by long inter-glacial intervals. It was during these intervals, during which favourable climatic con-ditions prevailed, that the great African mammalians reached North Britain, and it will now be for the dogmatic critics to show that these mammalians could not have been accom-panied by the contemporary Eurafricans, who had never-theless followed them from Mauritania all the way through Iberia and Gaul to Britain, as far north as Derbyshire and Yorkshire. After declaring that in his opinion the finest of all the palæoliths "are of inter- or pre-glacial origin," Mr. Smith throws down a challenge, and invites whoever asserts that the "Palæo-Neolithic" objects brought some sixty years ago from the Shannon are not artefacts but natural forms to show that they are such (Chap. XIX.). He can now repeat the challenge in another form, and ask the dogmatic sceptics to show that early man did not or could not follow the African fauna from the Yorkshire caves into the Lothians. If they cannot do this, then our author may claim to be numbered amongst the *beati possidentes*. All unbiassed observers will conclude that he holds the field.

Reference is incidentally made to the assumed hiatus, or break of continuity between the two Stone Ages, a hiatus which is still warmly upheld by most English observers at least for Britain, but which Mr. Smith is disposed to reject, while wisely declining to dogmatise on the subject. He makes no appeal, for instance, to certain dubious forms, such as Figs. 398 and 410, which might belong to either period, and thus serve to bridge over the gap. Much ingenuity is at the same time shown in his interpretation of these objects, which for him betray a transition, not from age to age, but from savage to domestic habits. Thus certain typical Palæo objects originally fashioned for war or the hunt would have been modified for household purposes, and although the hiatus itself is not formally discussed, the clearest possible distinction is drawn between the characteristic traits of the earlier and later implements.

Now comes the still warmly discussed question of the *eoliths*, those rudest relics of early man, which some hold to be antecedent to the palæoliths and to form tangible links between the savage and his anthropoid precursor, while others deny that they are of human workmanship, being merely natural forms roughly shaped by purely physical agencies. Here again our author maintains a reserved attitude, and speaks guardedly of these eolithic times, while Mr. Worthington Smith, once, I believe, their champion, now repudiates them. His opinion has justly very great weight on all subjects relating to human relics, and he now tells us in a recent number of *Man* that there are no such things as "eoliths," and that nine out of ten of the thousands sent to him for his consideration were nothing but natural flint fragments.

Now it so happens that the distinguished Belgian geologist, A. Rutot, has pursued the opposite course, and after long vehemently denying the human origin of the Tertiary eoliths lately found in Belgium, has at last admitted his error, and recognised them as true artefacts in as strong language as he had before rejected them. So it has ever been, and, as Dr. L. Reinhardt remarks, pioneers with new ideas in advance of the times have always been laughed at, and even persecuted where possible. But the more these objects are studied, the more their genuine character becomes apparent (*Der Mensch zur Eiszeit*, 1808, p. 31). A fresh illustration of this perennial truth has just been afforded during the building of a railway station at Aix-la-Chapelle, where some rude objects, at first regarded as ordinary stones, are now believed to be stone implements, in fact eoliths (*Athenæum*, Oct. 10, 1908). The reader will here be reminded of the grudging admission made by the late Sir John Evans that some of the flints produced by Mr. Lewis Abbott from the Cromer forest-bed "were probably made by man" (*Natural Science*, Feb. 1897).

A sort of *a priori* argument has been raised by some objectors against the Pliocene, and especially the Upper Miocene objects claiming to be wrought by man. The objection is based upon *the great number* of the so-called eoliths occurring, for instance, in the "Silexteppiche" of Professor Engerrand of Brussels. As the same objection may be raised against "the great number" of palæoliths collected by our author in North Britain and Ireland, the criticism may here be anticipated by a very simple explanation suggested by the great abundance of available materials occurring in those Upper Miocene beds, and all over Scotland, where the absence of flints and cherts was more than compensated by several other suitable rocks, such as granite, basalt, quartzite, various traps, dolomite limestone, and ironstone-band. Thus the easily worked materials came to be used extravagantly, often just touched up and then cast aside, or replaced by others, as at present amongst the Andamanese islanders, the Bushmen here referred to at p. 154, and other thriftless wild tribes. Now if a thousand persons used only three a day, as we recklessly use lucifer matches, in a thousand years such rude flakes, chips, and other retouched stones would number one billion. This is Reinhardt's estimate for a given district, and it undoubtedly falls far below the reality. Thus we need not conclude that the numerous relics even from the Upper Miocene are necessarily the products of natural or accidental forces, but may well have been produced by the intentional act of intelligent beings. It is not therefore surprising that the late Professor John Young, an expert in Scottish petrology, accepted several of Mr. Smith's specimens (Figs. 8, 9, 10, 12) as true artefacts, although not showing Sir J. Evans' "bulb-of-percussion." To expect this as a necessary and universal test of all ancient human relics would indeed be "a blind way of leading the blind" (ib. p. 26). Equally good and illuminating tests are supplied for the wonderful collection brought together by our author, whom I may take the liberty of here designating the "Boucher de Perthes of Scotland."

A. H. KEANE.

The Stone Ages

CHAPTER I

The Origin and Scope of this Work

On a day, now forty odd years since, a small glass case, eighteen inches long and eight broad or thereabout, was placed in the Woodwardian Geological Museum, Cambridge. And in that case were shown—I can hardly say "exhibited"—some six or eight specimens of presumed Palæolithic weapons—"celts" they were ticketed, and only that one word was attached, or that is my impression. They were shown much as an apple-woman displays her fruit—piled up into a pyramid. But while the old lady's display is a trophy of excellence, and the best face of every specimen is in evidence, the "celts" seemed to be a trophy of embarrassment; for every example appeared designed to hide away its neighbour. Whatever may have been the value then set upon those specimens, they are now, or should be, valued by at least their weight in gold—I presume they are still somewhere in the New University Geological Museum (the "Sedgwick"), for they were presented by M. Boucher de Perthes himself.

The great English inquiry into the genuine character of these relics had only a few years before been made by Falconer, Prestwich, Flower, Evans, and others, and the truth of M. de Perthes' assertions regarding a prehistoric man cautiously, and in some cases somewhat grudgingly, conceded. Mr. Henry Keeping was then Curator of the "Woodwardian," and he it was who had been engaged to watch the workmen in what we may call M. de Perthes' own pits at Menchecourt and other places in the Somme Valley; and such was the precaution taken that, when a typical specimen was discovered, it was not allowed to be touched by the hand, but was taken directly into sheets of paper, and then subjected to the closest scrutiny under magnifying glasses in order to detect any possible prior handling, or disturbance of the material of the pits by the workmen. Finger-marks could, I presume, have been detected by such means; in any case such care at least showed the extreme caution with which the inquisitors approached their ultimate decision.

It is not perhaps surprising that a dubious mode in the exhibition of these relics should have been adopted in the Woodwardian, since by many leading men of the University they were still regarded with much suspicion and no little real alarm. But there was one, a mere youth, for whom that little case of "celts" had a profound fascination. And when one day the Curator raised the glass cover and allowed him the privilege of examining and even handling them, one purpose at least was marked out for that lad's life, and that was the persistent inquiry into the history of the ancient owner of the relics. That inquiry was begun *per saltum*; for two great ideas dawned on the youth's mind, and have remained there ever since, fixed, like the directors of a finger-post to point out the way. These were:—

(1) An assum[illegible] that if that ancient man had no metals he must [illegible]ade other things than these weapons of ston[illegible] [illegible]illed an animal, with what did he flay it, and [illegible] he cut it up? *He must have made and used oth[illegible] forms*; that was one inspiring idea.

(2) This was also an assumption; but it was founded upon actual observation, which arose out of the fact that the youth was experienced in the splitting and fracturing of flints; he had devoted boyish but enthusiastic years to the breaking up of flint nodules with the view of procuring sections of embedded ventriculites (fossil forms) allied, as was then thought, to sponges, but may be classed as something else now for aught I know. Most beautiful sections of structure were sometimes obtained; red (occasionally) or whitish, or perfectly white, in a grey or black setting. Thus the lad was, in a way, an expert in flint fracture. He knew that there was generally a certain expression, not always definable perhaps, in flint surfaces that were intentionally produced, as against natural fractures. This was the lad's view—he was much struck by the distinctly artificial and "clever" look of the fractures which had produced these recognised forms. If those ancient men were thus clever, they certainly could and naturally would have made other forms as various necessities suggested. And this was the

lad's second idea, viz. that the man who made these weapons so cleverly never started in his efforts with such work, or with such forms!

Who will say that this was beyond the mind of one still in his teens, and especially at that time of day? If any had said so he had only to point to the numberless efforts that he had made to split flints exactly as he wished; and to the numberless times in which he had failed. And here were men whose every stroke produced exactly what was intended—neither less nor more—and who could skim the surface of a flint as easily and delicately as a maid skims milk. The young man was fired with an enthusiasm to see for himself what those ancient men did; and that effort has never ceased to be made for full forty years.

He at once began to make investigations, in his own way, and quite irrespective of what had been found of that ancient man's work. He spent hours and whole holidays in examining heaps of gravel or material strewn along the roads; and many a day was spent in gravel-pits in quest of evidence of that man's work. He soon discovered that few of the *typical* forms were likely t   ʻo *his* hands: for already the workmen had been coached in   ʻo look for. So here at the first move he was checkmated, for he ...a seldom sufficient means with which to satisfy the workmen for these things.

To this day he is not sorry that he had to give up the first design of a collection of "type"-forms, illustrated and illumined by other objects yet to be discovered. He soon was so absorbed in the attempt to read what was not yet realised that the prospect of seldom or never coming across the type-forms seemed in no sense a disappointment, but rather a stimulus in the effort to discover other possible samples of that ancient man's handiwork.

He did discover what he conceived to be various forms and phases of that man's work. But they were certainly not the things which the workmen would look at; nor were they likely to be seen by such as carried on heated discussion, as was then the mode, about such things, on the basis of what could be discovered in their studies. It was a delight to examine the stones for himself, not by merely giving a passing look at a heap or by visiting this and that pit in order to purchase the specimens saved, but by handling and inspecting stone by stone; so that a heap—much to the astonishment of the road-menders—was at times found to be not where it had been placed by them, but upon a new site.

What did he find ? He found in those early days certain almost geometrically faceted stones, some of whose facets exhibited what he thought was artificial smoothing. These were the first marked objects. Then came certain very boldly flaked forms with none or very little of the fine surface-flaking upon them such as characterised the typical weapons. These were possibly knives and flayers. He would readily have admitted at that time that there was a strong spice of romance in the investigation, but that was kept in check by a strong desire to be able some day to show that the bold yet clever flaking was indeed man's work. There also occasionally appeared what must be described as weapons, but of less delicate elaboration and without the refinement of form shown in the Somme-Valley types.

The young man's efforts to persuade others that what he had found was something more than the outcome of romance, met with rebuffs that were not encouraging; although he occasionally produced a new form so distinguished by a " bulb " or " bulbs-of-percussion " that some concession was made in face of evidence. But as a rule his specimens were condemned by the merest glance, as though it were beneath any one with a mind, even for a moment, to look at such things. His friend the Curator was, however, more generous as to the youth's request that the stones should really be examined ; for *he* invariably examined them most closely with the aid of a powerful magnifying glass such as had been used in France, although he as invariably declared that nothing was visible of the agency of man. The lad was never astonished that he so answered, since the ex-pression of intention which he saw in the forms, coupled with the style and combined result of the bold flaking, could be infinitely better seen by the naked eye ; but possibly a naked eye for any purpose connected with science was thought vulgar. It may be so ; but all the lenses of man's making put together could neither have helped nor retarded the piece of work which the lad had set himself to perform.

The youth must now give place to the man, who has carried on the work for the greater part of an ordinary lifetime, not in England, where the work was begun, but in North Britain, where he feared, as he had reason to do, that the work could never be carried any farther than where the young man had left it. But, in point of fact, the long-continued quest in Scotland has resulted in a full and very graphic corroboration of those early finds in the gravels of East

Anglia. After spending close upon thirty years in North Britain, with that ancient man's history ever before his eyes, he had not only corroborated the forms that had claimed the youth's attention in the gravels of East Anglia so many years before, but had found other forms that more broadly and characteristically represented that ancient inhabitant; and the man had to return to southern England to find corroboration of these striking Scottish extensions of the relics. And in the same southern gravels which had so long ago been ransacked, he found the complements of the newer Scottish forms.

The story of this quest can be put into few words, although it might be extended to many a chapter. But, to put it briefly, after some six or seven years' search among the East Anglian gravels in that early time, a collection of flint objects was formed. He was, besides, forming a large collection of Reptilian and other faunic remains from the Upper Cretaceous beds, mainly from the Upper Greensand of south-eastern England. The flints were retained, but the Palæontological collection went to the Royal School of Mines, Jermyn Street, London, because, alas, the collector could not afford to keep it. Circumstances invited and, perhaps, in part drove him to Scotland, the experimental collection of flints of that early time going north with him, where he has now been following up the quest of that ancient man's history for thirty-six years.

I am not aware that any one save myself has made the experiment of seriously attempting to show whether or no that ancient man ever existed in North Britain. I have come across a considerable number of scientific and other observers who assumed, without taking the trouble to put the matter to proof, that that ancient man never had existence in Scotland. And this view has been insisted upon, often with such vehemence, that one is tempted to conclude that the mere suggestion of such a primitive being as Palæolithic man was considered an insult to North Britain.

To one acquainted with the fine work and the excellent forms of M. de Perthes' specimens,—and I suppose no one unacquainted with them would have ever dreamed of making the experiment of looking for these same forms with identical elaboration in Scotland, —it was almost like looking (say) among endless quantities of coal for veritable diamonds. The difference between the common rocks of Scotland and the flint of which M. de Perthes' typical specimens are made, is not inaptly suggested by the difference between common coal and the diamond. The common rocks of Scotland were not susceptible of such delicate treatment; and if they could have received it, they would long ago, in the large majority of cases, have lost the delicacy of such elaboration in the chemical changes which exposed surfaces are for ever undergoing; and that, coupled with the greater abrading and degrading forces that exist in Scotland, in comparison with such influences in the flint areas of southern England and north-western Europe, left little chance of perfect specimens of any kind ever being found. But if Palæolithic man ever were a denizen of North Britain, his relics should be made to tell their story, in whatever state they may now exist. Flint was practically indestructible. The Scottish rocks were as a rule the converse of this; but that characteristic had to be learned— a lesson that was not to be acquired in a day; indeed, it was many a year before its full meaning was apprehended.

But in the learning of that lesson many a corollary sprang to light; one was a reversion to the youth's first notion that the ancient man of the flint areas never showed a "'prentice hand" in M. de Perthes' æsthetic forms; or, rather, it was an elaboration of that view.

I had (in Scotland) come across certain weapons and other forms of so bold a style of fracture, but, withal, clever workmanship, that the elaboration suggested a freedom and power and cunning of hand in marked contrast to the dilettanteism so characteristic of the typical flint forms. It suggested that where man had the freedom of rocks to select from everywhere, his freedom was reflected in the style of work. If one stone went wrong in his "free-hand" strokes, it was thrown away and another selected. Not so with the man of the flint areas. It was not easy in many districts to find a flint nodule; and when found, it was always a question what the nodule itself was capable of, more than of what the man might actually have desired. The nodules were more often than not of limited size; but the largest of them presented other limitations in the way of eccentricity of form. No two nodules were of the same shape or size, or presented identical conditions of compactness in texture. It can be seen in many a weapon and implement of flint that the fabricator had very carefully to work in complete subjection to the form and other attributes of the nodule in hand. A nodule that would yield a weapon of good size and form was a rarity—certainly in places; and if the projected form could be obtained, it had to be by cautious and most skilled work. Here was in my view the origin of the often extremely delicate and refined treatment. It was the outcome of necessity; but where that necessity of restraint was not felt, it was, as seems to be illustrated by these Scottish forms, natural for the man to use his bolder and freer hand.

Nor is this possibility illustrated by the Scottish forms alone. The bolder, freer work is, so far as I have seen, characteristic of the Somaliland, Indian, and other forms; the human elaboration of which I presume no one doubts.

In his *Man the Primeval Savage*, Worthington G. Smith gives illustrations (pp. 11-14) of crystalline quartz and quartzite implements from Madras, which are complements in style and form and workmanship to those of Scotland.

I have found, not one or two of what are to me convincing examples of Palæolithic weapons in Scotland, but about three hundred. Some of these must have been, in their newly produced condition, equal in form and in cleverness of elaboration to the better examples of M. de Perthes' types.

But the result of the quest in this long-tabooed region is so remarkable, that even though my collection were deprived of all these weapons—*i.e.* of the particular forms that make up almost entirely the priceless collection at Abbeville—I have yet such conclusive proof of that ancient man's handiwork in subsidiary forms, in mullers, flayers, knives, choppers, clubs, etc.,—the very forms, with additions, which were found of such interest in the early Cambridge days—that I should be proud of the opportunity of demonstrating this before any audience of educated and scientific men. It is demonstrated in this work.

It is doubtless remarkable—it has surprised none more than myself—that what must be styled for the want of a better term *domestic* forms, should offer stronger and more graphic evidence of the whilom sojourn of Palæolithic man in Scotland than do his weapons. It distinctly is so. Series after series of these less expected relics have come to hand—their cumulative evidence of mere form alone being overwhelming. But when there is added to this the evidence upon many of the individual objects, of the various uses to which they have been put, as is indicated by certain worn, smoothed, or semi-polished surfaces, the cumulative evidence is enhanced. And when a feature of these forms which could never have originated through any combination of all known and conceivable accidents remains to be added, the evidence is unassailable.

This last-named "feature" is the conception which Palæolithic man had of the advantage in these domestic forms of a *handle*. This handle appears everywhere, and is devised by a multitude of more or less primitive methods—a mere hand-grasp in some : a hand-hold arrived at by the simple process of laterally knocking away a piece from the hand-grasp end, by which that end became a handle. In others, handles are elaborated, *i.e.* sculptured out in the making of the implement ; and these often at an angle to the direct line of the fabrication. In some instances the implements are so excellent, and the handle so well contrived, that their counterparts in form, though not in material, are to be found in use among present-day civilised communities.

The unassailable nature of the evidence of these Scottish forms is astonishing. It was this, and especially the presence of the handle, that sent me down at intervals during the past twelve years, for altogether six or seven individual months' search in the English gravels. This of course is an absurdly brief piece of research as compared with the hunt for these things north of the Border. Still, the result is a perfect corroboration, from well-known Palæolithic gravels in the South, of Palæolithic man's efforts after the handle, etc.

A further "hall-mark" of very pronounced character, already referred to, is seen upon many of these Scottish (domestic) forms, and that is the evidence of actual use. In many instances the *method* of use is distinctly indicated, and from this method of use it is not difficult to infer the probable application of these implements to the necessities of that ancient man's daily life. This is further exemplified by illustration, and in the text.

One series of Scottish forms (domestic, as I presume), and this a large series, which comprises a good many examples also from the English gravels, is particularly interesting and suggestive. It exhibits, as I conceive, the passage from certain common forms which are distinctly Palæolithic into the Neolithic *polished* axes— the true "celts" as they have been styled. In some series the evolution, not only of the *forms*, is illustrated, but that also of the æsthetic *polishing*, which was not primarily an invented and added refinement, but the result of the *use* to which they were commonly put ; that use, and especially with the Scottish rocks, produced a natural smoothing or polish, which polish was accepted in Neolithic times as part and parcel of the new axe-form ; this again, with the more perfect figure and highly refined workmanship, was finally extended to the whole form as an æsthetic addition; since it was intentional, and no longer limited to the merely operating end of the implement where it was naturally polished by work. It will be seen, in the proper place in this volume, that the pointed offensive weapon was gradually lost in the growth of the use of this broad-ended domestic form, which ultimately took its place as the Neolithic battle-axe.

One naturally asks where, and under what circumstances, these presumed Palæolithic relics have been found. They have been found, in Scotland, under much the same conditions as their counterparts are found in England: viz. in ancient river deposits, in the material of ancient deltas, and they have been occasionally turned up in deeper ploughing. They have occurred more frequently in river-beds, and on the margin of the sea, particularly in the greater estuaries—those of the Clyde and Forth basins. *Some* of the forms have also occurred in the Scottish boulder-clays, from which I myself have extracted them. At times these boulder-clay specimens are crushed and highly glaciated—at times they are crushed or broken and yet show no glacial striae. Glaciated specimens have been found by myself in ancient redistributed boulder-clay material, as in ancient river and delta deposits. They have been found distinctly glaciated on the seashore, and notably in the Forth area.

From my experience in Scotland I am led to the conclusion that the best relics, in the shape, at least, of *weapons* of Palæolithic man, witnessed the beginning and development of the last great glacial phenomena; by the grinding movement of which the evidences of the residence in North Britain of Palæolithic man were largely obliterated, and *with* the relics, the osseous remains of the "great mammalia." That the great mammals are represented in Scotland I shall show; and that, in accordance with such finds of the animal remains as have been recorded, those remains are generally to be looked for in or under the Scottish "till" or boulder-clay.

It is now generally recognised that the type-forms of southern England and north-west Europe represent either an *inter*-glacial or *pre*-glacial man, and possibly both. An examination of such forms as I have, during the past ten years, collected from the gravels mainly of the Thames Valley, confirms in some respects this view. The assumption is, of course, that while the glacial phenomena in North Britain were of so destructive a character, they passed away with much less violent effect in the South. This argument will also be more elaborately followed out in due course.

It will be seen from the above statements that the quest for relics of the ancient fabricator in Scotland has been, and is, one of a very different character from such quest in (say) any of the flint, or chert, or obsidian areas throughout the world. Where these silicious rocks abound, there the work of Palæolithic man is not only practically indestructible, but exhibits to this day, generally speaking, every stroke of elaboration which that ancient man gave to his work. In North Britain the very reverse of this may be said to obtain. Any and almost every exposed rock undergoes more or less complete decomposition—the strokes of work in many cases of elaboration have entirely disappeared, and only the mellowed general form is retained. It is not so in all cases, fortunately, and so one has been able to deduce from better-preserved forms the verity of the more obscure.

Add to this the greater abrading and destructive powers of the natural physical forces in Scotland, and it will be realised that the search necessitated persistent and patient application; the question of whether or no Palæolithic man had been a denizen of Scotland could only be answered by an abstruse and patiently prolonged study; and that not in one's cosy room, by the aid of one's books and of other men's work and opinion, but by constant work in the field of natural phenomena—by the naturally or artificially exposed cliff; in quarry and pit; in the summer-dried river-bed; up in mountain recesses, and down to the stone-strewn margin of the deep sea-waters. From Aberdeen to Berwick-on-Tweed, and to Stranraer on the south-west, it has been my privilege to explore for full thirty-six years in Scotland, and to this I must add the six or seven years' search by that young man in East Anglia; and thus forty odd years have been exhausted in the quest.

And to all this add the momentous factor of the difference in the use of *gravel* in southern England, as against its use in Scotland for road-making. Whereas in flint areas gravel is constantly being excavated, the country roads are bordered with gravel heaps, or are strewn with that material, in Scotland it is a rarity to see a road "metalled" with gravel. Various basaltic rocks are the almost universal road-making material. Only in the digging for sand, and in the sifting of the stones from the same, has the searcher a chance. He has, as a rule, to be content with the examination of natural exposures of the superficial deposits. The task in Scotland has been by this one factor alone rendered a thousand times more difficult than it would have been in southern England. It need not surprise any that river-beds and ocean shores have been persistently ransacked for their evidence. Nor need it cause surprise that these sources have been most largely productive. It need not mean, and does not mean, that the shores of Scotland and its river-beds have a monopoly in these things; it simply means that persistent search in such areas as offered possible results yielded up their evidence, as is the case in similar positions in southern England, when persistent search is made. The shores of South Britain have yielded many a splendid find to the casual hunter. I know from my own experience upon southern English shores, that they offer magnificent results to the man who can devote himself to their prolonged ransacking.

But the common use of gravel in South Britain has been the direct means by which the recognition of ancient man's work has for so long been narrowed to the most ornate, most easily detected of his productions. The navvy who worked in the pits is the man who has had most to do (in the selection from the pits' material) with what is and what is not representative of Palæolithic man. He was primarily instructed in his "bit" of the work. He knew the form and style of what he had to look for. He, naturally, saw nothing else. "Collectors" bargained for the supply. If the pits were visited it was in order to purchase or to make "sections" of the material. The ordinary stones were not worth looking at.

Thus our collections are almost entirely composed of the typical and "orthodox" forms, nearly all replicas of each other; as though ancient man's life-history's work began and ended with highly elaborated battle-axes. We shall, I believe, in this volume, catch sight of at least the profoundness of the human history that has been lost in England and elsewhere by the assumption that early man put such limited restrictions upon his own productions; and by trusting to vicarious and ignorant labourers to do the collecting! While it may be argued that there was no alternative but to let the men collect the forms, that can be no argument in excuse of the entire neglect of the study of the general contents of the Palæolithic gravel-beds.

I was fortunate in that my work was begun with actually an aversion to what the navvies were put to find. Their finds represented a thrice-read chapter. It was suggestive and interesting to turn to other possible chapters. When I arrived in Scotland I *had* to find the very title-page for myself; and I am thankful that no vicarious agents ever stood between myself and what was to be found. In the effort to discover the known I have turned and read many a chapter of the unknown, which a vicarious agency could never have seen.

It is, however, curious and interesting that away from the circle that environs the "official" forms of Palæolithic productions (those of the navvy collector at home), as in Egypt, and India, Somaliland, and other regions, these other (domestic) forms have been freely collected; and I find the Scottish forms, and some from the English Palæolithic gravels that are not generally recognised in England, marvellously illustrated, especially by many common and fully accepted (Palæolithic) Egyptian forms. Some comparative illustrations of this follow in the text.

Much has been done in the elucidation of this or other ancient man's history during the past sixty or seventy years. Much wonderful lore has been culled from the hitherto hidden recesses of caves; "kitchen-middens" have been laboriously explored, and in more distant parts of the world discoveries of his relics have been made under many varied circumstances. But it is not my province and not my intention to attempt a *résumé* of what has been done by others in this wide and as yet mainly unexplored field of research; my intention is to place the results of my own piece of work, so far as is possible by illustration and text, before the reader, who will, as I with some confidence anticipate, agree with me that forty years' serious search has supplied ample matter, and that *sui generis*, to at least fill an ordinary volume. By the way, as we proceed, comparative use of illustration and text of other and often widely separated discoveries will fall into appropriate place in this volume, which is designed as a record particularly of what has been discovered in North Britain, and now in Ireland. Much also may be suggestive and illustrative of what remains yet to be done in still unexplored regions in which that more ancient man is known to have dwelt.

It is known that in areas of the recognised occurrence of the typical Palæolithic weapons, they are as a rule looked for in vain in the soils. There is the proverbial exception to this; but such exception is an accident in the geological and geographical history of such areas, and it is a fact that the orthodox Palæoliths are not indigenous to such soils. The meaning of this phenomenon is that the geological and geographical features that now characterise such areas came into being after the last of the Palæolithic axes had been fabricated and left on the ancient hunting-field, for the soils of such regions have come into existence since that " orthodox " Palæolithic man possessed the land.   This factor in the *occurrence* of Palæolithic remains can be more definitely stated of northern France and southern England than of Scotland ; since, in this last region, the physical phenomena have not the milder character of the two foregoing areas.   In some parts of Scotland the older diluvial deposits are actually the soils, inasmuch as little depth of " vegetable " soil has ever been there formed because of the active nature of ordinary physical phenomena.   In such Scottish areas the soils are the ploughed-into and ploughed-up diluvial beds ; and there the orthodox Palæolithic forms are indigenous to the soils—but this again is of the nature of recent accident.   Practically and actually, the truth is in Scotland what it is in England and France, namely, that Palæolithic man had disappeared before the superficies of these countries received their present configuration ; the event which initiated and manufactured the now superficial geology and geography of these areas, *i.e.* their main features, was the last great glaciation.   In my view the orthodox Palæolithic being disappeared from such regions with the beginning and development of the glacial phenomena of that remote period.

In Dr. A. H. Keane's *The World's Peoples* (1908) the following occurs in reference to the " Javanese Man," whose osseous remains are believed to be the oldest human relics known.   " In this ' first man,' as he has been designated, the erect position, shown by the perfectly human thigh-bone, implies a perfectly prehensile (grasping) hand, with opposable thumb, the chief instrument of human progress " (p. 4).

Nothing is clearer or more presistently shown through the whole range of the domestic forms in my collection, alike in the most ancient and in the possibly more modern, than the intention of the elaboration bestowed upon them with regard to the use of the thumb.   The " rule-of-thumb " is that which is so often the undeniable feature in them ; the intention of this curve, this hollow, this deliberate break, this purposely left projection, all speak with emphatic precision of the opposable thumb.   The reader will find that incidental reference is made to certain illustrations of this in the volume, and will find out others for himself.

One aspect of the title and contents of this volume gives them an utter lack of proportion. While Ireland takes an important place in the title, the quantity of matter with regard to that part of the British Isles is very limited. This is not the result of intention, but entirely accidental. A most important, most graphic discovery was made in Ireland when the writing of this volume was drawing to a close, but this important Irish evidence, though perforce brief, is of the finest quality as bearing on the aim and contents of this work. In a single chapter we have illustrated, and corroborated by specimens from Erin, what it has taken me thirty-six years in Scotland to realise; but the realisation gave me the power to profit by the most fortunate and unexpected opportunity which natural phenomena held out to me in that country. I anticipate that my readers will agree with me that the value of the Irish discovery gives Ireland full claim to its prominent position upon the title-page.

I have, among other and great obligations, to thank Dr. A. H. Keane for the happy suggestion of *The Stone Ages* as the title of this work—a title that is in every way satisfactory to myself, for two reasons: (1) That there is, as the Doctor himself said, a bold and broad ring about it; and (2) that it does not commit me to any particular time or circumstance, to any special term or theory. Hence, such title was a great relief from an embarrassing position; and for this relief I am deeply indebted to Dr. Keane. The embarrassing position I will now try to explain.

If I limited the title, as I proposed to do, to *Palæolithic Man*, the limited and measured conception with which I began this quest, it would not at all convey a truth of vast importance, which is one of the results of my researches, viz. that it is impossible to say where Palæolithic man begins or ends in the world's history, since there is no definable limitation to his career, which passes imperceptibly, as we shall see, into the Neolithic Age. I can in no sense define an ending for the former man, nor a beginning for Neolithic man. I am not aware that I have had to discuss Neolithic man's relics at all. I have never, in association with the relics of our argument, come upon a polished weapon, and never one single shard of " prehistoric " pottery. The more notable aspects of the finds are Palæolithic; their *occurrence* in deposits is decidedly Palæolithic; and they are often glacial. Those occurring upon seashore or in river-bed are of course of less definable age; and yet even there they seem to me to find their compeers in time, and style, and mode of elaboration, more in the relics in ancient deposits, and even in glacial beds, than in those which we style Neolithic. Yet, and here comes the relief to me, I have not needed, and do not attempt, to define and limit the "Stone Ages." Certain Neolithic forms run through the whole of the Stone Ages, Palæolithic and Neolithic alike, so far as my research has revealed the story to me. Palæolithic man used in most remote and prolonged times certain implements which, in a more refined condition, we have considered to be exclusively representative of Neolithic man. The ages in which these Palæolithic and Neolithic men lived are so vast, and at present so little comprehended by us, that I prefer to speak of such still unknown peoples, and unknown times, as they have presented themselves to me—by the relics, and by the revelation which they have made to me, rather than by what has been dogmatically laid down by my fellow-man, not so much from evidence and the result of research, as on subjective or assumed *a priori* grounds. The phenomena attendant upon the occurrence of these relics are so startling, and in some respects so astonishing, that we may well fear to dogmatise either as to time or as to peoples; and rather confess to profound ignorance in the face of so strange a history as in this volume we attempt to unfold, I trust not rashly, but with all respect for the mysterious past.

I use the term "Stone Ages" in the title because, though I do not define man or times, the weight of my argument falls almost as pointedly upon what we understand by the term Neolithic as upon what is conceived as Palæolithic. The Stone Ages as a title correctly covers the whole argument of the work. The relics of "Palæolithic" man alone probably represent ages *and* ages.

I would now refer to one or two other matters, and so anticipate some possible hypercritical remarks.

(1) I have drawn all weapons and domestic implements, with one or two exceptions, with their operative ends toward, and not away from, the viewer. I found that I could not draw a Palæolithic weapon with the thick butt-end toward, and the point away from, the eye. I could not see it perfectly, any more than we can see a cone or a pyramid with the broad base to the eye. I have reversed the position usual in illustration of such objects, and this position is maintained throughout the volume.

(2) Should any one point to the palpable absurdity of an object casting its shadow upon itself, as when two views of the same thing are shown with the shadow of the first thrown upon the second, let

him accept the fact of its impossibility, and allow the said shadow upon the second figure to be thrown from anything his imagination pleases; the effect will be the same—an artistic and defining effect, which I have thought too valuable to throw away before any possible critic's view. I have nothing further to apologise for, so far as I see. My one aim in the drawings was to be truthful; they are, I believe, as accurate as the average professional draughtsman's productions would have been; but as the employment of such a man was not possible, I have spent portions of the past ten years in making the drawings myself. Without any definite hope that they would ever be utilised, I still felt that it was a duty to prepare a record of the results of my prolonged quest, and there, if need be, leave the matter. And there it would have been left, if I may judge by the almost entire lack of appreciation which has been shown to me for all these years north of the Border. But there have been just the isolated exceptions which prove the rule; and my friend of a good many years, Mr. Walter W. Blackie, B.Sc., has been the greatest of these. But for his constant encouragement, I question whether even my enthusiasm would have stood the strain of the making of 520 careful drawings, with possibly the wastepaper-basket at the end. But in his appreciation of what I may venture to call the important result of forty years' work, he has come to a courageous resolution in the interest of science; and the record is accordingly to see the light of day. May I hope that the substance of this volume will prove a revelation to the scientific world? It has been such to myself.

It may help some of my readers to realise better the actual size of the objects illustrated, if I point out that by their reduction to what is styled "half natural size," this being the general rule of reduction in this volume, they are reduced to one-fourth of their actual surface area. If a square, for instance, be reduced half its length and half its breadth, only one-fourth of its area remains.

CHAPTER II

On the Trail in North Britain

A FRIEND once assured me that he had been following my example, and had been looking for Palæolithic implements on a certain Scottish stony seashore; and he seemed aggrieved and inclined to be "sceptical about the whole thing," because he had not found anything that was like the things in my collection! "How long did your investigation last?" I inquired. "For perhaps half an hour!" he replied. Comment was needless; but by way of illustration I remarked that I often gave eight hours at a stretch to such search, and thought myself well rewarded if I found one good thing in that time.

I had brought my way of searching from England. It was as easy and interesting, at least in the years gone by, for me to search for eight hours or more on occasion, as for my friend to exhaust thirty minutes in the same way; and to become, as was evident, himself exhausted by the effort.

None will, I presume, contradict me in the assertion that mine was the right way of searching, provided one knew what was to be looked for! I assumed that I did know what I wanted to find, when I began the quest north of the Border. But the very nature of the rocks of the country, their way of weathering chemically or becoming rounded physically, their coarse crystalline, gritty, and earthy nature as compared with the flints of the South, soon undeceived me. Partly by intuition, but more by experience, I came to apprehend that one need not look for absolute identity in the work of an ancient man in Scotland with his recognised work in southern England.

It was scarcely possible that that ancient man could give, and certainly he generally never attempted to give, to the rocks of the North such elaboration as he bestowed upon flint objects in the South; and when he may have done so, where were the rocks that would retain the expression of such elaboration as the flints imperishably retained it? And as he generally did not give such work to his fabrications, what was his work like ?   What were his weapons, in form, and style, and design ?   What his domestic forms, assuming that he made them ?

As soon as this stage of the investigation had been reached, the long days' ramblings and searching ceased almost at once to be, as they had often hitherto been, unrewarded.   Something, or some things, were sure to attract attention : a dilapidated weapon—one, at least, in form—would demand a considerable " brown study " ere it was discarded ; a less recognisable form, but mayhap unaccountable in its facets of apparently bold flaking, except through a human intervention, would at times be as great a strain upon one's mental powers as a deep mathematical problem.

Fortunately, I have retained a few of those earliest Scottish finds —"problems," I often called them ; and they are particularly interesting to me now, since they have been verified over and over again, and are no longer problems.   How many that would now be interesting items have I thrown away in the effort to understand ? and how many good things that had actually been found have been lost in the changes and chances of thirty-six years, it is vain to attempt to calculate ; but a few unique specimens that have so disappeared will haunt me.   Several are in my memory—but, alas, are there only—that would now be to myself, and notwithstanding all my other specimens, " worth their weight in gold " ; for they put diamonds and rubies out of court in the value of association and circumstance.   Nothing can be substituted for those lost examples. It will be apparent that, notwithstanding my asserted indifference to the typical forms in England, my one leading desire was to find in Scotland the very things which in a sense I had decried, and which the pitmen were sedulously picking out of the gravels of the north-west corner of Europe.   Though possible Scottish relics might not be identical in form and feature, what I desired to find were still to be that Palæolithic man's weapons of offence or defence ; and in that broad view they were bound to be counterparts of those of the South.

In my disparaging mode of reasoning, it will, I think, be seen in what follows that I underrated the possibilities of the anticipated relics of ancient man in Scotland ; for many forms *are* identical in figure and design and style of work, so far as the material admitted, with those of the flint regions ; they are, however, mainly less well preserved.   But that broader view of anticipating modification and variation in possible Scottish relics was a power that has brought into recognition whole series of undoubted fabrications of which none seem to have dreamed. Preconceived forms, preconceived methods and modes of work for Palæolithic man, were at first an insurmountable hindrance to discovery. It was only when I could throw away all sense of what I *ought* to find, and replace that with a sense of ignorance of what I *might* find, that the search became absorbing and vivid with anticipation. And now I trust that we are ready to seriously follow the illustrations and descriptions of what have been found: to which, with the geological and geographical "occurrence" of the same, this volume is wholly devoted.

Almost the first specimen found in Scotland of what I consider to be a typical hache, was perhaps the most characteristic that I have found in North Britain. Its form and actual work was that of a Somme-Valley type. It was of a compact, *i.e.* fine-grained, basalt: it had been fabricated—the work was very distinct upon it—from a highly rolled pebble, which was evidenced by a small portion of the original surface being left unworked. This interesting specimen, discovered in 1873, was in my possession for twenty-five years, when it mysteriously disappeared from a number of specimens which I had sent to a friend for inspection. It is possibly now in some over-enthusiast's cabinet in England. I have lost that specimen, but 1 had fortunately made rough drawings of it, and here they are (Figs. 1 and 2). Only one other example has come to me in Scotland that exhibits the same kind of *typical* work so demonstrably as did the lost example.

Fig. 1.   Fig. 2.

That early specimen was thrown out from some drainage trenches on the higher level of the Tay Valley, above the north bank of the river Almond two miles or so above Perth. Its point end was gone and it was "fretted" here and there along its margins. The

Philosophical Society, Glasgow, in 1898, or at a meeting of the Glasgow Geological Society in 1899, where this stone and others were shown, or the late Professor John Young, or Mr. J. Lewis Abbott, see that it *might* have been a mere hammer-stone?

I give, by way of illustration of how such a proposition or the like proposition might destroy one's faith in any and every thing,

a drawing of a small hache (Fig. 4) which I purchased at Abbeville, Somme Valley, in 1883 —one of the four only that I ever purchased. It is but half an inch longer than Fig. 3, before it lost its point, and of just the same width at its broadest. To suggest that this was also fabricated by its use as a hammer-stone were, in my view and knowledge of the work of Palæolithic man, just as legitimate as to suggest it of Fig. 3. Where is such an argument to be barred? All the typical Palæoliths that I have seen might have been used along their edges as hammer-stones. Of these two illustrated the Abbeville specimen would have made the better

Fig. 4.

hammer. Mr. Fisher finally, at my suggestion, forwarded the specimens and drawings to Dr. and late Professor A. H. Keane, the well-known ethnologist and exponent of anthropology. At Dr. Keane's most generous suggestion I myself had the privilege of paying him a visit, and of exhibiting to and discussing many specimens with him.

Not only was Dr. Keane satisfied with the verity and intention of the human work of Fig. 3, but he agreed with me that Nature works miracles if the constant repetition in form and design which groups of the other specimens exhibit were the result of accident, and not of human intention. This frank and generous admission by Dr. Keane I am anxious to acknowledge, with the great interest he, the Rev. O. Fisher, and certain Yorkshire and other scientists south of the Border have shown, since such recognition has given me courage to attempt descriptions of about 500 drawings which I have devoted some years in preparing, with the now greater hope of the volume for which they were prepared being published.

Another specimen (Fig. 5) is also small, and also exhibits the characteristic work of the typical flint-forms so far as crystalline quartz, from which it is fabricated, is capable of exhibiting it. This

I found in what I took to be boulder-clay thrown out from a railway excavation at Bowling, Clyde Valley, in 1894.

Let us now mark that it is, to say the least, a curious coincidence that the three Scottish specimens, as shown in our illustrations, are damaged in a very striking manner. In Fig. 1 the point is gone; and, as I have said, it has been fretted since it was fabricated, along its edges. We have also noticed that the point end of Fig. 3 has been, so to describe it, snapped off. In Fig. 5 the breaks, which certainly are of subsequent occurrence to the fabrication of the specimen, are of a very suggestive yet puzzling character. I say puzzling, because I do not for a moment suppose that these breaks were intentional, any more than the loss of the points in Figs. 1 and 3 were intentional. But while it is not only conceivable but natural that the points of weapons should have

Fig. 5.

been at times broken by actual use, it is difficult to understand how fragments could by any conceivable *use* have been taken out from the body, and especially from a small though compact body of stone such as Fig. 5. These fragments were not removed by any ordinary and intentional effort; but, as we shall see, the implements show in this and many other instances that such breaks are the result of some power that is not, on the ordinary face of things, apparent. It is more as though, if it were possible, they had been bitten out, or as though an unheard-of power of finger and thumb had broken or snapped them out.

If we examine, *i.e.* if *I* examine Fig. 4, the specimen from the Somme Valley, for my readers, I find that that also shows some, though much more slight fretting along its margins. We need not, however, here attempt to infer anything from this phenomenon of fretting and fracturing, but let us notice this feature as of interest and importance at this very beginning of our study of these stones, and the meaning will become clear, just as it dawned upon and came to myself by the cumulative force of repetition. Let us meantime try to see the value of the evidence of these breaks in the mere *morphology* of these stones. It matters not in what manner, or to what extent these presumed fabrications are broken, their restoration, if made upon the suggestion of what is left of the original form, invariably reproduces the perfect Palæolithic weapon. Will my readers kindly think this out? Now let us mark that these frettings and breaks, where rolling, marine or river, or subsequent decomposition has not reduced the whole to a more modern and more shapeless production, invariably show newer surfaces than the original surface of the form *as a weapon.* Usually these destructive breaks are of ages contemporary with each other; but sometimes are not—though the great, or what we may call momentous breaks—I am of course speaking now of breaks that are not *natural, i.e.* not of cleavage or of planes of deposition or of thermal origin—are invariably of contemporary age in any specimen; lighter fretting may not always be so. So also, all the surfaces or facets that form what I conceive to be a weapon, *i.e. constructive* facets, are always contemporary in age except where—and this is always interesting and instructive— the surface of the stone from which the fabricator sculptured his implement is in part left. Then that surface is invariably seen to be of much greater age than the facets which have induced the weapon-form. Let us look at our position in this argument of " fabrication."

First: *These forms are always of ancient origin.* I have never yet found one which could be accepted as a Palæolithic weapon which owed its origin to any possible combination of *recent* natural breaks, cleavage, planes of bedding, thermal effects, or rivers in spate, or seashore action, or any such natural agents. I have never found anything recent which I could, or any one else would allow to lie alongside these ancient examples. The only rock which I have found to assume the form, and that without any expression of intention or work, is bedded schistose rock, which sometimes breaks away in lenticular masses; but one could never be misled by them.

Secondly: *All breaks of more recent occurrence than the age which is indicated by the common surface of the weapon have always destroyed the perfect form as a weapon.* These destroying breaks and frettings, or rounding by attrition, from whatever cause, have been and are still to some extent being produced; but whether from yielding at jointings, or planes of cleavage, or bedding, or from decomposition or rolling, the effect is always the same, viz. that of destroying and never of producing a weapon of Palæolithic or of any other form.

Thirdly: If these forms are now being destroyed by such agents as Nature provides, and if they show, as almost every Scottish specimen does show, that they have been undergoing the loss of the

pebble reduced to a surface-flaked condition by th
We assume that this is done; but my experience
series of years of continual observation is that
never fractured in such a way as to induce any f
surface. Thermal fractures have invariably an err
aspect that can at once be recognised by any
thermal petrological phenomena. Admitting, as
apart through various natural weak conditions, b
negative evidence.

Interested as I was specially in flints wh
Scotland, I was struck by ...ving that a
decorated with large, very i...gularly shaped
were in their natural condition; *i.e.* just as th
of their calcareous matrix. They had prob
Dundee as ballast. I watched these flint nod
years; and though they have lain out in all th
changes, they have undergone no change e
particles of chalk which were attached to t
flint. Nothing otherwise perceptible has
is no suggestion of surface-flaking.

Some of the flints which I submit
mentioned above I had found along the
them I believe to be fabricated. But
present shapes, which my friend said
their present facets, and therefore thei
them in some remote past, and, so far
them in some very brief space of tir
had those Ayrshire flints for ten years
convenient storage, been kept in bo
weathers in my garden since I found
are now; and, as I write, a blizzard i
shown any sort of thermal break.
not how long, scattered along the
possibly superficial deposits in Sc
to the greatest contrasts in temp
and their edges rolled more or les
occur. In 1883 I was in the S
thousands of tons of flint "pe
rolled on the shore at the Son
nothing else. If any recent fa

(B 987)

perfect (Palæolithic) form which they clearly indicate they possessed in some remote past, could it have been Nature, by the same agents as those with which she is now destroying them, that brought these forms into being? Could Nature so shape the stones up to a remote era, and then not only deliberately cease to so shape any more, but as deliberately set to work to destroy what had before been formed? If Nature produced these ancient forms there must have been a design and intention in her methods contrary to what is now her mode of work and her present intention; which position is inconceivable. If the agent which produced these ancient forms could not be Nature, as she now exerts her powers, it must have been some power of production which acted independently of Nature and her agents; and that power could alone have been the intentional energy of man.

Let us look at another argument that will take us to ages in the past beyond the era in which these forms appear, and to which, so far as is known, their occurrence in their pristine state is limited. Let us look at specimens of these presumed Palæoliths which show—and there are many such—that their forms as weapons have been elaborated out of highly rolled amorphous masses of stone, known as "pebbles": and our argument about Nature having reversed her mode of work since the period of the making of these forms is applicable to limitless ages on the remoter side of the era of the occurrence of such elaborations.

In that more remote period we see that Nature was for ever rolling and rounding certain rock-fragments over and over again, till every whilom ridge and angle became a thing of an extremely remote and obscure past. Some such fragments had become pebbles even in the era of the Old Red Conglomerate, and remained pebbles still throughout all the profundities of time as time is represented in the Secondary and Tertiary Epochs of the world's history till a certain comparatively modern era was reached, when Nature assumed another rôle and became the sculptor out of these self-same pebbles of the forms of Palæolithic weapons. And, having done such unusual work for an æon, she once more set about reducing all her material fragments to clays or sands, or to the rotund pebbles which sing in the streams and rivers, and roar in endless chorus upon her oceans' shores.

There are more pages to be read at Nature's hands concerning these ancient forms than that of bulbs-of-percussion and highly skilled flaking of purely silicious rock; and in these other pages,

E

the real and comprehensive history of t
long-lost efforts of that ancient man is to
My one anticipation through all
eventually show that the demand for b
æsthetic work, and insistence upon th
ancient man, is indeed a blind way
use another simile, like declaring that
only reign in English history. We k
we know that the guns and weapo
weapons of our late beloved Queen's
representative of the weapons and
the series of reigns prior to the la
our own history till the style and
not only utterly different from wh
in obscurity. But obscurity need
weapons did not yet exist.
Figs. 1 and 3 are cases in
rounded such fragments, till not
left; and these rolled pebbles
forces of Nature to give angula
of limited durance, since the
form was the result, not of a s
ing, of one comprehensively i
In some correspondence,
flints which I submitted t
logist and mineralogist, my
the specimens which did n
sion as " thermal " brea
natural, *i.e.* quite natura
shapes by variation of t
common cases of our rea
may safely be asserted
suggest that thermal b
occurrence is invariabl
which may all be des
admits air or water w
frost or natural deca
other " accidents," w
know from experienc
But how many

thing to find, it was not a thermal break, but, so to call it, a human one. The pebbles were brought up to St Valerie on rafts or flat-bottomed boats, from which girls landed them in baskets and shot them into enormous heaps.

I saw the same phenomena at Brighton in the year 1905; here the countless tons of flint pebbles which form the beach are for ever becoming rounder and smoother, and one may actually say, allowing the usual exception to prove the rule, are never flaked and seldom broken even in the most meaningless way by either the rough sea waves or thermal influence. Why and how did Nature produce such wonderful " thermal " flakings with such extraordinary results in the past, if she does not produce the like to-day?

The same negative evidence is given by all other rocks with which I am acquainted. Many of the forms which I have collected as fabrications in Scotland, of a great variety of material, have also been kept out in the open, and they have not suffered visible change during the course of years, or I should never dream of leaving them where they would, in accordance with the thermal assumption, be destroyed; or possibly, in accordance with the thermal theory, resolved into yet finer Palæoliths. That they would in time decay and disintegrate is certain; but that result would be the very antithesis of stones being fractured by temperature into Palæolithic or other recognised forms.

CHAPTER III

A Comparative Study of Relics

SUPPOSE we take two excellent specimens of the Somme-Valley type-forms and consider them from a Scottish petrological point of view. They are shown in Figs. 6 and 7. They are of course of flint, and exhibit, well preserved, the characteristic work which was given to them by their fabricators. They are both characterised by beautiful

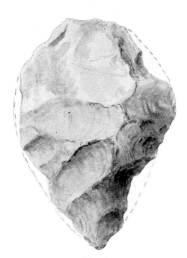

Fig. 6.   Fig. 7.

surface-flaking, and their forms are still perfect, except for certain marginal fractures, the character of which we have already noticed. No further destructive forces have materially affected them. They have been subjected to some river-rolling and to certain staining influences; but the ridges of the flakings and the lateral edges are almost as sharp as when they left their fabricators' hands. If we suppose any two similar specimens to have been fabricated in Scotland instead of in the Somme Valley they would almost certainly not have been made from flint, nor of any nearer approach to that highly silicious and glass-like material than crystalline or saccharine quartz or quartzite, or of one of the many volcanic or limestone or other rocks. We have seen what kind of work an agate in Scotland received and preserved intact; but no agate large enough for these could have been found; they must have been elaborated from one or other of the common native rocks. If we assume that any native material could have received such work as is indicated in Figs. 6 and 7, what would be their condition now? If of crystalline or saccharine quartz, the most silicious of Scottish rocks, save agates, their ridges and edges would have lost their individuality in the general surface; and indeed the character of the original work would have almost entirely disappeared. This I assert from thirty-six years' observation of such rocks. Such rocks are not only far more susceptible than flint to the friction they receive in rivers or upon the seashore, but are surprisingly affected by atmospheric or aqueous solvents; that is, by chemical agents. If they were formed from any of the other native rocks they were highly sensitive to decomposing agents, and were most of them easily abraded by river or marine action. The quartzites, highly crystalline and brittle when fabricated, have almost invariably lost their crystalline aspect, are generally so decomposed that they look like and indeed often are sandstones in character and aspect, and like sandstones, are smoothed and rounded by even slight abrading influences. I have thrown away excellent specimens in my ignorance of earlier years, under the impression that they were, and always had been, mere sandstones; of which material I assumed that that ancient man could never have made his weapons. The lesson of the metamorphosis of rocks and their return to their more primitive condition had to be realised beyond the mere verbal knowledge.

If they were of any volcanic rock, they underwent chemically a kind of mellowing of surface; so that facets, formerly angular, have assumed an indefinite aspect which gives to such fabrications an appearance of having been moulded from a species of cement or putty. Objects formed from (say) formerly brittle grey ironstone (the ironstone-band) are transformed into a peroxidised condition; some into actual red or yellow ochre. Certain dolomite and other limestones have preserved the work bestowed upon them as well as any of the rocks in Scotland; some of these we shall in due course examine.

If, then, our type specimens had been fabricated in Scotland, and presuming that such work as was bestowed upon flints in the Somme

Valley had been bestowed upon them, what would now be their condition? As certainly as the constitution of the Scottish rocks is what I represent, they would now have a softened, rolled, expressionless aspect as compared with anything elaborated in flint. They would present just such attributes in form and in indication of their elaboration as the Scottish specimens presented, which the late Professor John Young, of Glasgow University, had in his own possession for examination, and pronounced before the Philosophical Society of Glasgow in 1898 to be of human workmanship.

Scottish specimens cannot, and ought not to be expected to present themselves in other than these altered conditions, except in the rare case of fabrications from agates, or some material equally resistant to destructive forces. The late Professor John Young was an expert in Scottish petrology and geology; he could at once see how the items had become altered through certain processes; and he also knew that rocks do not naturally assume the forms of these asserted fabrications.

Figs. 8, 9, 10, and 11 are several of those upon which Professor

Fig. 8.   Fig. 9.

Young gave his affirmative opinion. Fig. 8 is a hard syenite-like rock that has resisted decomposition and only shows the smoothing effect of rolling. It was found in a deposit near the mouth of the river Esk at Musselburgh in 1884. Figs. 9 and 11 are of a black basalt, and were both found on the shore of the Ayrshire coast. They are characteristic of what I have called the mellowing effect of

decomposition, but not of decomposition alone. Their original elaboration left them doubtless with at least semi-angular facets; the

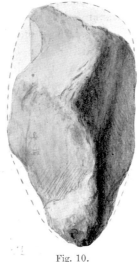

Fig. 10.   Fig. 11.

angles have entirely disappeared; the more demonstrative work is,
however, still indicated. The whole present
aspect is, I believe, the result of this se-
quence of events. In their earlier history
they were subject to considerable rolling,
possibly marine; it was then that they lost
the angles of their facets. They were sub-
sequently buried in the deep sea where the
mellowing proper has been achieved. Innumerable crystals (felspar, probably) have
been dissolved out; so that they have a minutely honeycombed surface, under which
process of chemical change they assumed
their soft, moulded look, like that of Fig.
12. I have found instances of this solvent
power of the sea in many marine specimens
and from many localities, i.e. in ordinary
stones. Fig. 10 is formed from a similar
trappean rock, and though it is somewhat
decayed, the felspar crystals having be-
come opaque and whitish are neither dissolved nor rotted out. In

Fig. 12.

this case the specimen was not found on the seashore, but in an ancient delta-deposit (*in situ*) on the north lower flank of the Ochils at Forteviot (in the Earn Valley) in 1896.

Notwithstanding that Figs. 9 and 11 were found upon the seashore they have not been subjected to modern rolling to any appreciable extent. They were brought up and ashore by the floating power of seaweed. They had lain illimitable ages under the waves and came ashore, as countless similar stones are annually raised from the sea-floor, and borne to land by storm-disturbed sea-wrack. Figs. 13 and 14 are side views of Figs. 9 and 10 respectively; they give a better idea of the style of the elaboration of these examples.

Fig. 13.   Fig. 14.

Once again we ask, what were the specimens (Figs. 6 and 7) now like, if they had been fabricated in Scotland? I am imperative with this question, because for many years—for full half an ordinary lifetime—it has on all hands been assumed and asserted to myself that the relics of Palæolithic man in Scotland ought to be, and must be, replicas, in form and style of work, of the typical flints. This is, with that ancient man, somewhere at least a hundred thousand years away in the past and his relics as far back in origin, an impossibility. It has or had come, in effect, in many minds to this—That ancient man's history must be found recorded in the manner and style which we anticipate, or he has had no history in Caledonia. This is in effect what has so long been postulated; and as identical relics in style and manner have not been found—I do not know that they have ever seriously been looked for—it has been assumed that that ancient man never existed in Scotland. But while he existed in southern Britain during a clearly indicated period of upheaval of enormous duration, and battled with, and held his own with, the "Great Mammalia," could he have had no habitation in Scotland, when the great mammals, as I shall show, had? If the great mammals were here, the area now known as North Britain was not submerged, as has been suggested, in order to account for the easily assumed absence of that early man. And if, as we also know was the case, the whole of the area of the now British Isles was, during part at least of the period of that ancient man's habitation, possessed of a milder climate than it possesses to-day, North Britain could not have been then barred to that whilom man by ice—another of the suggestions which have excused his presence here.

But to return to our specimens. I have said that that ancient man had to handle his flint nodules with considerable care and not less skill in order to make effective use of them. I have asserted that he was often reduced by necessity to a delicate dilettanteism in his work. I believe our example (Fig. 6) to be an excellent case in point. During at least a part of his procedure in the fabrication

of this Somme-Valley specimen he used a bolder freehand stroke, and only when that method could not be proceeded with farther did he resort to the delicate surface-flaking which is exhibited on what we may now call the obverse of Fig. 6. Let us turn the specimen over for the reverse—here it is in Fig. 15— and, as is at once seen, we have a freer, bolder, more barbarous style of work, if we choose so to name it. First of all, we see that the prospective weapon was struck off from a larger mass with a masterly stroke which released the piece as a fine thick flake. The newly produced facet was almost flat, as was doubtless intended. A large part of

Fig. 15.

this is left still untouched either by hand or by time, as may be seen in the drawing. The effect of a rough flat oval (on that side) is obtained by striking off fragments all along the edges of the mass, with the double purpose of shaping the weapon and of producing a cutting edge along the sides and a point at one end, the general outline being an oval.

This work, let us notice, is of the same kind exactly as is still clearly shown in Fig. 8 and in a less clear manner in Fig. 10 of these northern forms. It is the style of work commonly used in the Scottish specimens. Figs. 9 and 11 were also doubtless elaborated by means of the same species of work as that shown in the flint, Fig. 15. When the obverse, as in Fig. 6, was taken in hand, there was no material left upon which the bold stroke could be used without endangering the very possibility of the weapon; hence the delicate care and the great contrast in the style of work of the two sides of the same implement. If this specimen (Fig. 6) had been formed from a basalt and had received exactly the work it now so distinctly shows, assuming that it could have received such work, it would doubtless have been to-day as expressionless as Fig. 11. Or its condition might have been somewhere between the two, as in that of Fig. 10.

The companion type-specimen to Fig. 6, viz. Fig. 7, was elaborated in exactly the same way. There is an almost flat under-side with the more oval obverse, as shown in Fig. 7. Yet the mode of work has been identical in many of the Scottish forms with that of these two type-speci-mens, viz. a struck-off mass, which ex-hibits on that de-tached face often a conchoidal fracture, somewhat of the character of the struck-off flints. That side is often flat or flattish, like the flints; and the side on which the final elaboration was ex-

Fig. 16.   Fig. 17.

pended is oval, or of a flattened triangle in section. It is so in Figs. 8 and 10. In Figs. 16, 17, and 18 we have excellent examples of this mode of work. Figs. 9 and 11 have been more distinctly sculptured out bodily from a mass, both their faces, as in the flints presenting the oval line, and giving in section the more perfect oval form.

Fig. 16, with side view, Fig. 17, was found upon the shore at Troon, Clyde estuary. It is a fine-grained granitic rock. Fig. 18 is from the shore of the Forth estuary, and is of dolomite limestone.

Fig. 12, the Aberdeen specimen, which was found in a pit (an ancient glacial delta-deposit) almost under the whilom cathedral church of St. Machar, Old Aberdeen University, is a wholly sculptured-out specimen in Aberdeen granite. It lost its point end ages ago, was since highly (marine?) rolled, and is highly smoothed and rounded. There is a break (modern) on either side near the point end, one of which is shown. No equivalent form could ever have resulted from such natural breaks. Its section is a fairly balanced oval.

Fig. 18.

In Figs. 19, 20, and 21 we have the two faces and an edgewise view of a black basalt Scottish specimen, which is mellowed and finely honeycombed, as is usual with a marine example of that material. It is of the same oval figure as Fig. 6 (restored). It is an excellent specimen, and if but of flint would be assumed to be one of the best possible. It is from the shore, West Kilbride, Ayrshire. It has also lost its point end.

As to what is called "barbarous fabrication," let us consider it. With many, even down to to-day, and speaking of flint forms, anything less than the highly delicate dilettante work is not accepted; bulbs-of-percussion must also be in evidence, or that ancient man is not permitted to be spoken of in connection therewith.

But that ancient man only needed a stone with a point, or a sharp edge, for most of his operations. If the point were naturally there, and he could handle the stone, it was a weapon; and it was in such case generally every whit as effective as though it had been produced by the most skilled dilettante work. Now, who is justified in asserting, as many so-called experts do in effect assert, that Palæolithic man began and ended his career as a dilettante in his work? The position is inconceivable. Let us see what I

Fig. 19.   Fig. 20.   Fig. 21.

mean by being a dilettante! In his *Man the Primeval Savage*, p. 264, Worthington G. Smith gives a drawing as well as a description of the fabrication of a typical weapon, such as is shown in Figs. 6 and 7. The picture is of two individuals at work upon the one stone. There is an "anvil-stone"—literally an anvil—one holding a nodule of flint upon the anvil, while the other, hammer-stone in hand, strikes a "punch" of flint upon the edge of the said nodule. I myself think it exceedingly likely that such was the procedure when the beautifully delicate work was produced upon the obverse of Fig. 6. But see what it was as an attainment. The modern blacksmith, with his anvil and his tool and hammer and his assistant striker, is not one iota more advanced in the method of his work than was that ancient elaborator who demanded a second "hand" in his work. That ancient man no more began his making of implements by such a process, than present men began to fabricate weapons for the use of gunpowder by the making of what we now know as "machine" guns. Palæolithic man attained in such elaboration the highest attribute of his achievements. Many generations of men passed away ere such complexity and delicacy of method could have been attained.

But there is evidence, not only in the well-known Palæolithic gravels of southern England and France, but in many other areas

The more I examine this stone, the more wonderful the sculpturing seems to be. Most of the facets have been produced by what

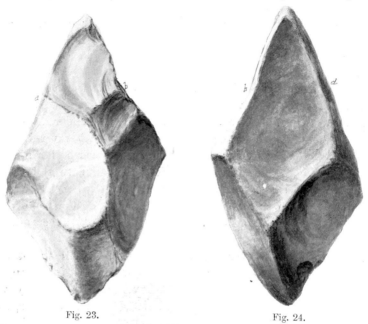

Fig. 23.   Fig. 24.

may be called surface (perpendicular) blows; the flakes have been removed by downward strokes, and not from the side. Well-directed side-strokes usually give bulbs-of-percussion. These facets present concentric waves which circulate about a cone spot, a mere speck, just the apex of a cone that is otherwise perfectly flat, save for the wavelike ripples. The strokes seem to have been given on the flat surface with a sideward direction. The result is exceedingly clever. I have frequently seen this kind of flaking in flint; indeed, it was mainly this kind of work that was only a year ago pronounced by a great expert, upon specimens which I sent to him, to be thermal in origin, to which I have already referred.

Let us notice that all the facets upon this flint are *of one age*; there can be no doubt of that; they were all produced in some remote and limited time. But one of the facets, *a*, is the unaffected original exterior of the nodule from which the whole was sculptured. This was intentionally left, since it forms a facet complementary to one of those sculptured out. That facet was designedly kept intact.

Now let us notice that, since it attained its present form, not one of the sculptured facets, nor yet the natural one, has been in the least affected by temperature or time. It must have lain an incalculable period in that old "coarse" "hill-gravel" bed ere it was deposited upon the heap by the roadside where I found it. When I found it snow was falling; it was a bright breezy day in December of 1883. It was an "April shower" day in winter; but the showers were snow, and the sun came out between them. How long the stone had lain by the roadside I know not. It was, however, perfectly thermal proof. That stone is as much the work of man as is Fig. 6, every whit, and is the more clever production of the two. It was, I judge, a hand weapon; it fits either hand perfectly. I have given a third drawing (Fig. 25) to make the hand-grasp clear. It was a most effective weapon. The ball of the thumb fits perfectly into the curved facet *b*, and that with either hand.

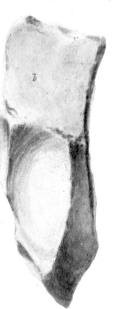

Fig. 25.

Let us take a passing look at several of the Scottish forms which were as evidently the result of a masterly freehand elaboration, exactly comparable with that exhibited in these last-discussed flints.

Fig. 26 is a splendid illustration of bold and skilful flaking. It was a tabular piece of quartzite, as is shown by two natural facets which were left unsculptured, of which *a* is one. The weapon is formed with eight principal facets, is wonderfully cleverly produced, and was and might still be an appallingly effective weapon, if hafted, as I imagine this to have been. We have here an illustration of the greater freedom with which Scottish Palæolithic man worked. There is a boldness and a directness in the fracturing which could seldom be practised by the fabricator from flint nodules, which were ever, not only eccentric in form, but of limited capacity to the sculptor. This specimen is unusually interesting. Except for the mysterious fretting along the edges, the cause of which will in due course become clear to us, it is hardly at all altered since it left the hands of its fabricator. It is therefore of almost the same evidential value as the flints as regards the elaboration. It shows at a glance that even with crystalline quartzite, the fracture is not of the same character as that of the flints—it is not so conchoidal, does not readily present bulbs or pits or waves of concussion, and the ridges of the facets are not nearly so clean and sharp as of the flints. It has been subjected to slight rolling —to such rolling as would scarcely have been perceptible in a flint, but which is plainly evidenced in this Scottish specimen. It was found (*in situ*) in a deposit in the Whitadder Valley, at the foot of the Lammermoor Hills near Duns (1901).

In Fig. 27 we have another Scottish specimen, not greatly rolled ; it is more mellowed by decomposition. It is of basalt, and still exhibits the facets of its workmanship distinctly, sufficiently so to show that if it had been formed from flint it would have been an excellent typical example of the bolder flaking. It is a Forth-shore specimen.

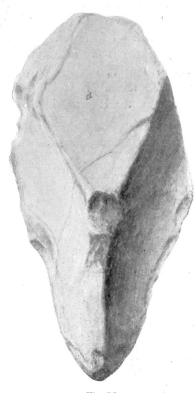

Fig. 26.

Fig. 28 is another illustration of that same bold flaking in a Scottish find. It is of a fine-grained granitic rock, and occurred in a high-level, ancient river-bed, some 60 feet above the present river Allan at Dunblane, and some 200 feet above sea-level. It is somewhat more water-worn than Fig. 27.

Fig. 29 is another of the excellent Scottish forms. It is highly marine-rolled, but is still of clearly defined sculpturing. It is of a hard, close-grained basalt ; it shows little or no decay, its smoothed condition is entirely the result of attrition. It was found in the bed of the river Whitadder, Duns, in 1901. This shows the condition to which many of the Scottish forms are reduced. If this had been a specimen of less design and character it would not now have been recognisable, and if were added to the attrition it has undergone the chemical changes to which these northern forms are subject, it is easy to conceive how difficult it is to recognise multitudes of the

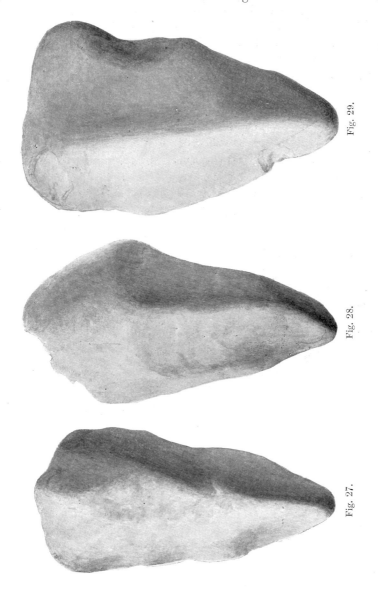

Fig. 29.

Fig. 28.

Fig. 27.

northern relics. The flints are exempt from most of these annihilating forces.

It should be noticed that Figs. 27, 28, and 29 have all of them

been subjected to some of the lateral fretting and crushing; it may
be noticed particularly in the excessively hard and compact material
of Fig. 29. Let us further notice in this specimen that the lateral
fretting took place subsequent to the marine-rolling which it evidences.
It was, of course, as I found it in the river-bed, still being affected
by river-rolling; but that is of slight account compared with the old
rounding. The fretted breaks are also somewhat rolled; they are
not recent.

CHAPTER IV

A Comparative Study of Relics (*continued*)

THERE is something contradictory and anomalous somewhere, when British collectors of the relics of Palæolithic man are ready, as they show themselves to be, to accept uncouth and often well-nigh shapeless elaborations from foreign countries, while they are fastidious to a degree in their acceptance of similar relics of home production. While Palæolithic implements from Somaliland, India, and other places are often of fine form and skilled workmanship, some in public and private collections are so poor, both in form and workmanship, that had I found the same in either England or Scotland, and formed withal of the same material, which is generally quartz, quartzite, or coarse-grained chert or allied rock, I should not have deemed them sufficiently evidential either of human work or human intention, and they certainly would not have been accepted by scientists at home. I have thrown away many, and particularly Scottish specimens, that were in my own opinion perfectly evidential of human work; but while better specimens were condemned as " purely accidental," it was useless for my purpose to accumulate inferior items. As a rule, the Somaliland and East Indian and other foreign relics are better preserved than those of this Northern region, owing largely to climatic and physical conditions—this being probably the attribute which has gained them acceptance.

While I have no doubt of the evidence of human work in these foreign specimens, it seems to me a curious fact that such are freely purchased by collectors who have been, as I have said, actively prejudiced against similarly poor work and rude forms, such as lie in the gravels and other superficial deposits under their feet, or are ground and crushed by the hundred, possibly by the thousand, along the roads of southern and eastern England every year. I have seen sufficient evidence during the last few years, during several limited holidays in the South, to realise that had I remained in East Anglia thirty-six years ago, instead of coming then to Scotland, I should doubtless have collected such a multitude of Palæolithic battle-axes and other implements as no ordinary house could have accommodated. I have, in place of that possible collection, made an

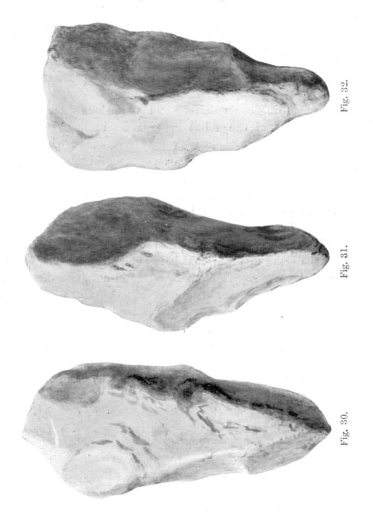

Fig. 32.

Fig. 31.

Fig. 30.

actual one of such proportions, even in Scotland, that it has been for years inconveniently large.

Let me illustrate what may be, in places at least, commonly found in the gravels of southern England, *i.e.* collected from heaps by the roadsides, or from strewn material, or pits. I have already (Figs. 22 and 23) given some idea of what may be found; let us take a general survey, so far as I can present it, of these almost wholly

neglected or unobserved forms of weapons. For the present we need
no description of these specimens, their general aspect being all that

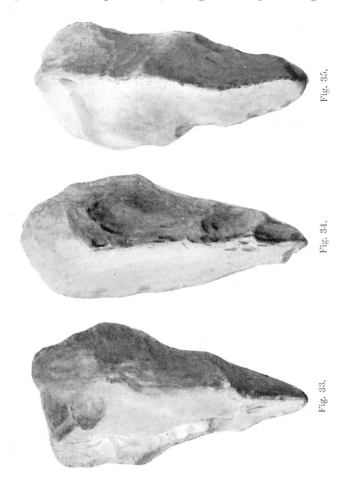

Fig. 35.

Fig. 34.

Fig. 33.

I here call attention to; and this the drawings will, I trust, give.
Figs. 30 to 39, inclusive, are some of those which I have collected
during those hurried visits South. I have just made a rough
calculation, and reckon that, if I had found them with the same
frequency as I did in my holidays South, I must now have had several
thousands of such weapons; not to mention perhaps twice or thrice
as many other forms (domestic and otherwise), to which we shall in
due course refer. I am postulating the possible past thirty-six years'
persistent search in England. For several years before his death,

Sir Joseph Prestwich had made something like an heroic effort to

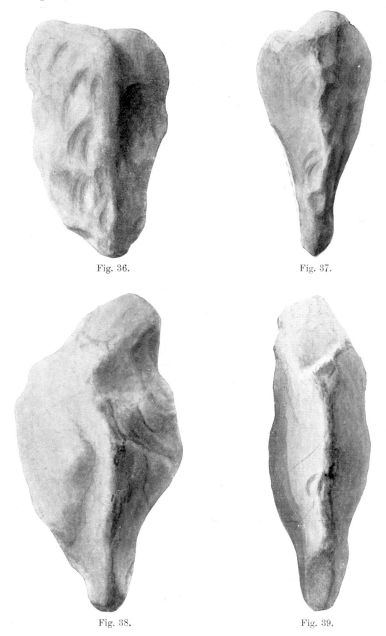

Fig. 36.   Fig. 37.

Fig. 38.   Fig. 39.

bring these evident elaborations into recognition, and especially on behalf of a type of a yet more primitive character—Mr. Benjamin Harrison's eoliths—with, in many quarters, questionable success. But to show that others besides himself were falling into line with him, at least as to the rougher Palæolithic finds, and especially with regard to the foreign finds, I quote from the then Mr. Joseph Prestwich :—[1]

"Mr. Montgomery Bell informs me that he has certainly seen and rejected some of the old rude specimens, owing to the absence of the bulb-of-percussion, which he then considered essential." [2]

All the specimens (Figs. 30 to 39) may be said to be characterised by the absence of bulbs-of-percussion.

If I take up such a modern work as Worthington G. Smith's *Man the Primeval Savage* (1894), the last of the British issues which treat essentially of the fabrications of Palæolithic man, I look in vain among the 242 illustrations for forms with such bold, plain work as characterises the specimens here shown (Figs. 30 to 39), except in two or three instances, which are foreign. I do not in any way desire to disparage Mr. Smith's work; his discovery of ancient (Palæolithic) "floors," *i.e.* buried land-surfaces upon which these ancient men worked, his replacement of the very chips which they had struck away from recovered forms, and his restorations, not only of broken implements but of the actual nodules from which they were sculptured out, are monuments of heroic patience, and his results are among the most romantic achievements of scientific investigation. Yet Mr. Smith worked in a narrow zone, as is evidenced in much that he says in his work. It is indeed only when he is brought face to face with the work of foreign investigators, *i.e.* of Englishmen or Europeans in other parts of the world, that he seems to apprehend the "Greater Britain" of his "primeval savage."

I have made drawings of two Madras (India) specimens (Figs. 40, 41, and 42), from W. G. Smith's book (pp. 11, 12), which are both more indefinite in form than any specimen which I have assumed to be a fabrication from Scotland. In reference to the first (Fig. 40), the author says (p. 10): "The most massive human-made implement of which I have any record is now in the Government Central Museum, Madras. It is made of quartzite, measures $9\frac{3}{4}$ by $5\frac{3}{4}$ inches, and weighs 6 lbs. 4 oz. This tool is engraved from a drawing kindly

---

[1] "Age of Plateau Drift," *Quart. Journal Geol. Socy.*, May 1899 and May 1901.

[2] Mr. Montgomery Bell was more appreciative of my exhibited Scottish specimens than any other of the members of the British Association who inspected them at their Meeting in Edinburgh in 1892.

forwarded to me by Dr. George Bidie. . . . Another very heavy
implement, formerly in my own collection, but now in the British

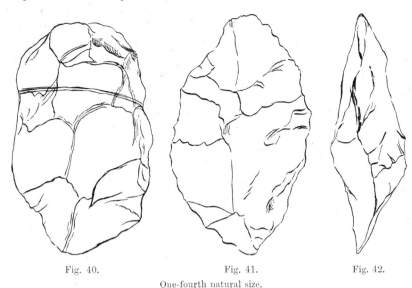

Fig. 40.　　　　　　　　　Fig. 41.　　　　　　　Fig. 42.

One-fourth natural size.

Museum, Bloomsbury, is also a tool of quartzite from Madras,
procured for me by the aid of Dr. Bidie. It measures 9¾ by
5⅜ inches, and weighs 4 lbs. 7¾ oz." It is of importance from what
we shall ere long have to consider that we notice the size of these
Indian specimens; their style of work and their size together will
help us to a better apprehension of the Scottish finds. But while
we are criticising the narrower outlook of a now nearly extinct school
of investigators into these relics, and while we have the admission of
these Indian forms in view, let me point out that my assertion that
Worthington G. Smith gives no illustration of these more barbarously
worked items from his own country, is modified by one exception.
Upon p. 131, *Man the Primeval Savage*, three views of a weapon,
which is of identical work with Fig. 2, p. 12, same volume (from
Madras), are given by Mr. Smith, who has replaced a flake which the
ancient worker struck off. But as the specimen is not Indian, but
English, in this more barbarous manner, the author apologises for its
style, by describing it as an "implement in an initial condition." Are
not the Madras forms equally to be described as in initial conditions?

It has been the habit of many, and of some down to the present,
to thus ignore the intention of the maker of a simply produced

implement; and if the same cannot be suggested to be unfinished work, to close discussion by denying its human elaboration *in toto*. It was with something like surprise that I read Mr. W. G. Smith's implied unacquaintance with large weighty specimens of European or British origin until the Madras items attracted his attention, since in M. de Perthes' collection, which I had the honour and pleasure of inspecting on two occasions in 1883, there were certainly several weapons of exceptionally large size. My notes give the following :— " Musée M. de Perthes, July 25, 1883.—Magnificent collection of implements (weapons), several specimens very large, one being 12 or 14 inches in length. Some of these large specimens are very rough in character, others are beautifully wrought." I well remember being struck with those very large objects. Perhaps because I was thus interested in the abnormally large specimens at Abbeville, I had an eye henceforth for possible like finds. At the end of that same year I was in Cambridgeshire for the second time, and among other places visited Hildersham, whence an interesting specimen, before referred to, was obtained. I was wonderfully successful on that occasion, and found so many interesting objects that two large specimens—one very large and well-shaped—had to be left behind. I hid them in a hedge, intending to return again for them, but time, and perhaps " means," ran short—they may or may not still be where I hid them. They were from the coarse hill-gravels.

I was, further, a good many years ago impressed by the presence of two large implements which, if I remember correctly, were over a foot each in length, in Lord Northesk's Collection, then on exhibition in the Museum, Chambers Street, Edinburgh. I attempted to make notes and drawings of these two, but was ordered to put my notebook away, as the collection was a private one and only on loan.

We shall, I think, see, if we take a rational view of the exigencies of the life of that ancient man, that what we may choose to call great implements were a necessity of his being, of his everyday actions and undertakings, and therefore common and natural in his day. One can understand Mr. W. G. Smith's wonder at the size and weight of the Madras examples when we learn his view of the physical and moral condition of that ancient savage. On p. 56, *Man the Primeval Savage*, Mr. Smith writes as follows :—" Primeval man is commonly described as a hunter of the great hairy mammoth, of the bear and the lion ; but it is in the highest degree improbable that the human savage ever hunted animals much larger than the hare, the rabbit, and the rat. Man was probably the hunted rather than the hunter." This reads oddly, especially after a paragraph immediately before (p. 55) to the effect that, "Stone-implement-making would be a great industry. The old males and females, aided by children, would be despatched to look after suitable blocks of flint, to push such flints out of the chalk, stiff clay, or earth with sticks, and bring them to the human haunt. There by the fireside, the more skilled and light-handed human creatures would, with anvil, hammer, and punch-stones, fabricate pointed stone weapons and keen-edged oval choppers and knives." And all this, as is suggested, in order to hunt the hare, the rabbit, and the rat! No wonder the large Madras implements came with the force of real thunderbolts, particularly as the writer suggests the possibility of his ancient Palæolithic fabricator having come to Britain westward from India (p. 9), in which case that ancient man made the gigantic weapons ages before his descendants, supposing them to be such, could have reached north-western Europe. It is clear that the weapons, great or small, were for use. The man must have been a great hunter, as indeed we shall see he was; as we shall also see, he was instinctively a domesticated and an intelligent being.

But though it is important to have raised an interest in what are thought to be abnormally large fabrications, our main point at this present juncture in our study of that ancient man's work is that of the *style* of his elaborations, and its possible and probable variation, at different periods of his existence; and under the different circumstances of variation of material and other physical modifications which his passage from one region to another naturally imply.

As I have already suggested that such poor forms as the Madras specimens (Figs. 40, 41, and 42) would probably, ages ago, under Scottish atmospheric and physical conditions, have become unrecognisable, it follows that having collected what I conceive to be highly recognisable specimens in Scotland, they must be of more characteristic form, and often of better workmanship, than the two said specimens; and that I consider to be the case. Let us now return to our comparative study of the Scottish forms.

Let us briefly compare several of the roughest of these Northern forms with the more primitive specimens (Figs. 30 to 39) from the Palæolithic gravels of England. These English forms are generally ruggedly, but often skilfully, sculptured from the natural flint nodule, the form of the weapon produced being, as a rule, governed by the natural form of the nodule, in which case the unwrought surface of the flint enters largely into the actual form of the finished weapon. In Fig. 31, for instance, the lightest in colour of the three comprehensive facets shown is the natural exterior of the nodule. It runs, as is indicated, around the butt - end, and passes about one-third down the underside; all the rest of the weapon was sculptured out from the nodule.

Here is a Scottish specimen (Fig. 43). It never was a nodule (there are no native (flint) nodules in Scotland), but it was a naturally tabulated piece of basalt. And the ancient man did in Scotland exactly what his coeval did with the flint nodule in England. He designed his weapon from the suggestion of the actual form of the naturally tabular mass, by striking away such

Fig. 43.

portions as were necessary to his purpose, and leaving such natural facets as already conformed to the figure of the proposed implement. The large upper facet and a similar one on the underside were natural to the stone when he chose it for his prospective weapon. Fig. 44 is of the same rough-and-ready type. In this specimen all the facets shown are the work of the fabricator; but most of the underside is of more ancient aspect, i.e. is more rolled, and shows that a cylindrical stone was chosen, very possibly a damaged and yet more ancient weapon, which a few strokes of well-directed masterly blows reduced to its present form. Compare Fig. 43 with Fig. 31,

Fig. 44.

and Fig. 44 with Figs. 32 and 33, and we have fairly corresponding
forms with exactly similar work and the same intention shown in
both English and Scottish items.   Fig. 45 is a very boldly struck-
out specimen ; which, so far as one can judge (for it is highly rolled),
was fashioned from a yet more highly rolled stone—one so rounded
that we should have called it a pebble.   Fig. 46 is of the same type
of work, but it was wholly sculptured out of a mass of basalt.   This
last is scarcely at all water-worn, but is mellowed and minutely

Fig. 45.   Fig. 46.

honeycombed in the usual way by long submergence at the bottom
of the sea, and has lost its point.   This is an Ayrshire-coast specimen.
In Figs. 47 and 48 we have an interesting Scottish find comparable
with Fig. 38, and side view (39), from the English gravels.   The
English implement is formed from an oddly shaped flint nodule.   The
maker of the weapon was guided, as is seen, by the nodule's natural
shape, portions of the exterior of which are left untouched.   This
weapon, if hafted, and I presume it to have been hafted, was a
very effective one — the point end is skilfully produced.   The
Scottish item (Figs. 47 and 48) is a larger specimen, the former (the
flint) being 6¾, the latter 8¾ inches in length.   There is in both

specimens the same freehanded style of work; but as I have already pointed out, the man who used that freehand stroke upon flint nodules was hampered by restrictions which the form and

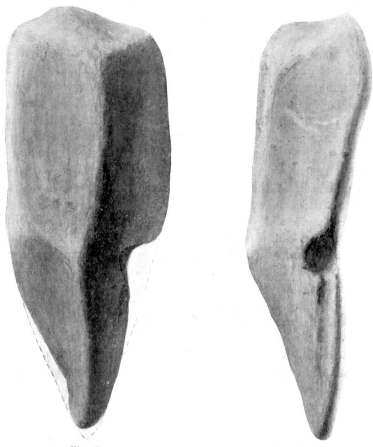

Fig. 47.   Fig. 48.

limitations of the nodules themselves imposed. In the use of Scottish rocks the freehand worker had much fuller play, as is well shown in this fine instance. It would have been actually a difficult matter to find any mass of Scottish rock so fantastically formed as are the flint nodules; and in Scotland if one fragment of rock did not offer scope for a prospective elaboration, it had only to be discarded and a better stone chosen. There could have been little such choice among the flints, except very locally. The effect of this greater freedom in the work of the Scottish elaborator is at once seen, not only in Figs. 47 and 48, but in 43, both of which are masterly productions. Their sculpturing is surprisingly bold and clever. There is not a sign of uncertain work, every stroke produced the intended effect: in this sense, although the work is much bolder, they are replicas of the English example which we discussed under Figs. 23 to 25. The form of Fig. 47 when perfect (note the lines of restoration) was excellent, and even elegant. It was, as doubtless was intended, a formidable weapon : I am assuming that it was hafted. Men who could make such weapons knew full well how to use them — we shall indeed see that they were as full of expedients as necessity demanded. I am convinced that Palæolithic man mounted these forms; that he was a great trapper and hunter; that he did attack even the largest of the great Mammalia; that he maintained his own during the prolonged epoch or epochs of the existence of that great fauna, in what are now the British Isles; and that he was a brave and courageous being—no mere scalp-hunter, and murderer of his fellows, but a man, as I have said, with a strong domestic strain in his nature, as will be evidenced in the record of these Scottish finds, and their corroborations from English deposits. This implement now under discussion (Fig. 47) is of a somewhat decayed quartzite, the cavity in the side being the result of a "core" rotting out, which released the lost lateral fragment. The other fragment indicated as gone from nearer the point might have resulted from that end of the weapon coming into contact with some hard body in actual use. There are eight distinct facets upon this weapon, all of which are unquestionably of one age, save, I think, part of the facet on the side on which the cavity occurs; that facet is older than the others, and points to the stone from which the weapon was sculptured out; and with what power and skill was that effected!

When I was, lately, corresponding with the Rev. Osmond Fisher concerning these Scottish forms, he expressed a difficulty in realising that that ancient man could have achieved such work; i.e. the work exhibited in large specimens such as that now under consideration. But the foreign items are helping us to a better realisation of that ancient man's capacity.

Mr. Worthington G. Smith alludes to what one might call the strength of the work, with reference to one of the Madras specimens before referred to, as follows :—" I have a rude tool of quartzite from Madras, made from a single ponderous outside flake, which weighs

3 lbs. 13 oz. The single blow which was sufficient to detach such a large splinter from a block of quartzite must have been delivered with terrific force" (p. 10, *Man the Primeval Savage*).

I do not think the said flake need have been the result of one blow delivered with terrific force, but of a series of blows, delivered with the final intention of securing the said outside flake, but which flake was *humoured,* so as to put it off the stone. I have seen a mason so carefully humour large blocks of sandstone into two portions, or a large item so taken from a much larger. I am not alluding to the rough breaking away of items with a hammer which we have all seen, but of the fracturing through a stone with a definite intention of flaking or dividing by starting a fracture and completing it by repeated blows. Our ancient man probably never attempted such a fracturing at one blow, as is suggested; but if he found means of attaching a weighty stone to a handle, then the one blow might even have detached the Madras flake, though such procedure was not, I think, necessary. See, for instance, what an effective hammer the butt-end of Figs. 47 and 48 would have made. *That* I believe to have been mounted; and if it were, what was to prevent a much heavier object being hafted in the same way and used as a hammer? But even then the spirit of humouring must have come in, or the hammer would have been as soon broken as the objective stone.

CHAPTER V

A Great Hunter in Caledon

WAS the man who has been in our mind in our comparative study of his relics a degraded and well-nigh helpless being; a man—hardly a man, according to the opinion of some—who fled from the face of every beast that was worthy of his resistance, who lived in constant hiding; a man without a spark of any of those attributes which are characteristic of mankind? That is the opinion of some who profess to have studied his relics, who profess to have a knowledge of his works and ways; it is the opinion of some who have devoted time and money in buying up every possible typical and "orthodox" relic, and in collecting a long array of his axe-like weapons. Herein is perhaps to be found the reason why he is considered to have been the helpless craven; for, though the same relics often show him to have had something approaching an æsthetic taste in form and workmanship, yet, since he (apparently) had only the conception of the one orthodox form, and not another idea, it is excusable perhaps to have thought of him as a helpless, incapable being, a coward.

But he was no coward, no craven, no poor creature with the one idea that alone marked him human. He was a man of heroic qualities, who was fully equal to the then momentous demands upon his courage, upon his skill in offence and defence; and this not in civil warfare, in man against man—the evidence is strongly against such a picture—but in his self-defence against the great mammals of his day; in offence by the exercise of his mind and the skill of his body in the necessity of maintaining his own existence.

We shall see when we come to his domestic (?) forms that he was prepared for great emergencies; that he could and did face the great mammals; that he hunted and trapped and slew them; that he flayed them and cured their skins; and the craven he is depicted could have done none of these things. A whole world of his history —his character, his doings, his habits are to be read, as I have for forty years endeavoured to read them, in almost wholly unrecognised relics, well-nigh everywhere strewn about us.

But meantime we must dwell upon this man's presumed one idea, and study his weapons alone. But here, in this one faculty of weapon-maker, we have every evidence of his heroic qualities, and not of these alone, but of the wonderful power he possessed of boldly and skilfully manipulating the rocks to suit the every instant demand; a power to adapt himself and things to the need of the moment. In a word, his weapons alone, as I believe every unbiassed reader will see, show this man to have been a skilled and great and heroic hunter.

It is impossible to dwell upon the merits of every type of his offensive handiwork which I adduce, but I trust that where every possible aid is given to the reader in illustration rather than in words, he will use his imaginative faculties so as to see the man himself, at least so far as he is represented by his works. Rocks, stones, relics cannot lie.

In Figs. 49 and 50 we have an elegant specimen of what we may consider a normal type; and of this more normal size and style let us make a study as a preliminary to more unexpected forms and sizes which follow. This specimen is of basalt;

Fig. 49.   Fig. 50.

it was somewhat water-worn ages before it found its rest at the bottom of the Clyde estuary (it is an Ayrshire-shore specimen), where some of its crystals were dissolved out—it has the usual mellowed and honeycombed aspect of that process. Portions have decomposed away from the edges, and a small portion will be seen to have parted at probably a prismatic plane, which parting has spoiled the excellent balance of the figure. Its point end, which was produced with admirable skill, is perfect. It is 7½ inches in length.

Fig. 51 is another excellent in form and preservation, and is of

a fine-grained, compact trap. It has, I think, never been subject to rolling, but is slightly mellowed by decomposition. The original work is still plain upon it; it is, however, fretted in what we may call the normal fashion, along its edges, and the point is gone, but one of its lateral edges is almost perfect, and that shows with what great skill the fabricator in primeval Scotland produced his weapons. It is a highly interesting specimen, for two main reasons: First, it was one of the earliest of my finds in Scotland, and, second, it comes from a well-defined ancient deposit, from which I have derived a few other equally interesting objects, which we shall more particularly consider in subsequent pages. The specimen is damaged somewhat by the passage of a cart, an accident which arose from the fact that several loads of material from the said deposit had been strewn upon a road at Forteviot, and I found it in a rut in

Fig. 51.

the said road. There is no doubt whence the material came. It is marked " 1875," so I have had the specimen now for over thirty years. It was, when perfect, about 7 inches in length.

Figs. 52 and 53 are another specimen from the Forteviot deposit which was found five years later, viz. in 1880. It is of grey, gritty, plutonic rock, somewhere, I think, between an ordinary basalt and Aberdeen granite. I obtained it *in situ* in the Forteviot bed. It is highly water-worn, and for that reason is the more interesting, since it must have received that smoothing by attrition, before it reached the Forteviot deposit. Except for the rolling effect and some decay, the specimen is perfect, as shown in the drawings. This specimen is a little over 7 inches in length.

Fig. 54 is a beautiful specimen, of a compact basalt, and of
elegant shape; its length is $6\frac{3}{4}$ inches, and on both sides it is

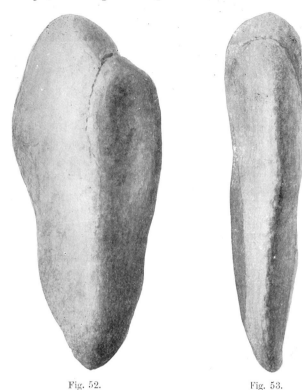

Fig. 52.   Fig. 53.

skilfully elaborated. In section it gives a depressed diamond-
oval. It is somewhat damaged at the point, and is fretted rather
extensively, though not roughly, along its edges. Though I found
this specimen in the bed of the river Whitadder, Duns (1901), I
have good reason for believing that it had been derived but a
brief time before from a certain deposit in the valley. This,
and all the foregoing in this chapter, would, had they been but
of flint, be considered "gems" as specimens.

In Fig. 55 we have a good Somme-Valley-like weapon, which,
although greatly rounded by marine shore-rolling, is of excellent
and still well-shown workmanship. It is of an intensely compact,
hard black basalt, of a massive build, and almost perfect save
for the rolling; and save for the fairly common feature among
these Scottish forms, that the point end has been powerfully

snapped off, in this case before the rolling took place.   In section it gives a rotund oval; its present length is $5\frac{7}{8}$ inches.   It is a Forth-shore specimen.

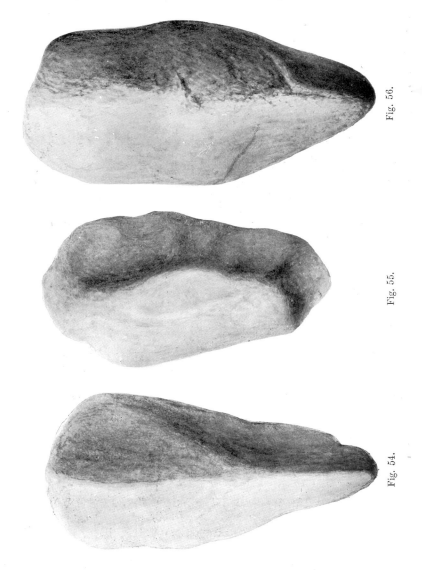

Fig. 56.

Fig. 55.

Fig. 54.

In Fig. 56 we have another cast up by the sea.   It is somewhat massive in build, but of excellent form, which form is perfect, in so far that it has suffered nothing further than ancient (marine?)

rolling, which rolling preceded the decay so apparent in the specimen. It is 7⅜ inches in length and gives a good oval in section—once again as clever a workman is evidenced by it as ever produced a Somme-type weapon.

Figs. 57 and 58 are to myself a highly interesting example. It is of a somewhat different type from the foregoing in this chapter,

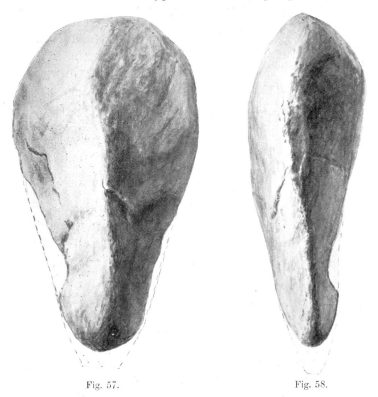

Fig. 57.   Fig. 58.

its butt-end is broader and more globe-like. It reminds me strongly of certain of the Somaliland specimens. It is a fine-grained Peterhead granite, is somewhat decayed, and highly rolled. It has lost a large piece from one of its facets—a thermal break, perhaps—which has greatly marred the form. Its point was, I imagine, damaged before it was subject to the severe rolling it indicates. I found it in 1896 (*in situ*) in an ancient delta-deposit, some 30 feet or so above sea-level at Aberdeen. Notwithstanding its water-worn condition, its bold style of elaboration is well exhibited. It is now just over 7 inches in length, and gives in section a diamond-oval.

Fig. 59 is a massive implement, in general form a replica of the last-mentioned (Aberdeen) specimen, but of larger build. It is in its present condition a trifle over 9 inches, and must have been fully

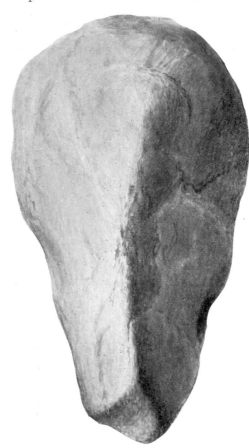

Fig. 59.

10 inches in length when it left the hands of its fabricator. It weighs over 5 lbs. 15 oz. It is of black, compact, heavy basalt, and is a Forth-shore specimen.

And now we are launched among some abnormally large (Scottish) finds which we ought seriously to study. There comes with this first larger specimen (59) a difficulty, or what is presumed to be such, in the question of how such a weapon was handled, *i.e.* made use of, either as a weapon of offence or defence. It has been, especially of late years, a habit of mind among certain investigators in this field to assume, as already pointed out, an infantile and helpless condition for our ancient man. It is a mere assumption, which has, I fancy, been insisted upon against actual evidence, or, to say the least, without real evidence in support of such a view. Such a habit of mind has, I believe, been largely responsible for the extraordinary way in which the larger examples of this man's work have been ignored. The weapon, for it unquestionably was such (Fig. 59), is of such form that it is not easy to conceive how it was effectively and securely hafted. Yet I cannot see that such a weapon was of any material use if merely held in the hands; two hands could alone hold it, in which case the holder might as well have had "gyves upon his wrists" so far as liberty of action was concerned, in which case also the least casualty must have driven the weapon from the holder's grasp. It is inconceivable to me that he who could fabricate such a weapon could not also adapt such fabrication to a usable condition. It is a mere assumption that he could not and did not haft his large weapons, or, as some assert, any of them.

That Palæolithic man was, and is, thought thus incapable of using his (larger) weapons, was the natural outcome of the prior assumption that such a being could not have made them. We have seen that Mr. Worthington G. Smith was astonished that the ancient man of Madras was able to detach and elaborate large masses of stone, and I have lately (1906) been told by more than one well-known scientist that primeval man had neither the means nor the power to produce such work. The assumption that such work could not have been achieved, cuts away, of course, all argument as to the hafting of such specimens.

But facts that may be adduced as evidence in the shape of actual weapons and other items, the production of which have demanded energy and strength and intelligence, are "chiels that winna ding," even in the presence of all the assumption the world has known and has to offer. There *are* the weapons. The implement shown in Fig. 59 is as evidently fabricated by man as any specimens from the Somme Valley or elsewhere, and being a piece of man's handiwork, the man did make it, and having made it, he knew how to use it. It is not conceivable that such a man could have designed and made an implement except from necessity, and the designing and making imply an efficient use of the same; efficiency demanded a handle, and that I have no doubt it had.

With a haft this specimen was a most efficient and even a formidable weapon. With such an implement in hand the man is immediately transformed before us; he is no longer a timid hunter of hares and rabbits and rats, but a hunter of noble game; a hunter of the mammoth and other elephantidæ, of bears and oxen and bisons; of the hippopotamus and rhinoceros, of fleet-footed horses and deer; a royal hunter indeed who faced the king of beasts—as why should he fear with his long-hafted (lighter) weapon, a swing of which was more effective far than a damask blade or spear or arrow or even a modern gun. Close quarters was the mode in that epoch; there may have been, and I think there were, spears and arrows even then, but these weapons of our present argument were all designed for heroic hand encounter.   The smaller, more serviceable weapons were for the man on the trail of his quarry ; the larger, such as Fig. 59, for the plotter, for the contriver of pits or entanglements, who watched and waited, or learning the news of a catch in a pit or in meshes, hurried forth with his ponderous axe over his shoulder to give the crashing death-blow to the mightiest of the mammals.

This was indeed the earliest conception of ancient man.   In Figuier's *World before the Deluge*, which I well remember reading as a lad, this ancient man was depicted as carrying his mighty weapon over his shoulder, and clad with the skins of beasts—a much more rational view in conjunction with the known relics than that he was a timid, despicable wretch.   His handiwork, as I know it, is proof to me of his broader and higher and greater instincts and attributes.   Socially and physically this ancient Briton was in no sense a man to be despised.   There has been of late years, *i.e.* during the past quarter of a century or so, a lowering of the views regarding this man.   I do not mean merely in the conception of what the man was, but real shortcomings in the method of using the actual evidence of that man's existence and surroundings. The why and the wherefore of such a failing mental attitude is, as seems to me, the setting up of groundless opinions, and the proclamation of them as eternal verities, instead of suspending the judgment while awaiting what may yet be discovered in the storehouse of Nature.   We have no more gleaned a full knowledge of that ancient man, of his capacity and works, and of his existence in time, than we have reached the moon, or shown that other planets are inhabited.

After thirty-six years' work and forty years' investigation literally among the rocks, among the possible and actual relics of ancient man in Britain, I feel that I am now only upon the threshold of the original habitat of that long-lost ancestor, and, but for the fact now so evident, that the years of my opportunity are nearly all with the past, and few with the future, I could start afresh from the present view of that ancient being's horizon, assured of what greater things can be done; but time and tide neither wait nor turn out of course, and so I am anxious to place on record the evidence of the relics as I have read them, and with that to be content.

Figs. 60 and 61 present us with another large and what may be called roughly formed example.   Yet such a weapon, mounted upon a shaft, and this would have   a more easily mounted than

the last (Fig. 59), was just as effective as the most highly elaborated
implement could have been.   It is most cleverly elaborated from a
mass of quartzite, the side view giving one an idea of the skill
of the bold flaking.   Its facets are all of one age, and that

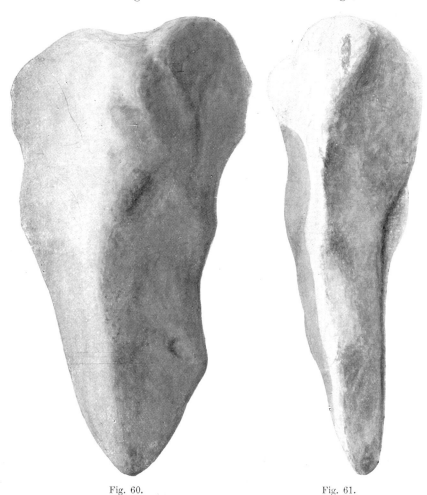

Fig. 60.   Fig. 61.

evidently a great one; and the weapon is in its form, with one or
two immaterial exceptions, as it left its fabricator's hands.   It is a
Forth shore find; its angles have rather been rounded by decomposition than by attrition; it cannot have been long ashore.   It is
9¼ inches in length and weighs over 5 lbs.
    In Figs. 62 and 63 we l. e a very striking specimen.   Portions

of its outline have rotted or been fretted away. I have suggested
its restoration, which gives in its broader aspect a fine figure. It was
boldly and most cleverly sculptured bodily from a mass of some

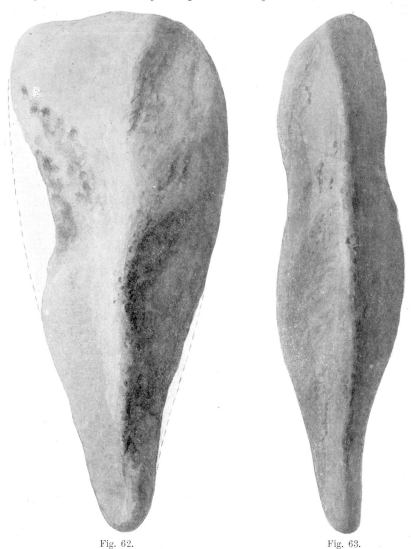

Fig. 62.   Fig. 63.

variety of trap. It still clearly indicates the masterly handling of
its fabricator. It was a weapon of which that primeval hunter
might well have boasted, as he possibly did. He would have been
a brave compeer who dared to face the owner with his mounted

work, and suggest that it wasn't a fine weapon—an instant experiment would have shown the maligner that it was a magnificent one —as indeed it is. I would call attention to the peculiar conformation of its side facets as seen in the edgewise view; we shall see that that may have some relation to the method of hafting. This specimen is 10½ inches in length and weighs 4 lbs. 10 oz. In its pristine condition it must have weighed a good bit over 5 lbs. It is a Clyde estuary specimen.

We have a magnificent example in Figs. 64 and 65, magnificent in its size, form, and the skill with which it was produced. "There were giants in those days"—giants in courage, giants in physical strength, though not necessarily in stature; although it is interesting and corroborative to find that the most ancient man at present known was of no mean stature. See excellent summary of the evidence of what is called the "first man" in the masterly treatise by Dr. A. H. Keane, *Man Past and Present*, pp. 3-6, which ancient man Dr. Keane describes as "the pliocene inhabitant of Java," who was of average height—"say, five feet six inches." That most ancient man is surrounded in the deposit in which his remains occur with his handiwork, his weapons—a fact which alone, especially if one has referred to his verbal portraiture in the said volume, will be conceived to be full of a profound significance. He was already a hunter, with artificial aids; he had already set out upon his mission of "replenishing" the earth and "subduing" it with the aid of his human attributes—his erect posture, his power to utilise the material things around him, and, above all, his mental superiority. He was "the Adam" of the set purpose of Almighty God in the world.

It is no longer a marvel that I should find so ancient a relic of human work and intention in Scotland, even though it be a ponderous weapon! It is rather infinitely more natural that such relics should occur in this region than that they should be absent. The *raison d'être* of such statement will appear in subsequent chapters.

But to our specimen, Fig. 64. It is in almost perfect condition. All that it has suffered is a gentle smoothing by attrition, probably marine. It is of a fine-grained quartzite, only slightly and superficially decayed; is a masterly piece of sculpturing from a mass the older surface of which is shown in one of the facets; that of the darker shadow in the drawing, which is represented as pitted smallpox-wise—that being the condition of the original surface of the stone from which it was fabricated. All the other facets are newer, and are all of one age, and that of the long ago.   Let us again

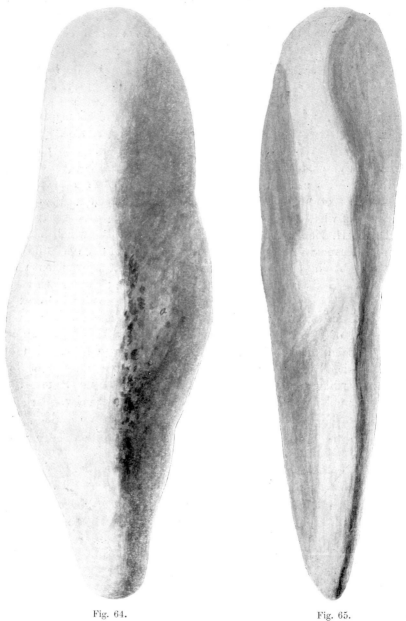

Fig. 64.   Fig. 65.

notice how boldly, how magnificently, the sculpturing was done !   It gives one a voucher of manly strength of purpose; of a real strength and an unhesitating directness in the execution of an intention; not only most admirable, but, I should say, with all our modern aids, with inimitable skill.

Let us further look at it as a thing to be attached to a shaft. If hafted it was indeed a weapon; unmounted, at best a club, but that too heavy for use in one hand; unmounted, it was by comparison with its assumed hafted condition a cumbersome toy.

Now, if mounted, and it seems to me to have been designed with the mounting in view, a split shaft of green or pliable wood, or possibly a "wyth" of stout ground-ash or hazel or some such tough though yielding sapling, twisted around the implement and bound with newly cut thongs from a "green" skin, were probably the commoner modes. We see in the edgewise view (Fig. 65) how, inserted in a split shaft, the split parts of such green shaft could have been made to fairly meet by strong binding at either of the lateral edges. Now let us notice the obviously intentional lateral expansion of either edge (in Fig. 64) about midway between the butt and the point of the weapon. We now see that the broadest part of the implement would be that which was mainly covered by the attached split shaft. If now the final binding thongs are conceived to be wound over and over across the two parts of the shaft and thereby over the two faces of and around the weapon, St. Andrew's cross wise, you have the weapon mounted in a fashion that knew no yielding; it could not be driven out of place either upward or downward unless the thongs should break or the shaft be splintered; but as the thongs dried, they grew hard, hard as steel, and tightened as they dried; there was thus no great fear of either casualty; and a shaft of wood was as strong then as it is to-day in, say, our sledge-hammer contrivance.

In the edgewise view of Figs. 62 and 63 we see that precisely the same effect is produced. In the example (Fig. 64), the "hold-fast" curves are produced upon the lateral edges, but in Fig. 63 upon the broad facets; the effect is the same identically, so far as utility is concerned; as the result is also, as seen in their different positions.

The same lateral expansive contour is seen also in Fig. 56, evidently equally intentional, and doubtless with the same object in view.

In Fig. 60 we have a much less regular outline than in the three foregoing; but there are also the lateral outward curves, or protuberances, that are admirably placed, if the intention was that they should serve as fixtures in the mounting. I have some few further illustrations of this interesting and suggestive feature. But other retaining methods are suggested which we may see as we proceed.

If there were no problems in this piece of research it would have had no interest for myself; but during all the years that I have had it in hand it has been full of a most absorbing interest in its problems. Here is a problem which has never ceased for several years at least to puzzle me. It is in this region of abnormally large specimens. When I found the fine specimen (Fig. 64) upon the shore (Forth), I imagined that it represented the biggest conceivable weapon or implement of any kind. I carried that specimen all the way home to South Queensferry, some six miles, with one or two other items on a hot day. It was, say, a lamb when I started, it was a sheep ere I reached home. Had I known when I discovered it how ponderous it would become in its carriage I might have doubted the possibility of its being a weapon. I soon recovered, however, from that sense of disgust, and felt indignant with myself for such weakness; for the weapon is worth a hundred miles' such toil.

What then could I think of a specimen, an undoubted fabrication in my estimation of at least 20 lbs. weight. I presumed I had found such, but when I found it I doubted and doubted, went away, and returned again and again; it was and is a fabrication, but I have it not. It is still lying, I presume, somewhere on the shore (on the Forth) where I left it. It might now be shifted by wave action any distance from where I saw it. It occurred in such situation that it was not easy to get a conveyance for it; and expense has always been perforce debarred as an aid in my work—not to mention the voices and opinions of friends as to the sanity of bringing home such a relic. So, there it lay still, somewhere on the shore where I had almost given it over to oblivion; when its possible importance was brought forcibly back to me by a more surprising replica appearing where I should not have dreamed of looking for one, and that was in Worthington G. Smith's *Man the Primeval Savage*. On p. 242 are two illustrations of an enormous flint nodule, which has by no great amount of elaboration, though still evident enough, been converted into some kind of implement. This is what the author says in regard to it: "As a contrast to some of the smaller tools, it may be well to refer here to the huge, heavy, and unabraded implement found and given to me by Miss Eleanor A. Ormerod, F.M.S., in gravel and brick-earth thrown out of an excavation made for the new Hounslow & London Railway, immediately south of Osterley Park, near Isleworth, as illustrated in Fig. 170. The engraving shows the implement one-sixth of the natural size, and exhibits a front and side view. The tool is two feet long and weighs 32 lbs." On p. 243 the author continues: "The tool appears to have been used as an instrument of heavy thrusting, as well as in a horizontal position as an anvil-stone. It would be idle to mention the possible uses of such a large tool as this, but any one who has formed ideas of the probable mode of life of primeval men will readily think of numerous purposes to which such an implement could have been put. The example is now in the British Museum."

The curious feature about this is, as seems to me, the readiness with which this find was accepted by the author as a fabrication. I have no doubt that it is such. I cannot, however, so easily conceive numerous purposes to which such an implement could have been put: more particularly by a people who are described as so incapable as only to hunt hares and smaller quarry, and who were "the hunted rather than the hunters." I can only see a reasonable use of such a bludgeon in the events of *trapped* elephants or hippopotami or equally thick-skinned animals. Such an implement could in such case have crashed in the skull even of an elephant; or if it could have been so wielded its point end would with its own weight have penetrated the skin-armour of the hippopotamus. It was impossible of course to have hafted such an implement. The man who used such a "tool" in any way was not a hunted creature, but a grave, strong-minded and strong-limbed resourceful being, who overcame what would be to us in like circumstances almost insuperable difficulties.

I make no pretence of assuming that my view that the weapons (generally) were hafted is a new one; it is not at all new. As I have pointed out, it was the early view of some of the continental explorers. It was Sir Joseph Prestwich's view, which he thus briefly expresses in vol. xxii. *Anthropological Institute Proceedings*, 1892: "Many of the implements were no doubt used in the hand; but a large, and probably the greater number, must have been fixed or tied to handles of wood or bone." This was, and is, the view of other English savants.

Had that ancient man never mounted his weapons, as some of our prominent "experts" still consider was the case, he would, and must, have been the craven being such as Worthington G. Smith conceives him to have been—and he would have continued to be such, and there would not, and could not have been, what we now see, a capable and an exalted humanity. It was by his going out into the wide world, and by the exercise of the greater attributes with which he was endowed, that he at last reached that land of "oil, olive, and honey," of well-nigh illimitable resources, and all because he was not the craven to be turned back on the very threshold of the promised inheritance.

But this man, the ancient fabricator of the weapons we have studied, was not one to be baffled; he sought and found, although it was stage by stage, the better region. To him, his advancement was his own work, day by day and through successive millenniums, and he triumphed in the strength of his purpose, in the presence of the great mammalia. And he achieved great things even in this northern Britain, as we shall see in the further turning of these pages.

Since this chapter was written I have made a further effort with regard to the large shore specimen; which I found again, carried two miles along a rugged shore, and having chartered a cab to meet me, the said specimen and I arrived home in triumph. It is an extraordinary example, which may have been fabricated from a naturally tabular mass—one of its facets is of the original stone; the rest is magnificently bold work, the point being cleverly produced. It is 1 foot 5 inches in length; the butt is massive, and the point slender in proportion. Upon further study of the same I should say that it *could* have been mounted and carried over the shoulder—a highly efficient deliverer of the *coup de grâce* to netted or trapped big game. It is of a doubtful quartzite rock, and was doubtless brought up from the ocean floor by the aid of attached seaweed.

If this ancient man were the strategic hunter I believe him to have been, what splendid implements for the "guillotine trap," as I think it has been styled, Miss Ormerod's specimen and this would have been! Suspended from trees in the paths of the mammals with their contrived (natural) cords, which the indignant elephant would snap at a touch, down would come, point first, the released guillotine. This is but a suggestion, but it seems to me a likely and natural possibility.

CHAPTER VI

Out of the Past

WHEN man realises what his position is in the world of to-day, in his commanding attitude towards the animal kingdom, in his relation with the physical environment, and considers his ascent from the remote past, he ought to be not only awed and impressed, but made to see how much more marvellous such an ascent has been than had the creative act endowed him there and then with all the attributes he now possesses.

The writer well remembers the awe, the bated breath, even the fear, with which Lyell's opinion as to the meaning of the newly realised evidences of the antiquity of man was awaited. We feared what God Himself had written regarding our own ancestry. We were afraid of what Nature's record had to reveal to us. We feared the verities of our own origin and history.

But what have we read of ourselves? First, that our ascent is and has been a part of the common method in creation, in accordance with laws that govern the creation of all living creatures. Man has been carried from less to greater positions and to greater purposes by an influence more potent than himself—from a dawn to the full day of his humanity, in association with identical processes upon lower planes in other creatures.

Our present chapter opened with an apprehension of the great antiquity of the human race. All the known data of the existence of this ancient man not only point to, but demand an enormous period of time to make his history even intelligible and consistent. This man is the noblest outcome of organic "evolution," as Dr. Keane describes him in a volume [1] where occurs a magnificent passage under the note, "A long period of time needed to meet all the conditions." [2] Let us look at one or two items of the data referred to above.

If the Javanese human relics, before mentioned, be "Pliocene"

---

[1] P. 58, *Ethnology* (Cambridge Geographical Series).
[2] Pp. 60 and 61, *Ibid.*

in age, then man must have lived in a period so remote from our own times that he could not have even seen many of the genera and very few species of the mammals that now inhabit the areas of his own origin and evolution.   He was then surrounded with animals and plants which, could we be introduced among them, would be as unknown to us.   Since the Pliocene man had his being, marvellous transformations have occurred in the world's *fauna* and *flora,* while equally profound changes have come about in the conditions of Earth's physical face.   Sea and land have even transposed their positions time after time.

> There rolls the deep where grew the tree.
> O earth, what changes hast thou seen !
> There where the long street roars, hath been
> The stillness of the central sea.

We have seen that the Javanese man's remains were immediately surrounded by relics of such extinct forms as *Hipparion antelopinum* and *Rhinoceros peramensis,* while *Mastodon arvernensis,* the hippopotamus of more than one species; the *Sivatherium*—a deer about the size of an elephant, and resembling an elk ; *Rhinoceros tichorhinus,* huge batrachian reptiles ; salamanders that still represent the great sauroid reptilia of the Secondary epoch, are his associates ; the horse, ox, and camel having later arrived upon the scene.   With such forms, that ancient man has not only left the relics of his person, but such implements as his then capacity led him to fabricate ; which implements, " chipped flints," Dr. Noetling, the discoverer of the human implements, declares unquestionably to occur in undisturbed strata with the above-mentioned Pliocene fauna in the Irawadi valley.

With the sense with which our friends go to the Continent and to greater distances to find scenery that can be matched and often surpassed in grandeur at home, we are more impressed by what may be discovered in remote regions than by similar discoveries at our own doors.   It is still seldom that a prophet is honoured in his own country, and we must believe from experience that it will ever be so. But let us see if we have not in Britain some evidence that Pliocene man may enter into the natural history of the land.

Some years ago, Mr. W. J. Lewis Abbott favoured me with a pamphlet entitled *Worked Flints from the Cromer Forest - bed.* It is a reprint from *Natural Science.*[1]   In this pamphlet the

[1] Vol. x., February 1897.

author carefully elucidates the occurrence of worked flints in that forest-bed, a plate of drawings of some of the objects accompanying the paper. I quote only the author's closing words: "In conclusion, ... I have submitted these worked flints to a number of the first experts of the day, who have accorded them unqualified acceptance as being man's work"; and I add Sir John Evans's opinion upon the same—as given by Mr. Abbott, not because it either detracts from or adds to the value of the opinion of the other experts mentioned, but as a curiosity in the world of expressed opinions. It is as follows :—"No. 4 may or may not be artificial, and the same may be said of No. 3, with even more probability of its having been made by man."

From the entire absence of any real opinion in Sir John Evans's statement one must infer that even a great expert can sometimes have little data to go upon ; or why not be able to give more of an opinion than the veriest tyro might with safety venture upon ? I myself take the statement from such a source, alongside the opinion of others referred to, as highly affirmative. If Sir John Evans had no negative data to apply to the character of the said specimen, it argues strongly in favour of the definitely expressed affirmatives of the other experts.

By the occurrence of these flint weapons in the "Forest-bed," assuming them to be made by man, and, judging from the plate of illustrations, I myself assume them to be such, man is set back to the Pliocene age, since both the animal and vegetable contents of this deposit belong to that era. Mr. Abbott indicates *Elephas meridionalis* as one of the mammals, and this animal died out with Pliocene times.

It is neither my province nor my intention to give exhaustive particulars of such collateral data. But let us look at another curious and highly suggestive piece of presumable evidence—

There is at Dewlish, in Dorset, a curious earth-surface phenomenon known as the "Elephant-trench." It occurs on the summit of a chalk upland or hill, which upland ends abruptly in one direction in a steep escarpment some 90 feet in height, the base of which rests in a valley through which a small stream is running. This trench was found as far back as 1813 ; that is to say, sand was found there, and in excavating that the trench was discovered, and in that trench organic remains, teeth, bones, and ivory, were found.

In 1887 the Rev. Osmond Fisher noticed two of the said

elephant's teeth in a museum at Salisbury, and at once concluded that they were teeth of *Elephas meridionalis*. This conclusion was verified, and the remains were traced to the Elephant-trench, Dewlish; since which time the Rev. O. Fisher and others have carefully examined and fairly cleared out the said trench. In it were found further remains of *E. meridionalis*, and of that species only.

The whole story is a most picturesque scientific romance, but is not fiction. The Elephant-trench is believed by the Rev. O. Fisher and others to have been the work of man. No other agent can be suggested that could—in its position—have excavated it. It is, as described, a "trench" which runs diagonally across the crown of the hill for considerably over 100 feet, terminating at the escarpment with an open end, and in the other direction on or just over the brow of the hill in an apse-like ending. It is formed with steep sides in solid chalk, with layers of flint, is from 12 to 14 feet deep, and was only a few feet wide. The Rev. Osmond Fisher, to whom I am indebted for most kindly given information as to this matter, is, and has been for many years, as I need hardly say, a distinguished and cautious observer, a widely known physicist and stratigraphist. Mr. Fisher's opinion is (nor is he alone in this view) that the trench was a trap or catch for elephants. This need not surprise us. As Mr. Fisher points out in his later paper (1905),[1] trenches are still excavated, and being covered in with boughs, etc., are traps for elephants. Sir Samuel Baker describes this method of taking elephants by natives of Africa.[2] A well-known feature along the margins of many African rivers is the presence of Elephant-trenches, some existing in districts in which the great mammals for which they were devised are no longer present. Some are very ancient, some modern—at times they extend almost without break for miles.

Now to our *British* Elephant-trench: The fact of its being such ought not at all to surprise us. To find such a relic is intensely interesting; but it is as natural to find an Elephant-trench in Britain as in any other part of the world, since elephants and other of the great Mammals have equally had their day in our own country, as elsewhere. *Our* surprise comes in with the necessitated age of such relics. But with the Dewlish Elephant-trench that surprise is enhanced by the *species* of the elephant which characterises that trench. The species is *meridionalis*, the same as that which is a

[1] See *Quarterly Journal Geol. Soc.* Nov. 1888, and same journal, vol. lxi. 1905.
[2] *Wild Beasts and their Ways*, vol. i. (1890) pp. 95-98.

characteristic accompaniment of Mr. Lewis Abbott's worked flints from the Cromer Forest-bed; which flints I here notice that Mr. Fisher states have also been found by Mr. O. A. Shrubsole and others. Our Dewlish trench therefore is of *Pliocene* age, *i.e.* it was constructed in Pliocene times, or that species of elephant must be assumed to have lived on into later times; for which view there is not a vestige of evidence. The presence of these remains demands, if that trench be of artificial construction, a man of parts even in that remote Tertiary period, a man who, as Mr. Fisher says, was sufficiently intelligent to co-operate in such an undertaking. So far as my own views are concerned from my long experience as a practical student of that ancient man's capabilities, coupled with a study of the excellent views of the said trench from photographs, I am quite in a line with the Rev. Osmond Fisher's view, that the trench is the work of man.

We may, I think with advantage, look at a further object of great interest which the Rev. Osmond Fisher has also brought into scientific discussion. It is a presumed "bludgeon," which was originally in Mr. Wincopp's Red Crag collection at Woodbridge in Suffolk. Mr. Fisher was greatly interested by this specimen as far back as 1865, for the reason that though it was a mineralised bone and had evidently come from the Red Crag with Mr. Wincopp's large and unique collection from that deposit, it had apparently been sawn or cut partly through at the ends. This specimen had disappeared when in 1905 Mr. Fisher made inquiries after the same by letter to the *Geological Magazine*.[1] It was and is in the British Museum. Mr. Fisher writes to me to say that he "has there seen it and taken casts of the ends of the said bludgeon. Sir John Evans has pronounced against its being worked. But I think he is biased against man being so ancient. When I showed the bone to Dr. Man he thought the ends had been cut."

Mr. Fisher kindly sent his casts of the ends of the Red Crag bludgeon for my inspection, and they appeared to me to be in the condition that any bone would present that was to-day partly cut or sawn through and then broken by (say) striking it upon the ground. At either end there is a sawn part smooth and the broken part rugged. An ordinary break of the said bone at either end must have presented a jagged surface completely across the break, whereas both these ends present the rough surface only about half across.

---

[1] December 1905, Decade v. vol. ii.

A striking feature in this item of history lies, I think, in the fact that the original possessor called it and believed it to be a bludgeon. He evidently considered it had been reduced to a usable length by the hand of man, notwithstanding that it was a Red Crag specimen and therefore of *older* Pliocene age. It is part of a rib of one of the great mammals. It weighs, according to Mr. Fisher's statement, 2 lbs. 7 oz., is 10½ inches in length, and 2 inches in diameter. It is interesting to notice that after Mr. Fisher's first inspection of the specimen in 1865, he again saw it in 1889 in Professor Prestwich's collection at the Professor's house, from which it will be seen that he also was interested in the said "bludgeon." "Of course," says the Rev. Osmond Fisher in his letter to the *Geological Magazine*, "the antecedent probability is against finding a specimen bearing signs of man's handiwork at such an early period as that of the Crag. But at every new stage to which his existence is pushed back there must always be a fresh find to break the record. The marine character of the Crag is not a serious objection ; for, seeing that Mr. Wincopp's collection was remarkable for the number of the remains of land animals that it contained, there is no reason why, if man should have lived among them, one of his implements might not have been found along with their bones."

I judge that the evidence and opinion is much more in favour of this relic being man's work than against such proposition. I state the case here as deeply interesting and suggestive, and as being illustrated, and in some sort corroborated, by certain stone bludgeons from Scotland. I have a note of some great authority who says that he is of opinion that the most natural and earliest known weapons of man were clubs. I cannot now find the said note.

There is believed by many to be evidence of a possibly yet more ancient man in the so-called *Eoliths* of the high plateau of the Weald, Kent. Mr. Benjamin Harrison of Ightham, in that county, was, I believe, the first to call special attention to these forms, which as a rule bear little evidence of intention ; indeed, they are often naturally produced flints, with only more or less presumed intentional chipping along the edges. They, however, exhibit certain characteristics even as to form, which are distinctly obvious when numbers are placed side by side. This "cumulative" evidence is also very strong in the feature of the marginal chipping, which is more often than not from one lateral direction only, but occasionally from both right and left, and sometimes the chipping is almost regularly and consecutively alternate. In fine, the chipping, when numbers are studied, has an undoubtedly artificial aspect.

The late Professor Sir Joseph Prestwich strenuously supported Mr. Harrison's view, that these finds represent a *most* ancient man— hence the term *Eolith*. (See paper by the late Professor, with notes by Messrs. B. Harrison and De Barrie Crawshay.[1] And see paper by Mr. A. Montgomery Bell,[2] who says that he himself "during the years 1883-89 obtained a collection of this kind (the plateau forms) from the surface-soil near Limpsfield in Surrey.") The collection was seen by various competent persons, "none of whom doubted that it came from Palæolithic times." In reply to certain criticisms of these forms by Professor Boyd Dawkins and others, Mr. Bell remarks :[3] " Hitherto it can hardly be said that they (the plateau forms) have had a patient hearing ; it is not fair that the conclusions which have been reached by competent investigators by patient research, extended over a series of years, should be rejected in as many minutes after a hasty glance."

I have purposely stated sufficient to show that the question of the human work upon the plateau forms is disputed. Some assert that the chipping is natural, others that it is artificial, *i.e.* human work, but of Palæolithic age—of the same age as the Palæolithic forms of the higher-level "hill" gravels. Others assert that they are not only of human work and intention, but are infinitely older than the oldest of the Palæolithic forms.

This last view is probable. Mr. Montgomery Bell points out that the plateau *Palæolithic* forms are sharp and entirely uneroded. The plateau *types*, *i.e.* Mr. Harrison's, are worn and rounded, and sometimes found in patches of ochreous gravel.[4]

Mr. B. Harrison also points out that *Palæoliths* and *Eoliths* are found together *only on the surface : never in the drift deposits— in situ.*[5]

Mr. Harrison shows further in the said pamphlet, by reference to illustrated sections, that the plateau Eolithic types are so very ancient that they go back to a time when what are now the crests of hills were the floors of whilom valleys.

---

[1] *Journ. Anthrop. Inst.*, 1892, vol. xxi. p. 240.

[2] *Ibid.* vol. xxiii. p. 266.   [3] *Ibid.* p. 274.   [4] *Ibid.* p. 267.

[5] *History of Eolithic Implements*, 1904, p. 17 (pamphlet).

If these forms *are* of human origin they take man back to a most remote era.

It was my privilege to take part in a discussion upon these forms in the Geological Section of the British Association Meeting in Edinburgh in 1892, when Professor M'Kenny Hughes occupied the chair. Some of Mr. Harrison's eoliths were in evidence and excited no little curiosity. Some handled the specimens with the aspect of serious interest; others, after a hasty glance, put them down with undisguised contempt. The opinion of the meeting was divided, some for and some against a human agency. The impression I received of that discussion is to this day unpleasant. The *non placets* had no argument save denial; but the denial was delivered in terms so nearly verging upon the contemptuous for the *placets*—for men whose only object was to get at the truth—that something like indignation impelled me to speak on behalf of the discoverers and investigators into the question of this possibly ancient man. I myself, as I fear, incensed the chairman by postulating that the most learned among us, anthropologists, archæologists, or whatever we chose to style ourselves, knew nothing in comparison with what was yet to be discovered concerning ancient man; that nothing that was possible evidence ought to be treated with contempt; that things now reckoned of no account would be demonstrated to be of vast interest and importance. By way of illustration, I ventured to assert that the contents of some of the valley gravels of southern England, the very material of which they were made up, had been largely affected by the agency of man, and the materials to an appreciable extent supplied by man. I am glad to have the opportunity of repeating this assertion here, since I am more convinced than I was then that such is the case. *That* ancient man used the valley-floors largely as his workshop—his collected flints; the débris from the constant manufacture, his scattering of spoiled, broken, and lost implements for unknown generations, supplied large quantities of material. It was the province of the rivers to gather such scattered and refuse matters into beds, which we now call river-drifts. In some cases the drifts are certainly very largely expressive in their general *facies* of the ways and work of that man. The chairman referred to myself as—" And one speaker made the wild statement that some even of our valley gravels have been largely affected by the agency of man!"

Yet further relics bearing on this question of the antiquity of man are stated to have been discovered in France, Portugal, Italy, and in other countries by distinguished investigators : that, among others, of l'Abbé Bourgeois as long ago as the early 'sixties of last century, who discovered what he considered to be worked flints from *Miocene* beds—the Thenay " worked flints "—which have been corroborated by other finds from equally ancient deposits in other areas.[1]

---

[1] Keane's *Ethnology*, p. 91. See also De Quatrefage's *Human Species*, p. 149.

CHAPTER VII

Out from the Glaciers

Glacial Man in Scotland

IF Man has come from such a remote past as is postulated in the preceding chapter, it would be not only natural that his relics should occur in the boulder-clays of the northern latitudes of the world, it would be inexplicable if they were not found to occur in such deposits. It would be a phenomenon of a highly puzzling nature; since, if primeval man does reach back through not only Pleistocene times, the era of the great glaciations, but through Pliocene and possibly into Miocene times, the argument is that that ancient man occupied (say) the area of north-western Europe for an immeasurably longer period before the inception of what we know as the great glaciation, than he has occupied the same or any other area since such glacial event. But if we once conceive that this remote advent and prolonged ascent of man is not only possible, but, in accordance with all the w. .derful phenomena of Creation, is the only possible view of man's history, we shall be prepared for the phases of such history whatever they may be, and shall be only the more reverential in the handling and transcribing of the same. A human history of a million years is a vastly more venerable record than one of fifty thousand or a hundred thousand years. Man's age upon the earth must be, from what has been already gleaned, much nearer the million years than either of the two lesser periods suggested, notwithstanding the effort of some to reduce not only the age of man to a fractional minimum, but long geological sequences to the shortest possible periods of time.

When I began this quest in Scotland I no more dreamed of looking for evidences of man in the boulder-clays than I dreamed of looking for such evidences in trappean or granite beds. The position is now so much reversed that it seems to me to partake of presumption to attempt to reduce the duration of creative acts to the littleness of our own conceptions. As Dr. A. H. Keane points out, we can reduce time in association with such sublime events only by hiding away such phenomena as changes of climate and changes in the facial aspects of the *fauna* and *flora* of areas—all of which imperatively demand enormous lapses of time, or by postulating impossibilities in substitution.

This change of view, *i.e.* to the greater demands upon time and circumstance, is the natural outcome of observation; is rather the outcome of *natural* observation, for this last is the truth. The more we are led by the simple features of Nature, the nearer we are to sublime truths. In my own case, entirely irrespective of what was being seen and gleaned elsewhere, the profoundly greater antiquity of man dawned and grew upon me with the certainty that the dawn matures into day, by what I observed naturally and without effort, *i.e.* without effort of straining after results in certain deposits, and especially in the *glacial* deposits of Scotland.

A simple observation is at times a surprising one, as in what I may now try to relate. A part of my systematic observation in Scotland was, for eleven years at least, given to what I described as *river phenomena, i.e.* the phenomena of the distribution and accumulation of erratic material by rivers. In this quest it was extremely interesting to find, as I occasionally have done, mixed-up and ground-up river-deposit, or what had been such, in the boulder-clays. Not that they were in such cases clays; they were often rather mixed-up sands and gravels, where the rounded condition of the stones told the story of river-rolling, and possibly, on occasion, of prior marine, *i.e.* seashore, attrition.

I was examining such a deposit in the boulder-clay on the north bank of the river Almond about two miles north of Perth. I was inquiring into the nature of the contents of this deposit in order if possible to arrive at the origin of the material which there formed the bed. The condition of the stones, the utterly mixed state of the material, without the least suggestion of stratification, suggested to me simply pre-glacial river-deposits, which had been disturbed and mixed up by ponderous ice-movement.

The rounded and abraded or scratched and crushed condition of the stones formed the attributes of interest; beyond that I had conceived no possible interest. What was then my surprise when I picked out from this material, from the perpendicular face of a boulder-clay deposit, where there was no fallen débris nor detritus—

since the river was at this spot undermining and carrying away all that fell from above—a roughly shaped but well-contrived Palæolithic weapon? That it was such I had then no doubt, nor have I now, after over thirty years, during which time it has been in my possession and since which time it has been corroborated by other finds over and over again. It was a weapon, somewhat rolled, but as evidential of what it had been as though I had received it from the hands of its fabricator.

It was not a large, not an elegant, and not a perfect specimen. It was, as it is now, an object that evinces intention in its form and elaboration in pursuance of that form. It once had the perfect outline and general expression of the more cylindrically shaped Somme - Valley typical specimens of which those I originally saw in the Woodwardian Museum, Cambridge, were mainly examples, but this is smaller. It is over 5 inches in length, is of a close-grained basaltic rock, is not scratched or grooved, but for almost half its length from the point end one side has been forcibly broken away. Fig. 66 is a drawing of the same.

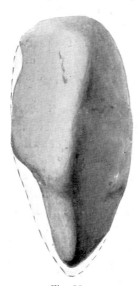

Fig. 66.

This specimen has received all its smoothing by rolling since it was broken; and the break itself could, I think, have been effected in its use by its fabricator—by a fracture from the point end. In any case, my first assumption that it represented a fracture by the ice-foot is not tenable, since it was found in unstratified "till," in the formation of which till it could not have received the rolling unless we assume complex changes which were indeed possible during the continuance of the actual glacial period. It suggests for itself a pre-glacial origin. The finding of this specimen under such circumstances made a profound impression upon me. It is marked 1874, i.e. it was found thirty-four years ago; although, for my own peace of mind, and for the sake of peace with others, I said nothing for years after of this glacial discovery. In several subsequent visits to the same spot I made other equally interesting finds—one a sort of "core" with a number of facets which were doubtless intentionally produced, two of which present what I consider from long subsequent experience and repeated corroboration to be artificial smoothing—smoothing by manual labour. Neither does this exhibit any glacial striæ (Fig. 67). Another, found in that early time and at the same spot, has always highly interested me. It is a specimen of a coarse-grained trap which is almost as fresh in its elaboration as when it was fabricated; it has never been water-rolled. Yet it is reduced by perhaps a third of its length by having been snapped towards the point end while along its lateral edges it has been subjected to rough

Fig. 67.

fretting and breaking. Although there are no very distinct striæ upon this specimen the break and the fretting are, as we have in anticipation already seen and will further see illustrated, highly characteristic of the destructive effect of the ice-foot. Fig. 68 is a drawing and suggested restoration which I made many years ago.

The butt-end of this specimen exhibits the always interesting fact of the item having been fashioned from a stone with a whilom highly decayed surface (basalt), a portion of which is still seen at the broad end, and there only.

In 1875 I passed from the neighbourhood of Perth to Dollar, south of the Ochil Hills, where I became Science Master in the then great school; and for several years then and after had little opportunity of revisiting the Almond-side section of the boulder-clay deposit. But in 1888 I became a chaplain of St. Ninian's Cathedral, Perth, when I revisited and closely at times examined the said deposit during two or three years.

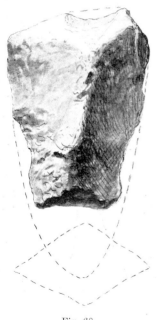

Fig. 68.

During this time at least three highly interesting items from that boulder-clay came to light. The first is an admirable specimen, which, except for the usual breaks and frettings, would be of an excellent Somme-Valley type as to form, and I may say also as to elaboration ; for, as can still be seen, the work bestowed upon it was, so far as a trap rock could receive it, of the same kind as that bestowed upon similar flint items. It was of a fine, well-balanced form, with excellently produced margins, and both faces are identical. The section is a diamond-oval. It is 4¾ inches in length. Figs. 69 and 70 are drawings—a suggested restoration with side view. Figs. 71 and 72 give another from that Almond-

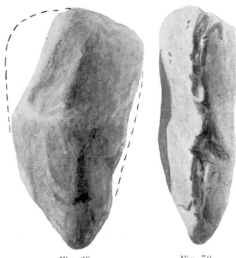

Fig. 69.   Fig. 70.

side boulder-clay. It is a much-rolled specimen, although its general form and expression are perfect. It is a decayed quartzite, and is neither damaged nor scratched glacially. It is odd that though this exposed area was so full of stones it was difficult to find a scratched or grooved one. I did occasionally find such, but not one of the six or seven undoubted fabrications from that source exhibits well-defined striæ or grooving. But it is well known that stones are not necessarily scratched because they occur in the boulder-clay,

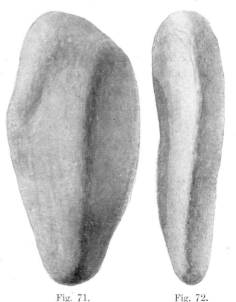

Fig. 71.   Fig. 72.

although in places such scratched stones are, as is natural, very common in that deposit. This specimen when fabricated must have been a beautifully formed and cleverly wrought hache. In its pristine crystalline state, with its then sharp edges and finer point, it would have paired well with the best Somme specimens.

My last find in this boulder-clay exposure of Almond-side was a remarkable one. It was a large cleverly and boldly faceted weapon of saccharine quartz. It would to-day readily have been mistaken for one of the finer Somaliland specimens. It was about 10 inches in length, with a heavy butt and cleverly produced point. In general form it was the counterpart of Figs. 57 and 58, but larger, and almost identical with 59 and about the same size, while its elaboration was much more distinctly evident. It was so perfect and of so good a form that I found it well-nigh impossible to make my best friends believe that it came from *in situ* boulder-clay. But alas! this is one of the lamented losses. When I left Glasgow for Dunblane in 1895 this specimen, with several of the other larger finds, was either stolen or thrown away. I never made a drawing of the specimen, and although it was photographed the negative appears to have been broken and destroyed before it was lost. My friend, Mr. Henry Coates, F.R.S.E., President of the Perthshire Society of Natural Science, would corroborate my description of it, since he was highly interested by it, and it was in his possession for about two years.

Let us endeavour to see how this boulder-clay is situated in the Tay Valley.

The exposure on Almond-side is in an escarpment or terrace about 60 feet in height which forms the north bank of the river at a spot about a mile west of its junction with the Tay; the Almond is here running across the flat valley-floor of the Tay, which floor, from one or less to two miles in width, is almost on all sides enclosed by a yet higher escarpment known as the " hundred-feet " terrace. That on Almond-side is practically a continuance of the same. It is close upon 50 feet lower than the well-marked terraces on either side of the Tay in the immediate neighbourhood, but it rises from its river-side margin by almost imperceptible degrees into the spurs or shoulders of the lower Grampian range to the north. The river Tay itself is in this area eating into and degrading a deep deposit of fine (Estuarine?) clays, leaving always in place of the removed clays rough deposits of rounded gravels and sands of at least a maximum thickness of 20 feet. The river Almond is, before its junction with the Tay, running over and eating into these same valley-floor clays.

But now let us examine the nature of the "glacial" deposit on Almond-side.

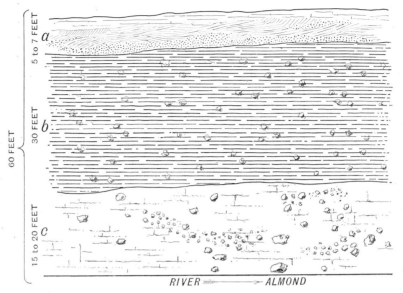

Section of Glacial Deposit on Almond-side, Perth.

The above is a section not drawn to scale. It exhibits, beginning at the top, an ancient river-deposit—an ancient bed of the Almond 60 feet or so above the river's present position at the base of the cliff. That old river-bed is in its material a great contrast to that offered by the present river-bed below, the reason for which we shall see as we examine the section. The ancient river-deposit (*a*) gives a foot or two of fine, somewhat highly rolled gravels: there are very few stones as large as a cricket-ball in this ancient deposit. These gravels pass up through false-bedded sands into horizontally bedded and finally into unbedded silts, which pass more or less perceptibly into cultivated soil; the whole not being more than from 5 to 7 feet in thickness. Below this river-bed there occurs a thick deposit (some 30 feet) of well-defined horizontally bedded clays without appreciable sign of gravels or sands, but with erratically scattered stones, sometimes rolled and sometimes angular and fresh-looking, throughout the entire thickness. This passes abruptly into the unbedded boulder-clay, which is here largely sand and gravel highly rolled, with large erratics from one to several hundred-weights here and there in the mass. This varies in thickness from 15 to 20 feet or so, and passes below the level of the present river-bed.

The horizontally bedded clays with the scattered erratics (*b*) would, if ploughed or dug into, be described as "till" or boulder-clay. It was unquestionably formed in glacial or, so far as this actual spot is concerned, *post*-glacial times. The scattered stones must have been ice-borne, and the stratified clays either estuarine or lacustrine, formed while ice still remained in the higher reaches of the then drainage areas. The amorphous mass of sands and rounded materials below the clays indicated at *c* can be no other than a *moraine profonde*, the gathered-up and stored-up and, for the time being, hidden-away pre-glacial débris; the fluvial or otherwise formed deposits of the valley-floor (or floors) of pre-glacial times. It was in this mass of presumed pre- or inter-glacial origin that the fabricated stones were found. They certainly came from that deposit, I myself having picked out most of them from the actual material. My visits to this spot, repeated at times during a prolonged period, were induced by the fact that the river was undermining the cliff and there was every now and again a new exposure. The present bed of the river Almond is characterised by excessively coarse material in contrast with that which is seen in the ancient river-deposit on the top of the terrace; which difference is explained and is at once an illustration that coarseness or fineness of material in a river's course has little connection with the size or strength of the transporting power of a river, but more definitely with the nature of the supply of detritus to such river. The explanation is, that when the stream, the present Almond, ran along upon the top of the terrace of its now north bank, such river was running in among the horizontally stratified clays, and the supply of coarse material was of necessity very limited. To-day the Almond is running in a zone below the level of the said clays, and is obtaining the coarsest possible materials up to gigantic boulders by the denudation of the boulder-clay itself.

From the time of that Almond-side experience I have naturally been interested, from a human-history point of view, in the contents of the Scottish boulder-clay. I have repeatedly examined it at various altitudes and under greatly varying geographical circumstances. In many cases, and especially in deposits of higher altitudes, I have found the boulder-clay completely destitute of such presumed fabrications. Yet there have been exceptions to this; and I should here point out that inasmuch as the exigencies of my daily round and common task have been mainly the dictators to me as to where I should make exploration, while choice has had little scope in the matter, my examination of the said boulder-clay has been neither so exhaustive nor so systematic as it might and would have been had circumstances and time permitted my following my own inclination and the result of my experience. Thus my researches in this deposit are less extensive, and on the whole less satisfactory, than have been my explorations in some post-glacial deposits or recent river accumulations, or in coast-line débris. Yet this till or boulder-clay has yielded remarkable evidence. The boulder-clays of lower valley-floors and the lower plains, as might have been anticipated, have yielded the most striking and suggestive evidence. Let us come down in the search to 1892.

Being then Rector of St. Luke's, Glasgow, my opportunities for the time being had almost wholly gone, when I received an invitation from Mr. Henry Coates, F.R.S.E., to meet the members of the Perthshire Society of Natural Science at Crieff with the view to an inspection of the then but partially completed excavations for the line of railway from Crieff to Comrie. My friend of many years, the late Dr. Buchanan White, F.L.S., etc., was at the head of that excursion.

By that visit to Crieff my interest was re-aroused to well-nigh boiling-point. In that hurried inspection, two or three hours at most, I picked out several objects from newly exposed or thrown-out boulder-clay which not only corroborated the finds on Almond-side but suggested wonderful possibilities. I made one or two return visits to the same spot, but of a hurried kind. Yet the result was so surprising and so suggestive of what *might* be done by a systematic and exhaustive search that it was an agony to me that such strongly desired effort could not be made. Only as pointing to what I believe to have been an irretrievable loss in this prolonged search do I refer to the actual circumstances. My responsibilities as Rector of St. Luke's, with my Mission of Garngad (Glasgow), were so onerous that I could not forgo them without providing a substitute; and the demands upon my purse in this work were so great that the provision of a substitute for the required few weeks was not conceivable; nor could I even afford further flying visits to Crieff; so there, at the very beginning of the most promising opportunity with regard to this boulder-clay aspect that I ever had, I had perforce to desist. Yet the result was (to me) as profoundly interesting as it was astonishing. On my first visit a fragment, a mere fragment, interested me intensely: I have it now before me. It is but 4 inches in length; is, particularly on one face, highly glaciated. Its point has been fretted off and it has been forcibly snapped at its broader end. One of its margins has been powerfully broken away, but the other, which tells the tale of its whilom form, is almost perfect. That more perfect edge, with the other face which has almost escaped the grinding and grooving, and which still shows the kind of elaboration once bestowed upon it, shows clearly that it was part of a once beautifully and skilfully formed Palæolithic axe. It is of a heavy compact basalt. The preserved lateral edge, and the general expression of the fragment, point to an unusually cleverly sculptured item. It was, I should say, when perfect, at least double its present length, and possibly longer. I made a drawing of it, flat and edgewise, a good many years ago (Figs. 73 and 74), but I then in the attempted restoration, indicated by the broken outline, suggested a radical error. Upon a study of the specimen now, as I write, it is clear that the broken-away margin to the left of the figure (Fig. 73) once extended to at least the distance indicated by a broken line which I have now placed beyond the original one. Had this fragment been the only specimen from that Crieff inspection of the boulder-clay it would have deeply interested me, though in its isolation it might have failed to interest others. There was, however, on that first visit another find of at least equally great interest.

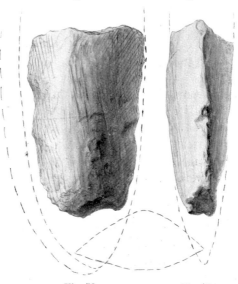

Fig. 73.   Fig. 74.

I had up to that date (1892) spent twenty years in this quest in Scotland. Now, one of the most common evidences of an ancient man I had found in shaped (pyramidal) stones—shaped for the hand: I had found them everywhere in post-glacial deposits; but, with the exception of the Almond-side boulder-clay, I had not found any in that deposit, and the specimen found there I have described as a sort of core—it is not so evidently one of these shaped (domestic) implements which, being described farther on as a group, I attempt no further description here. It is, however, interesting that with the above described fragment of a weapon I extracted from the *in situ* boulder-clay one of these shaped stones of the more typical form which was highly glaciated upon its broader facet and fretted all round its margin (Fig. 75).

Fig. 75.

We shall by and by see why this so interested me. It was, if it could be, more evidential of the presence of the ancient man in pre-glacial times than the preceding glaciated fragment. This shaped stone as a type I had long before denominated the " hall-mark " of Palæo-lithic man, since it became an axiom that wherever I found in any deposit such stones, there, with sufficient perseverance, other more orthodox elabora-tions were almost certain to be found. It is an axiom still, which I offer to all future in-vestigators in this matter. This Crieff boulder-clay specimen was, with the above fragment, sufficient to arouse my greatest interest.

On my second visit I stayed overnight at an hotel. This gave me a greater opportunity, which was not lost. My first discovery on this occasion was another broken specimen of an axe. I can hardly call it a fragment, since it is the heavier butt-end of a weapon, though it does not

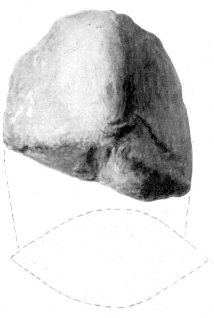

Fig. 76.

probably represent much above one-third of the length of the perfect implement. I think few would (nowadays) doubt in handling this stone its being what I assert it to be. Its form, so far as it exists, is still almost perfect. It has finely produced lateral edges, which are somewhat fretted, and the whole has been tenderly but distinctly glaciated. The striking feature about it is the powerful way in which it has been snapped across its thickest part. But this is a characteristic " butt-end," *i.e.* characteristic of the condition in which such glaciated relics often occur. A section is appended to the figure (Fig. 76) which shows the excellence of the form. It is of a reddish basalt with olivine crystals. As it is, the specimen is just over 4 inches in length and the same in breadth, and is at the fracture over 2 inches thick, *i.e.* from face to face. It suggests a most perfectly formed and beautiful specimen.

The next discovery sent me into raptures. It was a large and perfect example, as perfect as I might perhaps ever hope to find in a Scottish glacial deposit, and in a glaciated condition; and this was intensely glaciated. It is of a stout build, very compact and heavy—is of some trappean rock. It is roughly scarred and striated over every part of its surface. It has escaped that snapping fracture into two or more parts, but it has been fretted at the butt-end and at the point, and in places roughly along the lateral margins. The whole figure has been reduced in dimensions by the fretting and rounding in the process of the awful mill through which it has passed. I have never found a stone of any sort more glaciated than this is, yet I consider that the unquestionable intention and elaboration of an ancient (pre-glacial) man is there. In the drawings (Figs. 77 and 78) I have suggested what I conceive to have been the original perfected form. It was always of a ponderous build, the cause probably of its preservation. It is in its present condition $6\frac{3}{4}$ inches in length. If there could have been a greater surprise the next item provided it. It was a small implement, wonderfully well elaborated, in almost perfect condition, totally unrolled and unglaciated, but mellowed by decay so that it looked like a moulded thing. It was such a specimen that, if made of flint, it could not have been much more evidential of human elaboration; and if it *had* been of flint, it would have been declared, by any expert to whom I might have shown it, to be either from the Somme Valley or from southern England—probably the former. It would not then probably have been accepted as of Scottish origin. It is (or was) just under

4 inches in length. A youthful visitor in my absence on a time amused himself with a hammer among my specimens. Among other

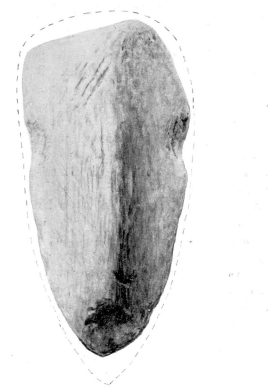

Fig. 77.

Fig. 78.

Fig. 79.

incidents he could not resist the tempting rottenness of the left top corner of the figure (79), and the specimen is now minus that portion. The extraordinary feature about this find is that it does not exhibit the sign of a scratch or any fretting. A break occurs at the point end on the face not shown, but that is, I think, of more modern origin. I picked it out from undoubted boulder-clay.

My third and last visit produced two interesting finds, although it was a flying venture — the first, a glacially damaged weapon, of suggestive interest equal at least to any of the foregoing (Figs. 80 and 81). It is of a heavy, compact, black basalt, is highly glaciated over all its surface, and has been snapped in the usual decided way, I judge, about one-third of its length from the whilom point. It has been badly broken along one of its lateral margins and also at the butt-end; but the other lateral edge, except

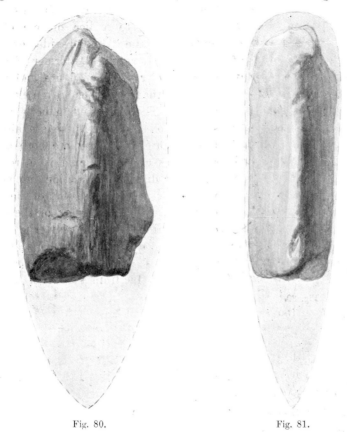

Fig. 80.   Fig. 81.

for being rounded by slighter fretting, is perfect. The specimen, as it is, is $5\frac{3}{8}$ inches in length, and must have been at least as large when perfect as I have indicated by the suggested broken-line restoration. Any restorations I have attempted must be accepted, as they are intended, as merely suggestive. One is guided, of course, by such evidence of an outline as remains; but it is well-nigh impossible in any case that I can have reproduced a facsimile of the original; I do not pretend to that. Further, if the reader sees that it is impossible to suggest anything save a formal outline in such attempted restorations, he will understand that they are perforce merely suggestive. Yet they are far removed from the sphere of mere conjecture. Compare, for instance, our present specimen with Fig. 77.

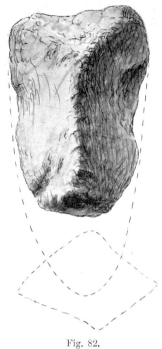

The last of the more important of the Crieff boulder-clay specimens is almost a complete replica of one of the finds from the Almond-side exposure (Fig. 82). It is, like the former (Fig. 68), of a rougher style of figure and workmanship than the other broken examples suggest. The point end in both cases is snapped off and fretted, as are also the lateral margins. They are both of the same size, and both exhibit a roughly produced diamond in section in contrast with the usually oval section of the other glacial forms. The former of these is a coarse-grained trap, the latter a highly crystalline quartzite. I have several other items of less, but still of real evidential value from the Crieff boulder-clay.

Fig. 82.

CHAPTER VIII

Out from the Glaciers (*continued*)

It was the further discovery of glaciated fabrications in the boulder-clay at Crieff in 1892 that induced me to venture to read a paper upon *Evidences of Palæolithic Man in Scotland* at the meeting of the British Association in Edinburgh, at the end of the same year. My evidences, of course, lay not in my statements in the said paper, but in the specimens themselves. As I have before said, few took the trouble to inspect them. Mr. Montgomery Bell, and one or two other members, took a real interest in the glaciated and other forms, and that gentleman remarked concerning Fig. 77, while he held it in his hand : "That is exactly what any specimen that was not entirely broken up by the ice would be found to present after going through the glacial mill." He and the one or two other members urged me to go on in the search ; otherwise, the approach to that great Society was the reverse of encouraging. But still there is the fact that I not only read the paper, but placed great importance upon the boulder-clay finds, particularly upon those of the Crieff and Comrie Railway cutting.[1] In the summary given there is, however, a misconception, in so far as it seems to imply that I began the search for evidences of Palæolithic man in Scotland in 1883. I began in 1872. What I said, or meant to say, was that after my visits in that year (1883) to the Continent and southern England, what I then saw gave me a new impulse, not an initial start.

Since 1892 more specimens have come to hand, some from *in situ* boulder-clay, and some which are glaciated, but were not found *in situ*. Some are finds which, although not now exhibiting glacial striæ, are so broken and fretted that one can assign their present condition to nothing other than the tread of the ice-foot. Butt-ends and point ends are fairly common ; and some, although they may have been found in river-beds, or on the seashore, or in post-glacial deposits, are distinctly glaciated as well as fretted and broken.

I have found *in situ* boulder-clay specimens in the Clyde Valley,

[1] *Report British Association*, 1892, p. 896.

at Dunblane and Cromlix in Strathallan, and now in the Forth

Fig. 83.

Fig. 84.

basin. I have made drawings of several of these butt-ends and of

Fig. 85.

a point or two, besides other drawings of what I take to be relics of once fine specimens. Let us examine them.

Fig. 83 is a glaciated (*in situ*) boulder-clay specimen from a shore exposure about a mile west of South Queensferry on the Forth. It is a massive piece of close-grained black basalt. The drawing sufficiently indicates its condition. I take it to be the butt-end of what was once a fine hache of the Somme type. Fig. 84 is another of these dilapidated butt-ends, and Fig. 85 is another. All these are highly glaciated as well as snapped and fretted. They had been, I have no doubt, derived somewhere from boulder-clay which surrounds the Forth estuary, and in places dips down to the shore and passes beneath the water, where it forms in part the actual bed of the Forth.   All the three finds are of basalt.

As one finds butt-ends, so, as has already been suggested, points or point ends also occur.   It is, I think, natural that point ends should not be so freely found as the butt-ends, since their greater tenuity exposed them the more readily to the destructive powers of the ice-foot ; they were more naturally broken into unrecognisable fragments.   Yet I have several that clearly indicate what they once were.

In Fig. 86 we have a magnificent point end. It was found on the shore (Forth), but it gives some indications of glaciation (*i.e.* striæ); a portion has been broken away from the under facet (not shown), and it is more or less fretted along all its margin. It clearly indicates having been snapped at its now broad end. It is of an intensely hard, compact felstone, and is, I believe, a good illustration of how certain stones may be crushed and broken, but yet show little striation. If this were about the hardest rock in any sub-glacial mass, it would have been a good tool for the striating and grooving of other

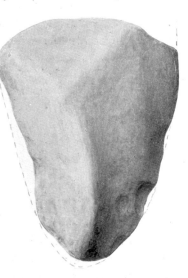

Fig. 86.

rocks, but would resist being itself scratched by softer stones.   This possibly explains why certain flints which I have found along the Ayrshire coast-line, and which often suggest having been through the ice-mill, never exhibit anything like scratches or grooving.   But this particular specimen was once the operating end of an excellently formed Palæolithic weapon, which I think was of pre-glacial fabrication.

Other finds suggest former specimens of fine form and size, of which Fig. 87 is an example.   It is of red syenite-like rock, and was found in the bed of the river Esk, Musselburgh.   This and other examples show little or no appreciable striation, although their snapped and fretted condition points, as I believe, unerringly to glacial destructive agency.

Though (in Scotland) the ponderosity of the ice-foot was naturally so utterly destructive, as is illustrated by the condition of the stones

Fig 87.

from the Crieff boulder-clay and these butt and point ends, I yet hoped, some day, to find a specimen which, while glaciated, should yet be so perfect as to need no suggestive restoration lines. But the years went on and nothing even so perfect as at least two of the Crieff finds came to hand. I found no opportunity like that lost one of the Crieff railway excavations for a ransacking of boulder-clay, but I persistently made the best use of such opportunities as did occur, and yet no more perfect specimen came to light for twelve years; then the unexpected happened. I had repeatedly ignored a certain very limited space of shore (Forth), because more extensive areas seemed to offer better prospects; but at length, in February 1904, I essayed a search at that spot. I had

hardly begun the search, when there lay at my feet the long-sought perfect glaciated specimen—a fine characteristic hache. It is distinctly glaciated over the whole of its surface, but in a tender manner. It was not found in boulder-clay, but had so recently been brought up from the bottom of the estuary that the seaweed which, with the help of the waves, had been its carrier from its long-hidden home, was still attached, and the shore waves had begun to do injury to it. That find was a red-letter day in the search for glacial implements. I am in a sense deeply grateful to that specimen; for though in its general form it might have been more "orthodox" (see Figs. 88 and 89), it well shows the correctness of my idea of what the highly glaciated specimens from Crieff and elsewhere represented; for they, or several of them, might be portions of just such a weapon. If, for instance, I take the fine point end last described (Fig. 86), I find that it corresponds so exactly with the size and form of the point end of this perfect specimen, that, *including my restoration line,* it exactly covers the corresponding portion of the perfect weapon, and is so good a replica

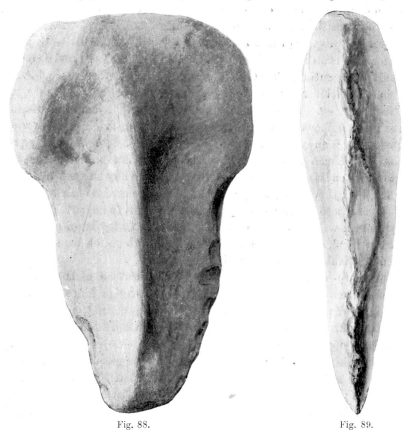

Fig. 88.   Fig. 89.

that, supposing the perfect glaciated specimen to have been only a butt-end, broken at a certain line, this now detached point would have given a perfect illustration of the complete weapon. Or, if we take the fragment (Fig. 73) from the Crieff boulder-clay, and compare it with Fig. 88, *i.e.* if the two are taken into the hand, it is seen that the former might be actually a part of the latter. It could be fitted, so to put it, into the lower end of this weapon (Fig. 88). There is, however, great difference in the material. The perfect specimen is a dolomite limestone, a substance which, once scratched or grooved, does not easily lose such tell-tale feature, except upon the seashore, where it is easily rounded.

This perfect specimen (Fig. 88) is, from a Palæolithic man point of view, a splendidly bold elaboration. Its under face, not shown, is the result of a masterly splitting from a larger mass, which exhibits conchoidal fracture, with something like a big bulb-of-percussion. On the face shown bold and skilful work is evident, with certain lateral chipping. On either side of the figure, about half-way from either end, is an indentation. Both these features were certainly the result of intention. That on the right was due to a piece having been most cleverly taken out; neither was caused by the usual glacial fretting. The clever way in which the right-hand indentation was made is shown in a lateral view of the same (Fig. 89), which view further gives an excellent idea of the great skill with which this pre-glacial specimen was produced. And further, let us notice that the lateral indentations are so placed, that they forcibly suggest the mode of hafting; they could, in my opinion, have answered no other purpose.

It seems to me to verge upon the ridiculous to suppose that such a specimen was only for use in the hand; it is too large and heavy for one hand, and the intention of such an elaboration for two hands is inconceivable. It was certainly mounted.

Our pre- or inter-glacial man was so skilful an elaborator, that it is to treat his powers with contempt to grudge him the wooden handle. We shall presently see that one of his earliest conceptions—limiting our view to what I believe to be Palæolithic man—was the necessity of a handle in certain other (domestic) forms. Concede that handle for this specimen too, and our pre-glacial ancestor was, as all the evidence, so far as I have gleaned from the boulder-clay, attests, a warrior brave: that I believe him to have been.

Figs. 90 and 91 represent another found at the same spot as the perfect specimen, but two years later. It is not in so perfect a condition as the former; but is of orthodox form, and in its present condition almost identical in size with the former. That is just over 8 inches, this just under 8 inches, in length. It is, I have no doubt, a glacial specimen. As is seen, a large piece has been broken out, and it is largely fretted. I have had to introduce restoration lines in the drawings.

If Palæolithic man be glacial, i.e. inter- or pre-glacial, in accordance with what I assume to be the evidence in Scotland, he certainly should, in his relics, so appear in England. And this should be

more particularly the case if my view with regard to Scotland and
the relics of that ancient man be the correct one, viz. that Palæolithic man in Scotland was well-nigh, if not wholly, glacial and

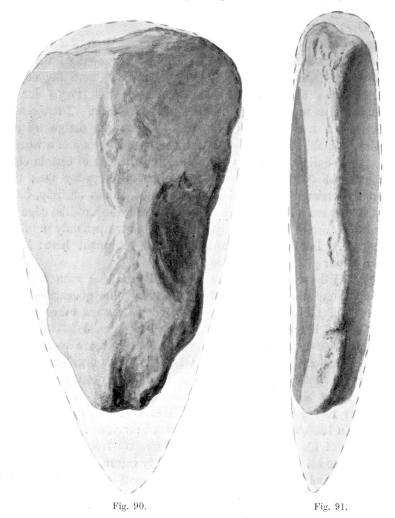

Fig. 90.   Fig. 91.

pre-glacial. It is clear that the most typical and the finest in form
and workmanship of his relics are of pre- or inter-glacial origin;
that they with the relics of the great Mammalia were overwhelmed
with the ice-inception; that both the mammal remains and the relics
of that ancient man were by that ice mainly destroyed. If there
were a post-glacial Palæolithic man, his weapons and other relics

were of an inferior character, both in design and workmanship, as compared with the glaciated remains.

I am inclined to the opinion, from what I have seen and collected in the Somme Valley and in and from the Thames and other areas of southern England, that the recession of the ice was followed by a man of greatly inferior calibre as compared with the man who made the typical forms of north-western Europe—that when the man of the more typical forms did return, if it were he, he had assumed such attributes in his work, and such forms for his productions, as to earn the designation of Neolithic. There was in no sense the necessity of any hiatus between the designated two peoples; the old Palæolithic point, as the operating end of a weapon, was, as we shall see, lost by the gradual substitution of certain chisel and axe like domestic (Palæolithic) forms of everyday use; they naturally ousted the pointed weapon almost, if not entirely, before Neolithic times. As domestic arts progressed, the axe-like edge was found to be useful in many ways: the pointed weapon only in offence or defence. But this must suffice for the argument here; let us return to our glacial Palæolithic man.

If, as I have assumed, the typical Palæolithic man was pre-glacial, there were certain regions where, the glaciation being naturally of far less vigour as compared with some other regions, both he and his relics were less affected by glacial action. Less vigorously ice-invaded regions would naturally have been, among others, south-eastern and southern England, and northern France, as compared (say) with North Britain. I hear on all hands of glaciated flint fabrications having been discovered in England. I remember seeing in the School of Mines Museum, Jermyn Street, London, in 1883, what I had no doubt was a fabricated flint, exhibited in a mass of its native matrix of boulder-clay from, I believe, the Yorkshire coast. Mr. J. Lewis Abbott lately informed me that he has found glaciated flint elaborations more common on the north, though also occurring on the south side of the Thames; while Mr. W. M. Newton also favoured me, by sending for my inspection a Thames-Valley find which was distinctly glaciated, and which also exhibited a bulb-of-percussion upon the glaciated surface. Mr. J. Russell Lukly also very kindly sent me two or three excellent specimens of *Eoliths* from Kent, one of which is distinctly glaciated. The glacial evidence is bound to be less demonstrative in such an area; but there must be such evidence.

In Mr. Worthington G. Smith's *Man the Primeval Savage*, although he denies the possibility of Palæo-lithic fabrications ever showing glacial striæ, yet he clearly, as I understand him, shows by means of diagrams that some of his " Palæo-lithic floors," *i.e.* zones upon which that ancient man actually lived and worked, were found below ice-disturbed drift. And I now learn from Professor Wright's *Man and the Glacial Period* of repeated discoveries of the relics of pre-glacial man in North America. For the introduction to the said work I am indebted to Mr. M. B. Cotsworth,

Fig. 92.

York, who has, as we shall see in due course, found a highly suggestive glaciated implement in the boulder-clay of the Yorkshire coast.

Fig. 92 is another Forth specimen which, like the last, seems to have been fretted mainly at its point end. Beyond this fretting it gives no evidence of glaciation. It is, I believe, a bleached dolomite limestone, very heavy, very ancient-looking upon

Fig. 93.

the face shown in the drawing, but much more ancient upon the side not shown. That side is the exterior of the stone from which the implement was fabricated. It occurred upon the shore.

In Fig. 93 we have a replica of Fig. 87, which has been snapped across in about the same place and manner, and gives an almost identical diamond-oval figure in section. They are not of the same rock, but were both found at different times at the mouth of the Esk at Musselburgh.

In Figs. 94 and 95 we have about two-thirds of a very fine and

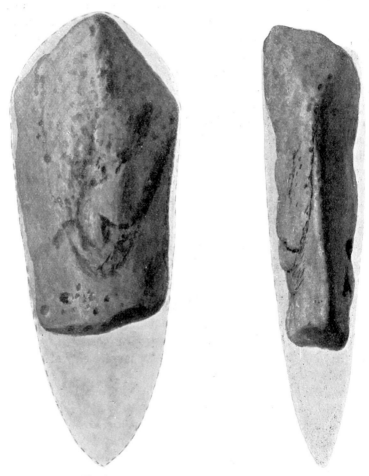

Fig. 94.   Fig. 95.

graceful weapon. Its antiquity is very evident; its deeply honey-combed and "mellowed" state is the result of decomposition during a long period of submergence beneath the estuary waters. It came ashore near Bo'ness.

It has not been recently rolled, but was subject to that process after it was reduced in length, and before it found a retreat beneath the waves ages ago. Beyond the dilapidated aspect there is nothing to indicate actual glaciation. It is of a trappean rock.

Nor is there evidence of the effect of the ice-foot in Fig. 96, more than is suggested by its fretted condition all around its margin; as in the preceding specimen, this fretting took place before it was subject to the rolling which its condition indicates. It was found by myself in a post-glacial river-deposit (a gravel-pit) 30 feet or so above the present level of the Dee at Aberdeen. Its immediate butt-end was detached from it by a workman's pick-axe. It is of a red pseudo-granitic rock.

Fig. 96.

Fig. 97.

In Fig. 97 is better illustrated the dilapidated condition resulting from glaciation. For though it is not striated I picked it out of undoubted boulder-clay at Dunblane. It was once upon a time a beautiful little axe. It has never been subject to rolling, and the flaking of its surface, where not broken away, is as distinct as though it were fashioned but yesterday; yet it must date from an extremely remote age.

The evidence is corroborative of an opinion that I formed many years ago, viz. that the relics of Palæolithic man in Scotland were destroyed or hidden away by the last great glaciation; that it is in glacially formed, the gathered and stored-up pre-glacial deposits, that the relics of this man are to be found.

I add two specimens to this chapter, which have come to hand just in time to be mentioned in this volume; they strongly support the view that a Palæolithic man was here, *i.e.* did occupy this region in glacial times, and that such relics may be found in post-glacial deposits, but that post-glacial man's fabrications are inferior in form, and weak in vigour and intention, in comparison with the much older glacial or pre-glacial productions, or that is my impression.

Fig. 97*a*.

I have made drawings of these two, but in order not to disturb the now completed arrangement of the illustrations, the figures must be numbered as 97*a* and 97*b*.

In 97*a* we have not an elegant, but what must have been a most effective weapon. It is of hæmatite, and is almost as heavy as though formed of malleable iron. It is nearly perfect, and still shows the elaboration, and particularly the effort, which produced the point. If mounted, as I have no doubt it was, it was all that could have been desired. It is more massive than the drawing suggests, being 2 inches through its thickest portion; and though inelegant it was fully as effective as the most refined in form. It was wholly worked out, except possibly the underside, which is not shown and is flat. It is unquestionably a fabrication, and being such, its importance comes with its condition and occurrence. It is glaciated, and most pronouncedly, according to the general rule, upon its flattest facet, and that is its underside; but it is distinctly glaciated upon other facets. It was found *in situ* in boulder-clay (Forth). It is 6¾ inches in length.

In Fig. 97*b* we have a finer and more vigorous conception, and something like elegance and refinement in form; it is of massive

build and is just over 9 inches in length. But its style of elaboration is quite as rough and ready as the last; its underside too is
flat, and possibly also re-
presents the only unworked
facet. That flat underside is
also clearly glacially grooved,
rather than striated : it is a
basalt, and is not now in a
condition to exhibit fine
striæ. But this grooving
is discernible under a side-
light over its other facets;
in fact, a close study of the
specimen shows that its
facets have been to some
extent actually moulded and
rounded by glaciation.

It was found on the
shore, where it was naturally
being gradually deprived of
its graphic ice-writing;
such striation would soon
have been obliterated altogether, and the stone thus
have lost its most striking
historic interest.

I have no doubt that
many of the now water-
worn fabrications of my
collection would, if they had
been rescued when they were

Fig. 97b.

first stranded on the beach, have told this same wonderful story of
their having passed through the advance and retreat of a glacial
era.

CHAPTER IX

The Glacial Story of Southern England

To pass out of Scotland into southern England was to leave a land where humanity is said to have had no history beyond Neolithic times, and to enter upon an area in which it is admitted that Palæolithic man played a great part in the history of what is known as the "Pleistocene" or the "Quaternary" period. He is known to have been present during some at least of the events of that momentous era. A period of profound changes in climate, and, as a matter of course, of equally profound changes in animal and vegetable life; a period in which what appear to be tremendous mutations in geographical and geological conditions took place. Land and sea seemed, according to some, to be for ever exchanging positions, heights subsiding and depths usurping their place. Now seas are shallow or altogether disappear, and cloud-capped mountains rear their heads. Now seas are depths, indeed, and the great marine leviathans are sporting in the late upland valleys. It was a period in which cold succeeded heat, and heat cold, with corresponding Arctic, temperate, or tropical *faunas* and *floras*. A period of great devastations and of great renewings; of great dispersions; of the complete exodus of this and that set of conditions and of living things; of the genesis, and yet again the genesis, of new conditions with a newer life.

It has all along been my opinion that the phenomena of this Pleistocene period have been vastly exaggerated. Exaggerations in the shape of constant changes of land superficies, and equally repeated changes of climate as per the "Great Ice Age," and similar assertions by other authors, which are in my mind.

How is it, we may ask, that the closing period of the great Tertiary epoch should be so full of what appear to be appalling events?

The first answer to such question lies, I think, in the fact of these events being so near our own times; of their being so actually connected with us as to be associated with such animals as are now

112

mostly familiar to us in some or other part of the world. The events to which we refer happened, geologically speaking, in our world, in our epoch. Most of the plants and animals which were ousted by the great glaciation are those which we now know in the world. Glacial periods, upheavals, and subsidences have come and gone with these creatures as part and parcel of their life-story; and they are a part of the human life-history; they, with their associated events, are of our circumstance, of our time. Man has come down upon the world's stage with them.

But why should this closing period of the world's (physical) history seem so appalling in its events, when it is asserted by many that more remote (geological) times were marked by phenomena much more profound than those of more recent eras?

Is not the answer to this to be found in our own inability to read into anything connected (directly or indirectly) with ourselves, the grandeur and the sublimity which we are ready to concede to events of the remoter history of the world. We have tried to read into these closing phenomena human conceptions of circumstance and time; momentous circumstance has become appalling, because of the limitations which we impose upon time in anything and everything with which man has any mediate or immediate connection.

Conditions have not changed more rapidly as the geological history of the world brings us nearer to the advent of man. Nor did his advent bring with it an acceleration of the earth's mutations. The general belief is that the reverse of this is exemplified in the world's history; we are not niggard as to time in connection with any circumstance in that history if it be but sufficiently far removed from any possible human concern and association. Where humanity is concerned we have tinkered away with mundane events in a spirit as little and as illiberal as ever was exemplified by faction in dealing with a nation's history. The world's history demands our every capacity for reverence, breadth of thought, open-mindedness, the deepest humility; in a word, it demands the very soul of liberality.

Sixty years ago the assertions of M. Boucher de Perthes that the flint weapons which he had found in the Somme-Valley gravels were indicative of an ancient man were decried by the then scientific world. It was thought that an admission of man being associated with an ancient gravel deposit would make him too old an inhabitant of the world for the then current views concerning that world and himself.

The admission was, however, finally made, with guarded restrictions as to the possible age of the gravels in which the implements were found. During the course of sixty years the world has become wiser and more liberal-minded with regard to things with which, notwithstanding his association, man has had and still has little or nothing to do. It is beginning to dawn upon humanity that itself is playing and has played a part in the world's history, which it neither devised nor knew that it was acting. It is beginning to come home to ourselves that the part which we have played in the world was designed for us by a dramatist who never consulted the actors. We have played our parts, as the humanity of the world, in accordance with the Designer and not as we choose to appraise such parts. We are beginning to submit to the inevitable in the truth, for the truth's own sake.

This is a reflection of the state of thought with regard to that ancient man in regions where his relics have been so long recognised. Let me, after forty years' interest, and thought, and investigation among these relics, give, with an utterly open mind, my views of the age of the typical Somme-Valley specimens.

In the year 1883, I twice had the privilege of inspecting M. Boucher de Perthes' magnificent collection at Abbeville. It is composed entirely of the Somme type-forms of weapons, similar to many which have also been found in certain of the valley gravels in the south of England. As I have said elsewhere, I never attempted to make a collection of these particular flint implements. Their general discovery in southern England began with the closing years of my sojourn in the South. They were forms which the pit workmen were trained to look for, and for which they demanded prices above my purse. My interest lay in yet commoner fabricated forms, which almost every gravel-pit I then entered disclosed to me.

It was a good many years later, viz. in 1883, that I spent ten weeks in the Somme Valley, when I purchased four of these said typical forms, one off a pitman at Abbeville, and three in a furniture dealer's shop at Amiens. These four specimens I have still, and in them, taken in connection with the outcome of my investigations in Scotland, I now have an almost profound interest.

For years after I had purchased them they were, more by necessity than by choice, stowed away, and I seldom saw them. In purchasing them, one only was critically examined by myself, for the simple reason that one alone suggested any possibility of its being a forgery.

One of the three from Amiens more than suggested that; but through curiosity, and as an object-lesson, I deliberately took the doubtful one. It is a most interesting fact—at least to myself—that after I had them in my possession for about ten years I turned them out for a careful scrutiny. It was the discovery of the Crieff *glaciated* finds, which suggested Somme-Valley forms, that induced me closely to scrutinise the Somme-Valley specimens.

The result made a profound impression upon me, and this impression still remains. I had looked upon them as the very latest work of Palæolithic man; as an evidence of his near approach to Neolithic times—Neolithic times then meaning an age of the narrowest limitations and of modern aspect. What was then my surprise when the close scrutiny revealed evidence, which I consider conclusive, that *three out of the four Somme-Valley type-forms are glaciated*; the only one which does not exhibit the least suggestion of glaciation being the doubtful specimen, *i.e.* the specimen which I all along believed to be a forgery.

Now see how some of us argue away evidence. On p. 89 in his *Man the Primeval Savage*, Worthington G. Smith gives a drawing of a fabricated flint to show that the portion of it which is not fabricated exhibits " presumed " glacial striæ. And he implies that because the presumed glacial striæ are not exhibited on the flaked surfaces, glaciated " flaked " surfaces are not to be found. This stone had obviously been flaked in post- or inter-glacial times, his only argument being that the original stone itself had been glaciated.

The author proceeds: " I have nowhere, either at Caddington or in the Thames Valley, seen a presumed true glacial scratch over an artificially worked surface." This we all readily concede—not a presumed true glacial scratch, because there is no presumption whatever about glacial scratches; they are what they seem, and they do not mean anything more or less than they signify. But a scratch is a scratch wherever seen and upon whatever kind of surface. The above sentence does not mean that Mr. W. G. Smith has not seen true scratches, but that they are merely not " presumed true glacial." In illustration of which the further statement is appended that " many of the implements and flakes—in fact, nearly all—from the Red Clay drift are profusely covered with slight superficial scratches, but these scratches are common on the stones of valley gravels, and are not glacial."

In a word, scratches that occur on natural surfaces may be

"presumed true glacial," but if they occur on artificially produced surfaces certainly not; they are only scratches without a suggestion of the cause of their being. If Mr. W. G. Smith had even hinted at a possible agency of the scratches the objection might have carried the weight of an argument. But an uncoloured statement that "they are not glacial"! arouses our curiosity.

What then are these scratches? That their occurrence in some of the valley gravels is "common," throws no light whatever upon their origin except it be from analogy with what I have found in this northern part of Britain; for here scratched stones are in places excessively common, and even though they be only "slight superficial" they are equally accepted as glacial striæ. Commonness is, indeed, as it should be, characteristic of scratched stones in a glaciated area; they should be very common, as they are in Scotland; and as appears in southern England and northern France also.

But whatever be the arguments against the glaciation of scratched stones, I am of opinion that the scratches which my Somme-Valley specimens show are glacial, and have no other origin. When I first discovered their scratched condition (in 1893) I had for twenty-one years been in the habit of handling and examining undoubtedly glaciated stones here in Scotland; and as I now write I have had thirty-six years' experience of the same. I now reaffirm the conclusion I came to as to the glaciated condition of these type-specimens in 1893, and assert that their scratches, though they are not by any means intense, are glacial. The possibility of their being in a glaciated condition is, to say the least, made a probability by the highly glaciated state of some of the weapons and implements which Scotland has yielded. Any one who has realised the glaciated condition of Scotland must naturally conclude that the condition of southern England and France would be at least what is admitted even by so determined an advocate of "post-glacial" man as Worthington G. Smith, when he asserts that stones are even commonly scratched and leaves the scratching an unsolved riddle.

Let me now endeavour to show that the *occurrence* of these "scratched" stones in England is exactly paralleled by the occurrence of glaciated stones in Scotland.

In 1902 I was in Colchester on two occasions. Most of my time there was spent in some high-level gravel-pits about 3 miles west of the town, and on about the same high level as the town, some 200 feet above the Ordnance datum line.

I was anxious to ransack some of the southern gravels with the set purpose of corroborating certain Scottish forms, chiefly of what I believe to be domestic implements. My search was hurried, but I could recognise at a glance what I wanted; careful examination was a prospect for some future leisure. I was successful in finding many specimens which interested me, but I left them with my friends in Colchester in anticipation of a further visit. This was paid in the autumn of 1904, when I revisited the same pits and found them closed, but opened at another spot, where operations were carried on, literally, by steam; sands and gravels of all sorts and sizes being produced all at once by machine-sifting and at once carried away. In consequence of this rapidity of action there was little material for me to examine. However, I added some things to my original collection, packed them up, and here they are in Scotland. And here they have been subjected to a careful scrutiny. There are about fifty specimens altogether, some being merely flakes. Now out of these fifty high-level Colchester specimens, some of which are unquestionably weapons of a poor type and others domestic implements, *eleven are distinctly glaciated.* We can call them "scratched" if we like it better, but it means glaciation all the same.

On the same visits (1902 and 1904) I was a few days at Datchet, near Windsor, and was then interested in some heaps of gravel which had been dredged from the bed of the Thames. I brought some seventy specimens from this gravel north with me (some very small), and they have yielded three specimens which are unquestionably glaciated.

. There is nothing in the foregoing, I admit, to positively show that the so-called glaciated specimens have not been scratched and polished — for polished or semi-polished surfaces are often the attributes of these stones — by the ordinary exigencies of "gravel-making," not only to-day, but in the past. Let us, however, turn to another of the results of my late visits South.

I spent as much time as I could of my 1904 holiday at Balham, London, S.W. I had not been in the neighbourhood a day before I discovered great quantities of the coarse gravel of the Mitcham (low-level) gravels strewn along some newly made roads. Nothing could have given me more pleasure than this discovery, since nothing could have been more favourable to an examination of the gravels with the purposes I had in view. The very last of these was the question as to whether the stones were glaciated or not. Had I examined the gravels with that view I should have missed to a great extent the corroborative evidence which I sought in other connection. To be brief, I collected between eighty and ninety specimens, small and large, inclusive of a few from an excavation at Croydon. This group, the largest of the three (comparing with the Colchester and the Datchet groups), has also been subjected to the closest scrutiny with the view of the "scratches"; but though the scrutiny has been repeated, with a sense of doubt of one's actual experience, I cannot find a single scratched stone among them. Not one; not a scratch that compares with those that characterise my Somme-Valley type-specimens, and that characterise some 23 per cent of the Colchester group.

Here is an interesting enigma! If rivers, or floods, or waves, or whatever forces we may adduce as having originated the valley gravels, be the agents which produced the scratches with occasional grinding and semi-polishing, why are they so entirely absent from the Mitcham group as not to be discovered, although almost twice as many specimens from these gravels as from those of Colchester are to hand? The Mitcham and the Croydon gravels are as coarse as could readily be found; they exhibit all sorts and conditions of battering and rolling, every attribute ordinarily exhibited by such gravels except the scratching—which, let me add, always has that precise, determined character which marks all glaciation that I have seen. Any single glacial scratch has that determined look; and three or four such scratches upon a stone are undeniable, in my view, as to their origin.

It may strike some of my readers as odd that, while the high-level gravels of Colchester should yield so many scratched specimens, the low-level Mitcham gravel should yield none; and that yet the bed of the Thames, the latest work of Nature, should yield a tangible percentage of the said scratched forms.

I cannot imagine that the Mitcham gravels are entirely without evidence of prior glacial conditions. *Derived* glaciated flints must, I think, exist in them; I speak simply as to what I found.

I do not conceive it to be at all odd that the bed of the Thames should contain the scratched stones, inasmuch as no river in a civilised part of the world can be held responsible for what it gathers together in its bed. The Thames Valley, for instance, has been the scene of agricultural labours for unknown generations. Cartloads of gathered stones from high and low levels have been shot into the river, not necessarily always as a ready way of disposing of them, but as a supposed defence against the stream's invasions of the banks at some points. The contents of the bed of the river are an exhibition of the result, to a great extent, of the interference of man with natural conditions—even the river's condition as a stream is not natural; its condition and the result of its work are artificially modified by human agency. But let me not be thought to suggest that the bed of the Thames could not and ought not *naturally* to contain scratched stones; it could, and of a certainty would, on occasion, obtain the scratched specimens of the higher levels or from any other source by natural means. Its own source and many of its tributaries doubtless rise in glacially affected deposits.

But let me ask why the scratches occur in older deposits and are more or less absent in more modern beds? and why stones are not now being thus scratched in the roughest of rivers, and on the most boisterous of seashores?

What I have already suggested as to the occurrence of "scratched" stones, *i.e.* glacial distribution, has come out clearly in my visits South; viz. that the glaciated forms occur both in Scotland and in England exactly as one ought to expect to find them. The Colchester high-level gravels are the washed-out and redeposited newly left boulder-clays of southern England, *with* the post-glacial efforts probably of a later race of human inhabitants. The Mitcham and Croydon gravels are both of a much later date, particularly the Mitcham series. If they contain stones derived from the original boulder-clays, as I have no doubt is to some extent the case, it must be very much at second-hand; so much so that no scratches are now visible. But these gravels are mainly made up of newer flints derived from virgin sources, *i.e.* direct from the chalk, or, perhaps better say *and*, from the post-glacial work of the newer inhabitants.

Is it not obvious that the agent of the scratching, whatever that was, had ceased to operate or at least to be effective when and where the Mitcham and Croydon deposits were formed?

This present chapter was, up to this point, written in 1904. I have paid one other visit to the Mitcham and Croydon gravels, viz. in 1905; and though I brought further specimens from both localities, and have since carefully examined them, the same puzzling statement has to be made—I have not found a single stone from either locality which presents the characteristic scratches which I consider to be *glacial* in origin. Such absolute negation I could not have imagined possible; but there it is, I merely state the matter as it has presented itself to me.

And further, I was in 1907 for several weeks in Surrey, where I had varied objects in view in ransacking the gravels wherever possible, this question of scratches being one; and I found splendid opportunities. I have the result here before me—over 100 finds; and though I have, by the aid of good sunlight, carefully examined each of them, I have not found a definite scratch such as I have in view in this argument; but I have found one, a semi-rotten cherty stone, that exhibits what might have been such scratches, but they are too indeterminate to be actual evidence in affirmation; that is the only result on the side of the presumption of universal scratches.

This is a puzzle, a problem; just the kind of problem that all along has given zest to the search. But this broad negation of what has been so plausibly and persistently asserted, viz. that the scratches are a natural attribute of " gravel-making," that they mean no more, nor represent more than is natural to the common gathering together of flints, by whatever means that may have been accomplished, is the reverse of problematical. There is, they say, no necessity for ice to step in here, since the stones are so universally and naturally scratched without that intervention. But is this the case *de facto* ?

The argument of the stones themselves seems, if we are not above listening to the argument from such a source, to be contradictory of the opinion that the said scratches originated in the normal conditions of gravel-making, and to suggest the necessity of the presence of some abnormal condition, that could alone be accountable for the said scratches where they do occur.

In this, my last search, I was located at Tongham, and was in the midst of a most interesting series of gravel deposits, of which, from my point of view, Farnham was the centre. Farnham was the chief field of my hunting. The town is mainly situated in a hollow, through which a small and sluggish river winds its way; but fairly steep rising-grounds surround this valley-floor, and bed after bed of extensive proportions of the gravels occur as one ascends to the highest levels. So far as I could learn (I did not see for myself) the gravel strata occur on the very highest plateau-like levels of the district. I collected my specimens from high-lying grounds as well as lower, up to perhaps 200 feet above the river at Farnham. And in neither high- nor low-level gravels have I found, as I have said, any evidence of the said scratches.

And now I would point out that the so-called "scratches" are something more than is implied by such word; they are, even the most delicate of them, much better described by the word *cuts*.

There is, as I have said before, something decisive about these striæ; that is an attribute which so drew my attention to the three of the four Somme-Valley specimens. Though they often are not deeply nor extensively striated, such cuts as they exhibit have that determined look which I have long recognised as characteristic of glacial striæ in Scotland. It matters not whether Scottish stones are much or but slightly striated, there is that decision in the lines that is hardly characterised by the word " scratch."

An incident in connection with the Farnham gravel, or at least in one of the high-level pits, is worthy of notice; it is this :—Steam sifting and assorting was in active operation, a process in which the larger flints in particular have a very rough time. This is " gravel-making " with a vengeance, for I saw that much actual breaking up of the nodules takes place, *i.e.* nodules are split into two or occasionally more pieces. A rougher time is represented in the passage through this mill than is ever exhibited on the roughest seashore or in torrential rivers; for the water in either case is an ever-present cushion or buffer, and literally acts as such. I never have seen, during over forty years' observations, stones broken up by any natural agency as they were broken up in that assorting steam-machine. This is, I should say, an illustration of the most vigorous possible style of gravel-making; and yet, though thirty at least of my Farnham specimens came from that higher-level steam-sifted gravel, I cannot find a scratch such as I am and have been looking for among them; they *are* not.

It is more than probable that scratches proper might be detected on these flints by the aid of a magnifying glass; but the "cuts" referred to need no such aid; they are perfectly and clearly visible to the naked eye, and are often so pronounced that they can be detected by the rule-of-thumb; they can be felt,—in a word, they are grooved.

I admit that I did expect to find that the steam-power had

produced tangible and visible scratches,—this is worth inquiring into by any one who is so situated as to be able to put this to thorough proof. I have not found such results. But even though the said steam process did produce the most vivid scratches and cuts, we should be no nearer an explanation of *the occurrence of striated flints in some areas, and their absence in others*—the occurrence and the non-occurrence of ice can, I believe, alone explain this, and here I leave the matter.

My readers will perhaps call to mind the fact that at least one of the three Somme-Valley specimens was pointed to as an illustration of the breaking and fretting along the margin of specimens which we now recognise as of glacial origin ; such breakage is generally associated with this scratching or striation.

CHAPTER X

Domestic Forms (*Scotland*)

I ASSERT that if we discard all the evidence of ancient (Palæolithic) man which we have seen and discussed in the foregoing chapters, *i.e.* if we discard all that is evidenced in Scotland by his *weapons*, we have yet such conclusive affirmation of his whilom presence in this northern region in relics which can only be described as *domestic*, as to be unassailable by any negative criticism.

This is doubtless to many a startling assertion, since both in England and France, the typical areas of the occurrence of that ancient man's relics, his domestic implements have scarcely been recognised. Not that they do not exist, but because the first apprehended forms—his axes or haches—were too readily accepted as alone exhaustively representative of that ancient fabricator; and this limitation of knowledge concerning early man is the penalty which has been paid for entrusting the search for his relics to artless gravel-diggers. While they have had that responsible duty thrust upon them, the weapons have accumulated to a vast extent, while the neglected domestic fabrications have been strewn by the thousand along the King's highways, and there reduced to dust.

Nor is this statement mere guesswork ; the more than surprising results of my quest in Scotland literally drove me to test, as far as possible, the occurrence of similar objects in the English Palæolithic gravels. And so far as I have been able to test the matter the result is a very striking corroboration of these Scottish domestic forms both in the older and more recent English gravels ; they are highly characteristic of such deposits as have yielded the best of the typical axes. They also possess peculiarities identical with those of the Scottish series, and evince the same modes of production, while perfect correspondence in their *use* is shown in the condition of the objects themselves. Among other features hand-grasps and handles are the common results of identical intention in elaboration, both in southern England and in Scotland. The ancient peoples' views of life were attained through the same course of events, and as they were doubtless one people, so their implements are of uniform type.

Yet the Scottish fabrications have their own characterising features. They are as a whole of better form, of a better style and mode of elaboration, as compared with similar productions from the English gravels. The explanation is, I have no doubt, that which I have given as the *raison d'être* of certain similar superior attributes in some of the Scottish haches, viz. the absence in Scotland of the restrictions which flint nodules everywhere imposed. It is perhaps even more clearly shown in the fabrication of these domestic forms that the flint fabricator's hands were governed and limited in their efforts by the exigencies of almost every object of his workmanship, while there is no indication of any such limitations in the Scottish fabricator's work.

The Scottish productions are, therefore, much more expressive of the actual intentions, as well as of the actual capacities of that ancient man; hence they are also more easily recognised than are the corresponding implements in southern England, *i.e.* when conditions have been favourable to their preservation.

I should no doubt have arrived at an understanding of these forms in England had my investigations not been transferred to Scotland. As it was, my observation of certain forms other than the typical weapons in the English gravels prior to my removal to Scotland in 1871 prepared me for such possibilities in Scotland. But I was in no sense prepared for the wonderful series of fabrications which has come to hand in this northern region : *I have learned in Scotland what to expect to find in the English Palæolithic gravels.*

It has been so persistently asserted as to have become almost a fixed (scientific ?) axiom that a combination of natural accidents, such as planes of cleavage, of bedding, etc., has produced these forms · r the same forms, as we have seen, "thermal" and other nat fracturing agencies have been made accountable. Even quite rece a well-known scientist has asserted the same to me by letter. I therefore a real pleasure to find this opportunity of laying before s apologists of the natural origin of these forms the following pages with their illustrations. It will, I believe, be conclusively seen that no chapter of natural accidents brought about these forms in the past, and that no such results from any known agencies are brought about in the areas of their occurrence in the present day.

There are certain forms of Palæolithic (and doubtless also of Neolithic) man's production that are almost as common in the more modern geological formations as daisies in a summer meadow, and yet they have not been seen. These objects are highly graphic, though they are of the simplest form and construction ; they are also very durable, and are therefore common because they are compact and not easily destroyed ; and they are highly evidential because of their numbers. Their cumulative evidence is beyond dispute, being based on their peculiar form, which is generally more or less perfectly shaped for the grasp of the hand, and the manual labour for which they were designed is often plainly recorded upon them.

They are characteristically simple forms,—a naturally flat tabular piece of stone,—a split pebble, or an object wholly sculptured out from a mass. They were mullers, rubbers, grinders, possibly on occasion pounders ; but in any case are easily recognised where we have not trained ourselves to assume that every stone under our feet is a naturally produced object. But, once apprehended we cannot fail to see them, for they occur almost everywhere, in what we understand geologically as superficial deposits.

They occur in all but the most recent deposits of the last geological age. They occur in all Pleistocene deposits which I have had opportunity to examine ; they occur conspicuously in certain of the boulder-clays. They occur in the soils, but not everywhere ; they are found among the stones of the brook, in the pebble-beds of river-courses, and upon the seashores. I have followed the plough and picked them up. I have seen them thrown out from deep cuttings in the streets of cities ; I have gathered them from heaps which have been culled from the paths of mowers and reapers ; I have picked them up from what must have been a fireplace and workshop of those ancient

...ples, even in Scotland. are ubiquitous, like s in autumn ; and leaves they tell the of departed times of a vigorous life.

Now to our examples. Figs. 98 and 99 are beautiful little specimens ; they

Fig. 98.   Fig. 99.

are both formed from cylindrical, highly rolled, close-grained basaltic

way in which the quite flat surface (*a*) was obtained was by striking away a projecting mass which left the concave facet (*b*). And so we go on, and see as we go the varied intentions of the ancient fabricators.

Figs. 107 and 108 are one specimen. We have here an instance

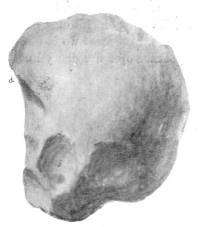

Fig. 107.   Fig. 108.

of a massive highly rolled stone, a crystalline quartzite having been successfully attacked, and a very effective skin-curer produced from it. A perfectly flat surface was obtained, and there is distinct evidence of a semi-grinding operation having been extensively performed with it. And while the exterior surface of the old highly rolled stone has a distinctly different aspect from the artificial flat surface, the rough thumb and finger places, which I have no doubt were distinctly intentional, are almost as fresh-looking as though made a few years ago. The projecting portion (*a*, Fig. 107) gives great purchase to the fingers when the thumb is placed in the hollow *b*. This is as large as an ordinary hand can comfortably grasp. Fig. 108 shows the flat highly worn surface. It is from the high-lying river deposit, Dunblane.

We now arrive at specimens which may be described as artistic, or fantastic, or æsthetic as we choose. There is certainly a touch of the artistic, and perhaps the foundation of our mathematics is here also. There is in Figs. 109, 110, and 111 not only the splitting or fracturing of pebbles, but the exhibition of something like mathematical precision in carrying out the intention; Fig. 109 is cleverly sculptured from a pebble upon which three facets have been induced, each indicating the usual smoothing effects of use. In the centre of this figure the hammered damaged portion is clearly indicated. From that point the two adjoining facets were struck off.

Fig. 109.   Fig. 110.   Fig. 111.

Figs. 110 and 111 are a transverse section of a cylindrical stone, one face of which is flat, while three facets were cleverly induced upon the other. In this triple-faceted feature there is that touch of profoundest sympathy with some of the now highest attributes of our humanity. It is the dawn of line and rule and figure; it marks the transmission of thought, the power of the complementary in design.

We come now to specimens which are much more actual pieces of sculpture in the sense that they have been elaborated entirely or for the most part from some larger mass. They had to be conceived just as a sculptor conceives his figure within the stone and works it out. These have a striking resemblance to each other in general form, as indeed they were bound to have, for their shapes are subordinated to the two chief requirements, viz. (1) as broad and flat a surface as possible, while the grasping by the hand (2) had to be kept in view. Some of these elaborations are quite small, some very large, as large as they could well be for the largest modern

Fig. 112.

hand. Some are probably highly marine-rolled; some are highly glaciated and fretted and broken; some show a slighter glaciation without being materially damaged.

In Fig. 112 we have a glaciated example from the shore near South Queensferry. It has been fretted and broken by the ice pressure, but was probably never a well-shaped specimen.

Another of much better pyramidal form, but also highly glaciated and fretted, from *in situ* boulder-clay at Crieff, is before referred to (Fig. 75).

In Figs. 113 and 114 we have an excellent type of the forms we

Fig. 113.　　　　　　　　　　　　　　　Fig. 114.

are now discussing. It is in all respects as it was elaborated, so far as its mere form is concerned. It was sculptured out entirely from a large mass. Its pyramidal form is excellent for the hand-grasp, and it well shows the result of labour upon the surface (*a*). The occurrence of this stone was of an almost startling nature. I took

it from a bed of wood ashes some four feet beneath the present surface at Dalmuir, Clyde Valley; which bed of ashes was surrounded in the same zone by a large accumulation of chippings and broken (Palæolithic) weapons and other domestic (?) forms. It appeared to be a Palæolithic hearth and workshop. It was so startling a thing to find in Scotland, that to this day I have almost a sense of awe when I think or attempt to speak of it.

Fig. 115 is another of the same general shape as the foregoing. This occurred in a delta-deposit at Musselburgh, near Edinburgh.

Fig. 115.

It is of a compact syenite; was cleverly shaped for the hand, and the flat facet has been finely smoothed; while the stone—which since its elaboration has been but slightly affected either by rolling or weathering—remains an excellent typical specimen.

Fig. 116 is another very fine and a highly interesting example. It is of quartzite magnificently sculp-

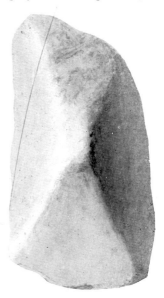

tured out from a once rotund mass, evidence of which is seen in the uppermost facet in the drawing. All the other facets, *i.e.* three and the underside, are the work of the fabricator, and have all been used, some more than others. This is the more interesting because I obtained it from an ancient high-lying deposit above the Whitadder, four miles from Duns, 1901.

And so one might go on *ad libitum*, making drawings and expatiating thereupon. But there must be a limit to illustrations; the object of this present effort is fulfilled by the giving of what one may justly call typical examples. Nor are those shown always the best that could have been adduced.

Fig. 116.

Some of the drawings were made years ago, as the finds came to

hand. Better ones have since been collected; better ones mayhap have even been picked up and thrown away again. I am not even certain that I still have all the specimens that are illustrated now in my possession.

Let us take two of my most recent finds, two, that is, which I thought it imperative to preserve and make drawings of. Both are from the shore within two or three miles on either side of South Queensferry. In Fig. 117 we have

Fig. 117.

a massive specimen of a close-grained trappean rock. It is glaciated in a sufficient degree to be at once evident. It is somewhat marine-rolled, which rolling was in

greater part effected before its glaciation occurred; and it has been
subjected to a further rolling from which I rescued it, the extent of
which is evidenced upon the surface of what I judge to have been a
glacial break.

This reference to *glaciation* is a natural opportunity for some of
my readers to ask whether, after all that I have suggested the stone
has gone through, the flat facet *could* show any indication of having
been subjected to human effort. Yes, it could and does; the effect
of labour is still plainly expressed upon it. The glaciation has but
slightly affected it. These flat semi-polished surfaces have been
assumed to be the effect of glaciation, but to one who has studied
the effect of ice it is seen that the more a stone is glaciated the
more uneven its surfaces become. Glaciation unmakes these surfaces
and never makes them.

But stones of this form, and with the attribute of the flat and

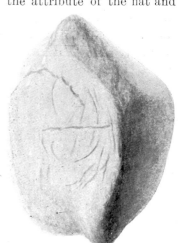

Fig. 118.   Fig. 119.

worn surfaces, speaking of their general occurrence, are *not* glaciated
one in a thousand. It is the great exception to find them glaciated
except in certain deposits. It was because of this feature (this
glaciation) that I deemed it imperative to preserve such cumbersome
examples as are now being referred to. Let us, however, look at another
glaciated specimen. The find, Figs. 118, 119, is of exceptionally
excellent pyramidal form. It is interesting to note that the facet
a can still be pointed to as the original surface of the stone from
which it was elaborated. All the other facets, with the exception

of a portion of *b*, are newer. These surfaces, since the stone is glaciated, are pre-glacial, *i.e.* the man who fashioned it was pre- or inter-glacial. If we turn its face to view (Fig. 119) we find it to be badly fretted and broken around its edges, and some largish fragments are gone. Its face, as in the preceding item, gives every evidence of the human use; but it is distinctly glaciated, and this in a very interesting manner. Its broad face is slightly *convex*, which fact, with the almost perfectly pyramid shape, would, to one who thought of such possibility, suggest a natural turning or rotary motion in any movement to which it was subject in a mass by ice. I have endeavoured to represent the ice-scorings upon its face, which cannot fail to be interesting, for they show that as it moved it actually did take that spiral motion. The face exhibits more of the curved scorings than I have attempted to represent. It is characteristic of glaciated stones, that it is always the surface which most easily yielded to pressure or movement that exhibits most the glacial striæ; *i.e.* the surface upon which stones would more easily slide or glide are always the more scratched or grooved.

Many of these skin-curers, or whatever they may be styled, are small; some apparently ridiculously so. I have found them with rubbed surfaces of not more than half an inch in diameter. They suggest a special purpose; but as we have only the stones themselves with nothing outside their own forms and condition to suggest their use, it is perhaps best not to make venturesome guesses. I would point to six drawings of three of the smaller, but by no means the smallest specimens (Figs. 120 to 125), in which we shall at once see not only a likeness to each other, but the wonted family resemblance to the large specimens of which we have just been treating. These all occurred in the delta material of Barbush Hill, Dunblane. The hill itself is

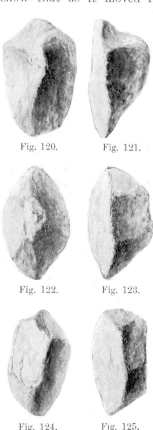

Fig. 120. Fig. 121.

Fig. 122. Fig. 123.

Fig. 124. Fig. 125.

composed mainly of sand, but is intermixed with larger stones, many of which are fabricated. I made a study of the contents of this old delta-deposit during five years in which I was Chaplain to Captain the Hon. Arthur Hay Drummond of Cromlix, the late proprietor of the hill, who had stones sifted from the sand, and part of a long drive metalled therewith. It yielded a large number of interesting finds mainly small; the larger stones, of which I saw very few, were discarded during the operation. I also paid a good many visits to the hill itself.

Nothing has interested me more than the finding of these same forms along the Ayrshire coast with as much expression of intention about them, and often with plain indications of use; *i.e.* they are in every feature identical with other Scottish specimens, but are *of flint.* I have italicised the words "of flint," because their occurrence in that material certainly gives them an added interest, since flint is not found *in situ* in Scotland; although some assert that once upon a time there was some flint-yielding chalk somewhere in the west islands. The nearest place, however, that could now be pointed to as a source of such material is the north of Ireland, some sixty miles in a straight line across sea from the area in which I found them. I have found them from West Kilbride southward to below Ayr; and I found one or two when, in passing through Stranraer, I had an hour or two to spare. Let us see representatives of these finds.

Fig. 126 is one of the more massive specimens. It is a section

broken from a cylindrical nodule, *i.e.* both ends have been broken away; the larger is reduced as usual to as flat a surface as possible, shown in drawing, while the smaller end has had some labour bestowed upon it that it might suit the hand — the edges have been rounded, *i.e.* struck off. Flint, as we all know, is much harder and therefore less impressionable to rubbing or even grinding processes than most other rock substances. But while it has not always so vivid a retention of the work to which it

Fig. 126.

has been put, this very attribute of hardness and indestructibleness is a great advantage in its rôle of recorder of its own history.

nasmuch as it generally retains the expressed intention of every stroke that the ancient fabricator gave to it in his completing effort, no matter how long ago that may have been. It is also worth our while to notice that the ancient operators found it no easy task to so fracture flint as to produce the desired flat surface. Its common habit is to split with conchoidal, shell-like curves, and often with a wavy or even semi-grooved surface. In the specimen before us it did not take a very flat surface; but it shows the greater wear on the flatter half of the face, as though the greatest stress was laid upon that portion by the operator. I had collected at least two other large examples of this type, both a good bit larger than this, and one in particular with a finely flat and much-worn face; but their size compelled me to leave them for a future opportunity of removal from the seashore, which opportunity never came.

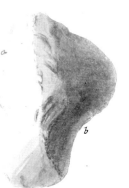

Fig. 127.

Fig. 127 is an excellent characteristic specimen. A good deal of labour was expended upon it to bring it into its present shape. By labour I mean that a good many strokes were given; but in the hands of a skilful workman the whole could have been finished in a few moments, and possibly it was so produced. The surface (*a*) is wonderfully flat for flint. It was produced by one vigorous, masterly blow. At (*a*) is the "bulb-of-percussion," with certain usually accompanying subsidiary fractures. This surface is highly artificially worn; as is to a less extent the surface on the underside of the figure (which is, of course, not seen here). It was elaborated from a nodule of which only one small part of its original surface remains. When taken well into the palm, with the ball of the thumb in the hollow (*b*), it fits the hand admirably.

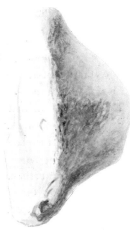

Fig. 128.

Fig. 128 is an excellent specimen, well shaped and smoothed on the flat surface. It was shaped from a nodule. All that is seen in the drawings, except of course the face, is the natural (nodule's) surface. The hand end has been reduced by repeated strokes, while two largish pieces have, on the side not shown, been cleverly struck out to give grasp to the fingers. It is also from the Ayrshire coast.

After the foregoing, Figs. 129 to 133 hardly need individual description. They are all formed from flint nodules, and all show the usual flat surface with more or less evidence of use, and have been further elaborated to suit the hand, or to prevent sharp points

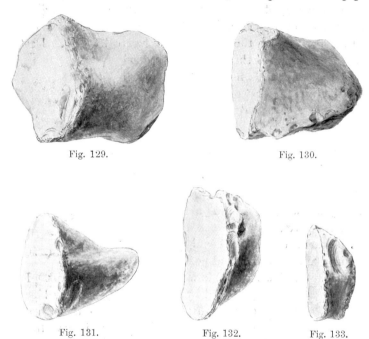

Fig. 129.   Fig. 130.

Fig. 131.   Fig. 132.   Fig. 133.

or rough edges from damaging it. I collected a good many of these flint fabrications, from forty to fifty at least, from the area named.

Figs. 134 and 135 are faceted flints of a different aspect, which might have been devised as knives or "scrapers." Their artificial aspect is clear from the drawings. They are part and parcel of the flints which characterise the Ayrshire coast.

I cannot attempt to fully discuss the question of their occurrence. That they are Irish flint I have no doubt; they must have come from that area. They are mainly brought up from the sea-floor, and I should say represent Palæolithic man during the "great upheaval"; when what is now sea between that part of Scotland and Ireland was dry land with a river or rivers only, forming a

barrier between the now separated countries. In those times
that great valley-floor was the chief hunting-ground of Palæolithic

Fig. 134.

Fig. 135.

man, since it was naturally the chief feeding-ground of the great
mammals. We cannot find space for further discussion of this

Fig. 136.

Fig. 137.

interesting occurrence of flint here in Scotland. It may be argued
by some that such flints are Neolithic. There is nothing but corollary
evidence to show that they are not Neolithic save the entire absence
of Neolithic forms among them, while Palæolithic forms do occur
with them. The four specimens illustrated (Figs. 136 to 139) are all

more or less fretted and broken, and are glaciated. They are all
Forth-Valley specimens, two having been extracted from *in situ*

Fig. 138.

Fig. 139.

boulder-clay and two brought up by deep ploughing; these also were
doubtless from the boulder-clay, since where I picked them up
boulder-clay forms the subsoil. They were drawn after this chapter
was written, or they would have accompanied the other (foregoing)
glaciated specimens.

CHAPTER XI

Domestic Forms (*England*)

To have anticipated these Scottish skin-curers, rubbers, grinders, mullers, or whatever we may style such elaborations, before my advent into Scotland thirty-six years ago, is not so surprising as it may appear in the eyes of some. Since for years before the relics of Palæolithic man claimed my interest, I was an enthusiastic hunter for Palæontological remains, molluscan, echinoderm, and sponge forms, which occurred not only among the flints, but in the matrix of the flint itself—in nodules and broken fragments. I spent years (as occasion offered) among the pits or roadside heaps or strewn gravel. When, therefore, the interest in ancient man came about, it was already a matured habit to ransack the flints; and in searching for Palæolithic relics I merely continued my boyish habit with a double purpose. I certainly found, *i.e.* I recognised, the faceted and *used* flint "mullers," and brought several North with me in my collection of presumed Palæolithic relics in 1871. But, as I have said before, they long ago disappeared. So, when the Scottish finds assumed their important aspect, I could not rest till I again found opportunity to hunt for renewed corroboration of the Scottish objects in the English gravels; for although a good many of these northern "curers" have been found in ancient deposits, by far the greater number have occurred upon the sea and estuary shores or in river-beds. It was therefore highly important, with the view to more definite age, to show that the actual Palæolithic gravels of southern England also contained them.

I was twice in England and among the gravels, in 1883, and during the last ten years I have been South with the same object in view some six or seven times—spending at least a month each time among the gravels and gravel pits.

I found full and, indeed, unlooked-for corroboration of the whole field of Scottish forms; and of these curers a series which fully corroborates my view that the majority of the similar Scottish finds are Palæolithic.

During my hurried visits South in 1883 I found several of these muller forms, two of which I have figured. Fig. 140 is not a large specimen, but it is well formed, being shaped, where the hand grasped, like the keel of a boat. It was skilfully fractured out, and its flat surface is for flint unusually smooth and illustrative of actual use. It came from Sedgwick's high-lying "coarse gravel of the hills" at Hildersham, Cambs.

Fig. 141 is another from the same gravels and obtained at the same time. It is also a small specimen, but shows well the used surface; and though most ancient and largely rolled, still shows the artificial sculpturing which produced its present form.

But for its stained condition, had Fig. 142 been found in Scotland it would there have seemed to be quite at home; for it is formed of a compact quartzite, and is a split, highly-rolled, iron-stained pebble. It was, however, derived from the high-lying gravels two miles west of Colchester, before referred to. Its flat surface indicates considerable use, and it is distinctly interesting as being undoubtedly glaciated.

A large specimen, Fig. 143, is a perfect replica of common, large Scottish examples except that it is of flint. It is also from the high-lying Colchester gravels. It has been cleverly shaped for the hand, and its broad facet is unusually flat for flint, but it does not show the result of labour nor any indication of glaciation.

Fig. 144 is another from the same Colchester pits. It is small, but cleverly produced. A small portion of its surface shows that it was fabricated from the heart of a nodule. Its larger facet gives indication of actual use, and there are slight suggestive striæ upon it.

Fig. 145 is yet another from that Colchester pit, and this is an interesting specimen. It is a portion of a nodule which was cleverly struck off transversely, and which was naturally suitable in shape for the hand. Its flat facet was skilfully produced, and it distinctly shows the effect of work. A few exterior flakings were given to it in the original making; and one or two flakes were boldly struck from it to give purchase to the fingers in the grasp—a circumstance which is often shown. This specimen is elaborately but finely glacially striated upon the flat facet, which would, as has been pointed out, be the gliding surface under ice-pressure. Nor need the said stone have been always placed facet downward in order to be glaciated most prominently upon that face; if contained in a sub-glacial mass of débris, *i.e.*

a "moraine profonde" in any position, that surface would yield

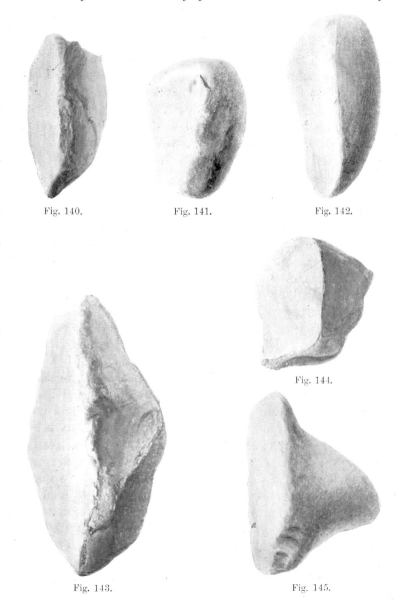

Fig. 140.   Fig. 141.   Fig. 142.

Fig. 144.

Fig. 143.   Fig. 145.

to pressure or movement, and so become scratched or grooved,
and on occasion furrowed. A fragment at a was fretted from it
in that glacial crushing. Although that break is old, it is seen

to be newer than that of the general surface of the stone, which was somewhat river-rolled before the last great glaciation came to pass.

But my visits to pits at Mitcham, Streatham, Norbury, Croydon and other places south have yielded the most striking and interesting specimens. I mention the pits in order rather to give their localities than to suggest that, as a rule, the search was made in them. The search was made generally upon newly made roads or paths upon which the rough sifted gravels were spread, as though for the convenience of allowing them to be thoroughly inspected.

If it should seem to any, ere my references in this volume to these southern visits are done, that I found an extraordinary amount of corroborative evidence in brief space—several months altogether— let it be understood that the circumstances were, as I considered, remarkably fortunate for my purpose. To give one instance: on a certain estate at Mitcham, a full mile from the pit whence the gravel came, almost a mile of new roads had been formed by using as the road-metal a thick layer of coarse flints, just as they were sifted from the pit material, i.e. not broken by road-makers' hammers.

This condition was equivalent to (say) my having engaged a host of men at a great expense for months in digging and sifting and carting, and finally spreading the product, probably (as I roughly calculated) between 2000 and 3000 cartloads over the roads. This is only one instance. I found other roads at Tooting, Balham, and other places similarly metalled; I lost no opportunity and no time, and it should be remembered that I knew exactly what I was looking for. My average day of search was eight hours at least, occasionally ten or twelve; but now and then it was too wet even to spend my day in such quest. So that reduced the average day's work. If it were as customary in Scotland as in southern England to dig and sift river and delta gravel for road-making, I am of opinion that we should be greatly astonished at what could be found. Broken whinstone or other bedded rock gives of course no opportunity, and that is the common road-metal in North Britain; but, judging from what I have found (in Scotland) on the rare occurrence of roads or paths being metalled from the gravels, I do not think that the finds would be at all less conspicuous or less interesting than they are in South Britain. What I found in the material of the southern deposits in, say altogether of late years, six months, would have demanded as many or more years in Scotland. And when we come to the boulder-clay in the North, the relics are naturally much more broken and unrecognisable than in corresponding deposits of the South. But to our examples:—

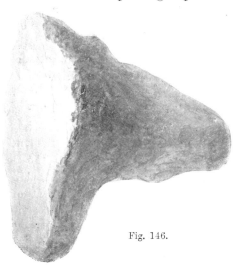

Fig. 146.

In Fig. 146 we have a remarkable illustration of a fact, already noticed, that that ancient man had a great eye for a natural *handle*; *i.e.* a handle that was already there in the conformation of any stone. The nodule (if it were such, as in this case) was so treated as to leave the desired handle or hand grasp with the necessary flat facet. This specimen, which I found in the great Mitcham pit itself, is as large as my hand can grasp. It is a portion of a once very irregularly shaped nodule. It was cleverly fractured through. The handle end has been somewhat extensively denuded of unnecessary excrescences, and reduced so as to perfectly fit the hand. The large facet is extremely smooth, and gives the characteristic evidence of having been considerably used.

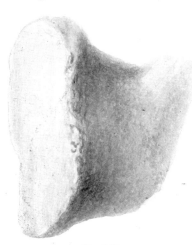

Fig. 147.

In Fig. 147 we have another excellent illustration of the adaptation of a natural handle. This specimen, like the last, is only a portion of a nodule. Its facet is flatter than in the last, although it is actually not so smooth. It gives decided evidence of artificial wear. As in the original nodule the handle end was rather too thick to be well grasped; bold longitudinal flakes were struck from the side the reverse to that shown in the drawing, and now it suits either the right or left hand admirably. I saw the excavation at Croydon, whence this specimen came, and if the material were not glacial drift it was a deposit resting within boulder-clay, in which case it was, certainly to some extent, rearranged glacial débris. Although this specimen does not show the least sign of glaciation, it evinces two erratic and forcible breaks along the margin of the large facet, and if these breaks be not due to some great natural pressure, they are the result of the deliberate intention of man. Such may possibly be their origin, but if they are not hammer-work, they must be a result of ponderous crushing.

Fig. 148 is a small specimen of the same type as the two foregoing; that is to say, it illustrates the deliberate choice of a natural handle. Its elaboration from a nodule is identical with that of the two previously described as well as of many of the Scottish specimens before discussed, which were obtained from cylindrical pebbles—"pebbles" and "nodules" coming side by side in this connection. My object here is not to give a history of each item, as it may be suggested to myself by certain attributes of the stones as well as of their occurrence; that would soon become tedious.

Fig. 148.

Fig. 149 is a longish example—a longitudinally split nodule. It has the rubbed look of such surfaces, which, by the bye, must not be confounded with the merely shiny aspect of many of the flints. Mere glossiness is not necessarily an attribute of a "used" stone. This feature of use is much better seen, as I have already suggested, in the Scottish, which are the more impressionable specimens, from which I learned the lesson. But it is often very evident also upon the flints, though not so generally. Upon this last example there are several flaked portions whose surfaces are more brilliantly glossy than the large facet, yet they have not at all the rubbed aspect. This is a Mitcham specimen. It gives no suggestion of glaciation.

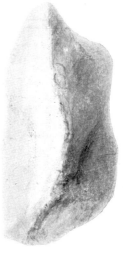

Fig. 149.

Fig. 150 is in elaboration more like some of the Scottish forms which, as has been seen, were designed and wrought entirely from out the matrix of a pebble or other mass of rock. This is cleverly produced from a split nodule, and like some of the Scottish forms is of excellent pyramidal shape. Two of the facets, as in some of the northern specimens, have, I think, been used. It is a good characteristic example of the wholly sculptured-out elaborations.

Fig. 151 is an admirable specimen — a length - wise split nodule with a facet almost perfectly flat and very highly smoothed. It is a black flint : but its exterior with the flat facet is highly patinated, which points to its great antiquity. It was left by its original

Fig. 150.   Fig. 151.

owner probably upon the open plain, where it became bleached (*i.e.* patinated) ere it found a burial-place. It not only still gives evidence of prolonged work upon its facet, but shows a semi-rounding, as though from use, where the hand grasped. The black fracture is the product of the modern navvy. At the end opposite to this break is a peculiar gap which deeply interests me. It has, as I believe, been struck out by wonderfully skilful splitting produced from opposite sides of the stone, by which process a piece like a wedge from a cheese was actually taken out. And that was done for the same reason that similarly situated fragments, as I have repeatedly noticed, have been removed in other instances, viz. to give a hold to the fingers, and often to the thumb. With the thicker end in the palm, the two forefingers take a natural and firm hold in that cleft. Where that item of the larger facet was lost in the making of that fingerhold, was the bulb-of-percussion that represented the stroke which produced the beautifully flat surface. The surface rises delicately in such a way to that end as undoubtedly to infer the point of impact and the start of the fracture which produced it. It is from the low-level Mitcham pit.

Fig. 152 is a sculptured-out example—only one part of the outer surface of the original nodule remains; its rougher facets seem to be of two distinct periods, but as the flat face, which is distinctly rubbed, is of the latter (more modern) aspect, the older facets may have been accidental, or they may refer to an earlier sculpturing. It is roughly pyramidal in shape, and suits the hand well. Another, which is of almost identical form and which I have not figured, is from the same pit as that of the foregoing, viz. Croydon. It is also a sculptured-out specimen. It is of a better pyramid shape than the last, and it has a well-produced square face, which,

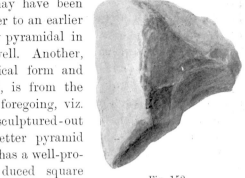

Fig. 152.

however, gives little or no indication of use. This fact becomes interesting when it is seen that, though its face presents quite an averagely flat superficies, two or three acutely jagged points mar its surface. An attempt to remove these would probably have made the irregularity worse. The story of the stone with these unusual prominences and its unused condition seems to be that, after its elaboration, the irregularities were found to scratch, or to tear, and so it was discarded. One does not of course assert this, but that is what the stone suggests to me.

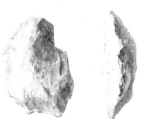

Fig. 153. 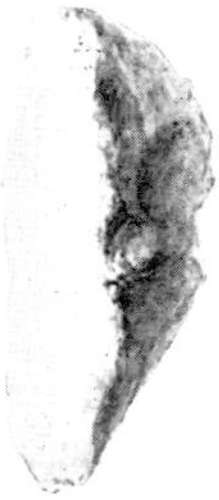   Fig. 154.

Fig. 155.   Fig. 156.

Fig. 157.   Fig. 158.

If I add three small specimens of which six drawings are given (Figs. 153 to 158), this must suffice for our introduction to these skin-curers. These last were obtained by myself from gravel at Cambridge in 1883, which gravel, I believe, came from a Wittlesford pit. They are more like the objects which are known as "scrapers," and generally associated with Neolithic man. Similar objects were among the specimens which first attracted my attention in the 'sixties, and were collected in gravels of East Anglia, mainly in the immediate neighbourhood of Cambridge. These specimens (of flint) speak for themselves.

Fig. 159 is another excellent specimen which came also from the Mitcham gravels at a subsequent visit. The drawing speaks for itself, and may be compared with Fig. 152.

These muller stones, with their facets and other elaboration, have been recognised by one or more students of Palæolithic man in East Anglia. And one in particular, being puzzled by them, says that they are usually large stones which have been more or less shaped and split so as to exhibit a flat or, as sometimes is the case, a concave (as also a convex) facet. This feature (the concavity), which is, I think, always an unintentional attribute, and often causes

Fig. 159.

the specimen to be well-nigh useless, led the said student of English gravels to advance the theory that Palæolithic man so shaped these stones that they might roughly fit around the base of stakes or posts, and so hold them more firmly in the ground. In this case it is suggested that that ancient man may have bound them to the base of the inserted posts.

While I cannot show that there is no basis for such a supposition, I can say that the very large majority of the specimens can never have been designed for such a purpose, since they are too small to have been of any service whatever, except in a mass as ordinary stones; and ordinary stones pressed into the post-holes would have done just as well. That theory need not, I think, in the least concern us. It is interesting, however, to find that the stones have been recognised by others besides myself both in Scotland and in southern England. In North Britain they have been associated with the polishing of the weapons of Neolithic man; and south of the border, as just seen, they have been made to secure very problematical posts in position.

I have discovered several of these larger specimens which exhibit highly *concave* facets—one from Scotland, and one or two from England. The Scottish specimen is of volcanic rock, the English of flint. It may be interesting to examine these.

I found three years ago (1905), in a pit at Croydon, a fine specimen. It is extraordinary if it be, as I think, a spoilt one, since it is more perfectly and skilfully shaped than any other flint example which I possess, except so far as its great facet is concerned, and that is highly concave. It has been more than usually skilfully sculptured out from a nodule; it is quite elegantly shaped for the hand-grasp, which sculpturing was done, I believe, before the nodule was split for the facet. I imagine that greater power could have been exercised in the sculpturing before the nodule was split. In any case the splitting was, from my point of view, a failure, since it took the great incurved surface. There was, I believe, an effort made to reduce the concavity after the splitting had been achieved; but that, instead of helping to produce greater flatness, took a yet deeper concavity and made the matter worse. There is a suggestion that an attempt was made to use it as those with flat surfaces were used. I have thought that some were used as "bone-crushers," but have never found indication of such use; and I think such work would have left its mark.

That the peculiarly shaped stones, of which the foregoing is a specimen, represent an ancient man, there can be no doubt.

As the Scottish concave example was found in the bed of a brook, and the concave surface was not the accidental result of a conchoidal fracture, but apparently of actual grinding, it may actually be one of the stones that were used in the polishing of Neolithic weapons.

If the foregoing be "skin-curers," as I have suggested, it follows that there must have been skins, and those in constant supply, if we may judge from the very general distribution of the said skin-curing implements. Would it not be almost startling if the next group of stones to be illustrated showed themselves to have been designed as flayers or skinners of animals? And not only designed for such purpose, but indisputably shown to have been put to such use? The next group will prove themselves to have been elaborated and used for such purpose. And so strong is the evidence of use upon some of them, especially in the Scottish forms, that it is almost certain that they were used mainly in skinning animals. It is at any rate difficult to suggest in many cases how the stones could have been worn in the peculiar manner which they evince by any other process. Some of them may have done duty jointly with the skin-curers in that operation; but both in their forms, and in the manner in which they show themselves to have been used, they almost as plainly as though they spoke declare their ancient use in the procuring of skins from the animals for the home or camp operation of skin-curing. There are many of these stones, and of many various forms; but all answering more or less perfectly the attributes of flayers.

In my visit to Surrey in 1907 I procured further excellent specimens of these mullers or skin-curers at Farnham, Tongham, Ashe, and other places.

CHAPTER XII

Palæolithic Man's Common Task

In the two preceding chapters we have discussed certain relics which often show that a considerable amount of sculpturing has been given to them in order to reduce them to a usable form. Such objects, whether elaborated much or little, almost invariably exhibit the result of manual labour upon one or more of their facets. These I have described as the simplest form of (domestic ?) implements. Yet I feel that I might, justly, be taken to task for such designation, since they were certainly neither the most primitive nor the earliest form of domestic implements.

Before such forms came into use or could have been even conceived, there must have been some urgent demand for them in the exigencies of that ancient man's daily life. If, as I have suggested, they were skin-curers, or skin-pounders, *i.e.* softeners, or were used for the removal of fur or hair from skins, or for the grinding or pounding of seeds, etc., such purposes, or some of them, certainly implied the prior use of other implements, which must also be described as domestic. These we can only conceive to have been knives, and flayers or choppers, or other implements *with* weapons of offence. If skins were "cured" by the animal fats being rubbed out of or scraped from them, and after drying, softened by pounding and rubbing, skins must have been procured ; and skins worth such preparation could alone have been obtained by the aid of knives and flayers. Knives and flayers in their turn postulate the use of weapons, for the skin-providing animals were of necessity slain.

We have seen that weapons occur everywhere, at least where these characteristic and widely distributed mullers are found, and so evidential are they of the presence of other Palæolithic relics, that I have long denominated them Palæolithic man's "hall-mark." We shall now see that the indispensable knives and flayers have come to hand in complete accordance with this postulated demand : they may be discovered wherever these "curers" are found ; but, as is quite natural, the curers are invariably (in Scotland) more numerous, and are therefore more easily found than any other of the domestic implements.

While knives and flayers certainly preceded skin-curers and skin-softeners, both knives and flayers, and especially knives, were from the necessitated attributes of their forms not only more readily subject to destruction from chemical decomposition, but from their tenuity and length they were the more easily snapped and broken, while the massive cube or ball-like curers or pounders could resist and almost defy the most destructive forces. The distribution of the curers, and their commonness, are exactly what should be expected. Even though they were not the earliest domestic implements, and need not at any time have actually been the more common forms, their general preservation is probably more the result of the accident of their particular shape than of any other factor in their history.

They occur for instance—in places—fairly commonly in the boulder-clay, or other ancient (post-glacial) deposits, where weapons also, more or less recognisable, are found. But knives and flayers are much less frequently met with in recognisable condition in such deposits, it being, as I have suggested, natural that it should be so. I do not mean that knives and flayers were not in use in pre- or inter-glacial times, but only that they have been for the most part destroyed. In more recent post-glacial deposits, and these not of Neolithic, but of, as I presume, Palæolithic age, as is distinctly shown in England, they do occur even commonly, sometimes more commonly than the curers. But the occurrence of the curers in the boulder-clay actually postulates the coeval existence of knives and flayers, whether or no we find them in recognisable form. Thus at length we have come to these knives and flayers and allied forms of domestic implements; and have thus arrived at what seems to me to be the most profoundly interesting phase in this quest. We have come to the fact that for many years I have had the experience of being introduced to that ancient man in Scotland, not only by the media of his weapons, but also by means of implements which bring him into sympathetic contact with many events of our everyday life, even in this beginning of the twentieth century.

By his weapons alone we see the man as at best a hunter,— possibly a slaughterer and murderer of his kind. In such implements we have no clear evidence of any of the better attributes of the man ; of any of those qualities which we recognise as " humanising " ! But with our skin-curers, and flayers, and knives, and choppers, and other associated forms, there comes a man out of the past—who stands before us, instinct with humanising traits; who was already in glacial and pre-glacial times a flayer of animals and a dresser of skins; a man already so far human as to have his home industries, his recognised and never-ending occupation of providing clothes and food for his women and children; and their turn came—the humanising "daily round and common task"—when, the skins having been flayed from the quarry brought home from the hunt, they effected the curing.

The above picture cannot with the evidence which I have gleaned be at all an exaggerated one.

Relics cannot lie, and the relics of this ancient man bear witness to an appreciably advanced state of civilisation, even before the last great glacial inception came to pass.

As long ago as 1872-74 I was puzzled by several objects which I had from time to time, during two or three years, found in what I have described as an ancient delta-deposit near Forteviot, in the Earn Valley.

These were, as I then believed, and am now assured, produced by man's handiwork. I took them to be weapons of a crude and uncertain form: there was clear indication of elaboration; there was always a more or less definite point end, and a broader butt. I took them to be weapons, as I say, but was for several years exercised in my mind by certain peculiarities which they presented, supposing them to be weapons. Let us examine them:—

Fig. 160.

Fig. 160 is the first of these puzzles which came to my hand. It is unquestionably weapon-like in general aspect; but two features struck me as at least peculiar. The one was the contrast between the result of the elaboration as seen in the two lateral margins of the stone. To the left of the figure the sculpturing has produced a rough, broad sort of "back" rather than an edge, while to the right an actual edge, more perfect than now, once existed, and was evidently intentionally produced. In the drawing the stone looks fairly well balanced; but in the hand a lateral view shows the contrasting character of the two sides.

The other feature of interest was the fact of the large facet (*bb*) being not only distinctly concave, but, as appeared, worn smooth by some mysterious accident, or by some human intention—it was a puzzle.

That specimen was obtained in 1872.

In the same year another was found in the Forteviot bed; not identical in form, not so weapon-like, but similar in certain attributes. This latter (Fig. 161) possessed the same characteristics of a broad back-like margin at *a*, a much better preserved edge at *cc*, and this time an undoubtedly artificial and highly smoothed facet *bb*. Both specimens had been considerably fretted and broken since they were elaborated. I have appended suggestive restoration lines to the latter—but, what were these relics?

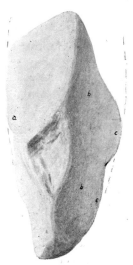

Fig. 161.

Both might originally have been knives, and especially the latter; but their use as knives could not have given the smoothing to one facet more than another on either side of the supposed cutting edge; whereas, in both these instances, the facets *bb* in the drawings are much more smoothed than the corresponding reverse facet in either. What were they?

The only answer immediately suggested was negative: they were not weapons, at least not of the ordinary type, for it was evident that neither of them was elaborated so much with the view to a point at one end as to an edge at one side. I cannot now be certain, but I am under the impression that I was greatly exercised in my mind for two or three years as to their conformation, and as to the effect of manual work upon them.

Up to this time (1872-74) I had not found, either at Forteviot or elsewhere in Scotland, typical haches, *i.e.* weapons of any great character or moment, and these things alone, though they intensely interested myself, were not much to base assertions upon. I was aware that few would accept them as either scrapers, or knives, or weapons, yet I was convinced that I had lighted upon not only human fabrications, but objects which also exhibited the result of human labour. Their indefiniteness, however, coupled with their place of occurrence, made me hesitate either to name or to describe them.

Yet another of the same general conformation as Fig. 160 was found at Forteviot in 1873, and this was much less like a weapon. Its back-like margin was more strikingly square, and its opposing edge more knife-like. I have given no drawing of this.

When it happened I now know not; but having this last find one day in my hand, while in an inquiring mood, illumination came. I had grasped it with my right hand by the back-like side toward the broad end, as upon *a* and *a* in Fig. 160, and the word "flayer" came to me; *they were flayers.* Whole series of this and other allied forms have come to hand during the thirty odd years which have intervened between that conclusion and the present time, and they all confirm the opinion that they were flayers, or, when suitable, probably knives, the two uses often occurring in one specimen, the knife becoming the flayer, possibly, as soon as the keener edge was lost.

That first apprehension has long since, from repeated discovery, become a system of Palæolithic domestic forms: forms of manifold aspect, of various design, and modes of production; of equally varied size, as circumstance and fashion dictated. And now we have a multitude of specimens, all of interest, and every one of some value in confirmation of the rest. We cannot do better than proceed in our discussion of these, upon the already suggested line of the simplest form first, since they naturally suggest and lead up to the more complex.

We are apt to assume that any elaboration of a stone, and especially when the operator could be aided only by the use of another stone, was a difficult and laborious work: an incident which I here quote, though we have little space for extraneous matter in this volume, will give us a different view of this, and will be suggestive to us in other ways :—

When Mr. F. H. S. Orpen, the Surveyor-General of Griqualand West (Africa), was on one of his tours of inspection in the western portion of the province, accompanied by his son, the latter, while out shooting with a Bushman after-rider, happened to kill a springbok in the middle of a large plain. When they wished to lighten the buck by disembowelling it and depriving it of its head, it was discovered that neither had a knife in his possession. In this dilemma the Bushman said that it was all right, and looking round, selected a couple of stones ; giving a smart blow by one piece above one of the angles of the other, he immediately struck off a long flake, found to possess a sharp cutting edge. With this he set to work, and in a short time opened the buck, dressed it properly, cut the sinews of the legs, and brought it into a fit state to place it behind the saddle. *He then threw away the implement* which had proved so useful. This production of a stone flake, merely for temporary use, seems to explain why so many of this kind are found thickly strewn over different portions of the old game country.[1]

In the above modern instance we have, without doubt, the capacity and procedure of the ancient elaborator brought vividly before us. An implement of most useful and effective kind is produced with a minimum of effort at a moment's notice. The work which demanded the production of the implement being accomplished, the means of its accomplishment is thrown away, as being only a burden, when the like can be so easily reproduced as occasion demands. This is certainly a highly illuminating and suggestive illustration of the probable, common procedure of primitive man.

But let us notice that the implement of the above narration was of the simplest possible kind—a flake struck off; that is all. The required edge was there as the result of the detachment from the parent stone : nothing could be more simply obtained except in the rarely possible occurrence of a stone naturally offering a sufficiently sharp edge. Such a natural occurrence must have been *most* rare when the required tool was a knife, but when the article required was not a knife, but a " flayer," where too sharp an edge was a fault, I have repeatedly observed among these Scottish forms that a naturally edged stone has been used with no elaboration whatever, or with such simple elaboration as was needed to give the hand the desired grasp. In the case of flints in the south, as I have seen, a knife was a simply produced surface-flake, or a section with a broad back and an edge struck from a nodule. If this were desired to be used as a flayer, it was a common habit with the flint-fashioner to hack the cutting edge away, and then, in flaying, the skin would not be cut. This feature of chipped-away edges, especially in the flints, is the usual accompaniment of the artificially smoothed surfaces, which are much more rarely seen in association with actually cutting edges.

With regard to such simply produced implements as the Bushman in the above narrative made, and used, and threw away, it ought to be clear to us that implements of similar simplicity, if formed from Scottish rocks, and cast abroad as thick as leaves in Vallombrosa, and especially if so scattered in a remote past, would scarcely be at all recognisable anywhere to-day. Most would have gone the way of all Scottish rocks, into a condition of disintegrated

[1] Stow's *Native Races of South Africa*, p. 66.

matter. It is only when we come to masses of more durable form, with some elaboration, or with smoothed surfaces, etc., that the human intervention can be seen. Flakes, *i.e.* knives, are therefore naturally much less evident in Scotland than flayers and choppers, and especially than the mullers, but these naturally postulate the whilom existence of the former.

One of the best possible examples of the simple adaptation of a stone to a purpose also comes from the ancient deposit at Forteviot. It is a piece of trap, which gave a triangle with one very acute angle in section, which was *naturally* a somewhat sharp edge. It might have been originally a knife ; but there is distinct evidence, or what I take to be such, that the stone was used as a flayer : both its broader facets — as *a* in the drawing (Fig. 162)—present artificial smoothing, and portions have been roughly struck from it in order to suit it to the hand, as seen in the darker portions of the drawing. That it is of Palæolithic origin is, I presume, evidenced by its geological occurrence.

Fig. 162.

Fig. 163 is another of very similar aspect, and I think of identical origin : it had been used in the same manner, and was adapted to the hand by the breaking away of portions from the " back " or hand-grasp. This specimen was found under circumstances which pointed to the actual occurrence even in Scotland of a Palæolithic workshop " floor," or " hearth," at Dalmuir, Clyde, before referred to, where were also several Palæolithic-like weapons, skin-curers, and a few unusually excellent knives, which are considerably broken.

Fig. 163.

I give here (Figs. 164 to 166) drawings of three of the presumed knives from the Dalmuir deposit. It is more than probable that I shall not find room for a full description of this most interesting occurrence in this volume, but we shall have casually to refer to other specimens from that source.

As soon as we pass from naturally produced, but artificially

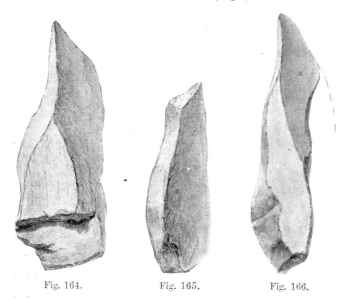

Fig. 164.   Fig. 165.   Fig. 166.

modified stones, we are on more tangible, *i.e.* more evidential, ground. We cannot take up a stone that has received its present shape through a human intention, no matter what its present condition may be, but that that intention is there before us. We may not recognise such expression, but that is the result of our own ignorance or incapacity: it is there. I can to-day point to many different forms, which had years ago no meaning whatever for me, till actual comparative study revealed the expression and the intention; and then, with patience, cumulative evidence has verified the revelation.

When, for instance, I first found a section of a pebble, in shape, say, like the section of a Dutch ball-shaped cheese, and imagined that it was intentionally produced from the pebble of which a portion of it showed it once to have been a part, there was nothing more tangible in it than the fact that it was the section of a once highly rolled stone, a pebble; or so a casual observer would say. But it appeared to me that several circumstances about the said stone were expressive of a human intention. There were (1) the fact of its having been the said pebble, rolled and rounded without being broken *for indefinite ages.* (2) That before the object could be a section from the parent mass, such mass must not only have split or divided, but another break whose surface radiated from the centre, like the

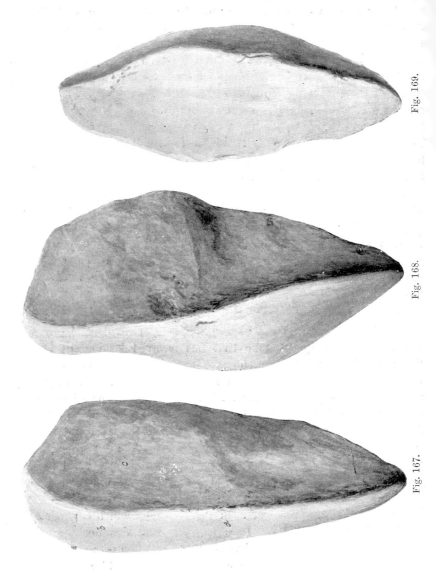

Fig. 169.

Fig. 168.

Fig. 167.

first, was necessary to produce the present result. (3) As both these detached facets are of the same age, as evidenced by their appearance and condition, and neither of them was the result of cleavage, or lines of bedding, or of any other naturally induced rupture, there seemed to me to be a real expression of intention about the stone. See Fig. 167, where the facet to the left shows it to have been part and parcel of a pebble; one of the more recently produced facets is the broad one to the right. On the assumption that it was an intentional production, the top left-hand portion is the hand-grasp. This specimen is marked 1880, and is from the bed of the Tay at Perth (Woody Island).

In Fig. 168 we have in every respect an identical form, with evidence of more perfect and probably more prolonged rolling as a pebble. There is also, I believe, the additional evidence of its having been actually used and smoothed, as indicated on the broader facets. This occurred on the "Black Rocks" at Troon, Clyde; it had been brought in from the sea-floor. The handle end is the top left-hand corner of drawing. In Fig. 169 we have another and admirable specimen of precisely the same type and exactly the same conditions :—a section from a whilom highly rounded, *i.e.* rolled, stone. This is from the Forth shore. In Fig. 170 is another not so evidently a *section,* but it was undoubtedly elaborated for the same purpose as the foregoing. This is from the before-mentioned ancient deposit of the Mill Burn, Whitadder Valley, Duns.

Fig. 171 is another most excellent typical specimen of these *sections —*

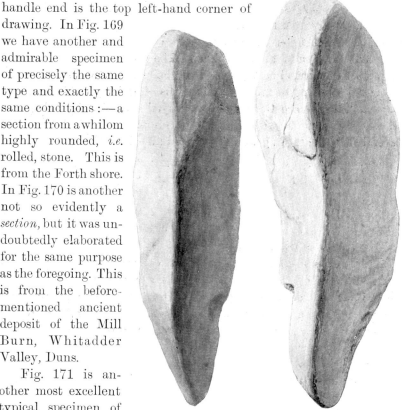

Fig. 170.   Fig. 171.

knives or flayers, or whatever they were. But all these three last show clearly the result of the manual labour referred to ;

and this is evident in Figs. 169 and 171, in an incontrovertible degree, on both the broader facets of each, but is yet distinctly more conspicuous upon one facet than the other; in both cases it is the flatter and the naturally more usable facet that is the smoother. In the one the more used surface corresponds to manipulation with the right, in the other with the left hand. These also demonstrate what may be accepted to be a general rule with such items, viz. that the evidence of work, as is natural, is much more decidedly marked *toward the point end*, as opposed to such evidence at the "handle" end, where the smoothing is reduced to a mimimum, and is often entirely absent. I would here point out that the fact of there being a handle end precludes in my view the possibility of these stones being, say, "scrapers" or skin-curers. They might, of course, have been used for scraping skins, but such application to a skin placed flat upon the ground would not have resulted in the peculiar limitation of the smoothing. The peculiar *use*, as indicated upon most of them, almost proves that their application was more for the actual skinning of animals. It is also highly probable that the larger of these—once the animal was flayed—were used as choppers, *i.e.* were implements with which the animal was hacked to pieces. Several of the foregoing would make admirable hackers, with which

Fig. 172.   Fig. 173.

I would to-day undertake to cut up the carcass of a sheep; and in case of necessity, would hack to pieces even that of a bullock. Figs. 167, 168, and 171, for instance, are from 8 to 9 inches in length, and weigh between 2 and 3 lbs. each.

We shall, however, see farther on that this ancient man had much more effective implements than these — at least in Scotland — for the dismemberment of carcasses of the larger animals.

Figs. 172 and 173 represent another section, possibly more a knife than a flayer, from the Dalmuir fireplace. This has never been water-worn or rolled, as all the others have been to some extent. It is identical in character with the preceding.

We now come to what is to myself a most interesting phase in this search. My readers will call to mind references which I have made to certain forms from the Palæolithic flint gravels of East Anglia, which I had collected before my advent into Scotland, most of which specimens disappeared twenty-eight years ago. Among them were forms which I had, as I have said, supposed to be barbarously shaped weapons. These were repeatedly and strongly recalled to mind by what I have since their loss discovered here in Scotland. This constant reminder was the strong factor in my great desire to return to the gravels of the south of England during the last twelve years. Without further ado, let us see how far our present aspect of the Scottish forms was responded to by the renewed southern investigations.

I give a few illustrations of these; but I have quite a series of identical forms, *sections* of nodules, of the most corroborative and convincing kind. Fig. 174 is the drawing of an excellent specimen, as like any of the foregoing in this chapter as could well be. *a* is the exterior of the *nodule* in place of the exterior of the Scottish pebble; *b* is an operative facet, the edge is of course to the right of *b*: the other operative facet is not shown; *c* is the hand-grasp.

Fig. 174.

It will be seen that such fabrication, with its broad butt and point, would, with the identical Scottish forms, on first acquaintance suggest a weapon. This specimen is from a high-level gravel-bed at Croydon. That the stone is a fabrication cannot be questioned; but it does not show the *use* as many of the Scottish specimens do—none of the flints would or could be as susceptible to the effect of manual labour as are the Scottish rocks.

Fig. 175 is of identical style and origin. But it is interesting as showing in the clearest possible way the method adopted for reducing a too sharp edge to the requisite bluntness. The edge has been broken away by a series of strokes given consecutively from the broad end to the point; all the strokes except the last at the point, were given in one direction. This item again seems to indicate actual work; but it is indefinite.

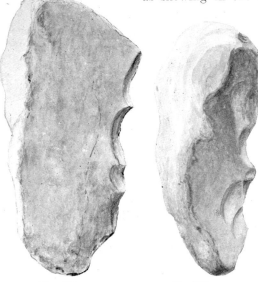

Fig. 175.   Fig. 176.

Fig. 176 is a smaller but admirable specimen, this time from a low-lying pit at Mitcham, Surrey. It occurred in association with a fragment of a mammoth's tusk which I brought North. This has also been hacked along the edge, from one side only, except again at the point where the stroke was in the reverse direction. Like the others, its expression of actual use is indefinite.

Fig. 177 is another flint specimen, but this is Scottish, and is from the Ayrshire coast. I have already referred to the occurrence of these flints, which I have no doubt are of Irish origin. It is not iron-stained, as most English specimens are, more or less. It is also a section from a nodule, but was obtained apparently with comparatively considerable effort: it is thicker and more clumsy than usual, and there was a considerable amount of elaboration bestowed upon it after the actual section

Fig. 177.

frettir
the st
It
glacia
" flaye
1902-
can b
expre

was obtained. The elaboration is very distinct and definite, and is characteristically " human." Upon the facet, not shown, two fine bulbs-of-percussion are in evidence. Neither does this, while it suggests it, actually show the result of manual labour. In order, however, to reduce the cutting edge, considerable work was given to it; again, almost entirely from one side.

I have found several of these flints on the Ayrshire coast, where, as I have shown, they were associated with other flint forms, which I take to be Palæolithic weapons of a poor and primitive type.

Since the majority of these Scottish examples have been found along the coast-line (mainly within or near the mouths of the larger estuaries), or in river-beds, it is quite legitimate for any to suggest that at least some of these finds are *Neolithic*. I am ready to concede that some may be such. I am myself quite unable to say where Palæolithic elaborations end and Neolithic begin. Indeed I do not believe there is either any ending of the one great group or any actual beginning of the other.

There is, however, a vast deal of evidence that points to the very great antiquity of these relics, and little that suggests a modern origin.

Even though found upon the seashore, that position is rather for than against their antiquity, since they are either brought up from the sea-floor by seaweed attached to them, or are derived from deposits by coast denudation. By far the larger part of my coast specimens have come from the sea-floor. One can tell, by taking trouble, whence they come; and when they have come from beneath the waves, they invariably have a very venerable look, and are in a highly antiquated condition.

Such stones are not indigenous to the seashore—to what we call the littoral zone—any more than they are indigenous to the King's highway. They are ever being derived from some source or other, and stranded there, where they are for ever being reduced by decomposition or friction, or by the two destructive agencies combined, to unrecognisable condition, and finally to utter dissipation; sands and clays at last representing them elsewhere.

Stones in river-beds, and especially in the channels of the Scottish rivers, occupy such a position for only a transitory period; they, too, are ever being derived either from the soils of their drainage areas or from denuded deposits, and they are ever being " moved on." So evident is this that I have in a few instances traced the source of

CHAPTER XIII

Some Palæolithic Puzzles

EXCEPT for the one or two introductory specimens from the ancient deposit at Forteviot, our last chapter was taken up wholly by a consideration of implements of great simplicity so far as their elaboration is concerned, for they are little more than segments or sections, as they had been broken out from more or less globular masses.

This particular form might have been a very early conception of primitive man; it might have been a mere passing fashion in form and style of a comparatively modern period in his prolonged history—an accidental variation. Yet our last-considered glaciated example suggests that this particular form was indeed most ancient. My experience leads me to believe that the more clumsily made weapon or implement need not necessarily be older and may be ages younger than others more elegantly or more elaborately formed. Geological and geographical position is much more reliable evidence of antiquity than mere form and style of work. Hence, although we make a kind of progressive series of these fabrications by way of giving a sort of system to their study, it must not be concluded that we are (necessarily) studying the mode and manner of the development of either domestic implements or weapons. I have no desire to mislead even by suggestion.

We are proceeding from the more unwrought and clumsy to the more skilfully designed and wrought: but we must bear in mind that it is a comparative study rather than one of progressive development; we must know much more than I pretend to have mastered, before we dogmatise as to which form or mode of production led the way to higher types. The spirit of our present procedure gives us doubtless the true aspect, viz. that the better, more æsthetic form was at some time or other evolved out of the poorer and less refined, the same being true also of the style of elaboration; but the vicissitudes of the wondrously prolonged life of this man are, we may be sure, responsible for great enigmas both in the modes and manners of elaboration and use and in the distribution of these forms. Let us to our study of the same : and for the present we are still engaged with a particular type of domestic implement—flayer, knife, chopper, and such-like objects.

There is a difference in the conception of an implement that results from, say, the splitting of a pebble and the further elaboration of one of the halves of such pebble, and an elaboration wholly or for the most part from the centre of a mass of stone, pebble, or rough rock. The following, although mainly of identical form and conception with those which immediately precede and show that they have been used in precisely the same way, have generally been sculptured out from the mass, a method of procedure which demanded the use of the same mental activities, i.e. calculating and judging, and in a less degree the same operative powers as those which are exercised in the production of a statue from a block of marble by the modern sculptor.

In Fig. 180 we have an illustration of this sculpturing out. The specimen is of close-grained trap. Its figure is decidedly that of a flint hache. It has, however, received the usual characteristic treatment of the foregoing examples, in that one side, the lighter-shaded in the drawing, is reduced to an edge much more definitely than the opposite side. There is also the further characterising feature that the said lighter-shaded side of the implement exhibits in a marked degree the effect of manual work—particularly upon the facet a. This specimen tells the story of its elaboration in a graphic manner, by the fact that the crown of its broad end is a relic of the decayed exterior of an originally round mass of trap. As

Fig. 180.

a relic of the rind still adhering to an orange implies that it has been peeled, so we infer that this object has, so to say, been peeled of its more ancient coat, which was rotten and rusty, presenting a complete contrast to its existing surface save at the crown of its butt. It was found in the bed of the Whitadder, Duns, in 1901.

Fig. 181 is another very similar specimen—not so weapon-like in outline, with more the expression of a domestic implement designed for use in the hand. It is a wholly sculptured-out flayer, with a decided back-like hand-grasp; and a cleverly produced operative facet, which corresponds exactly in position with *a* in Fig. 180, which also gives clear evidence of use. This was found on the shore at Prestwick, Ayr, in 1897. It is of dolomite limestone.

Fig. 181.

Fig. 182 is another sculptured - out specimen, very weapon-like in appearance, but with a decided edge to the right of the darker facet, and a rounded hand-grasp on the left of the butt. The point end has been so cleverly produced that it actually bears the aspect of a weapon; and this brings us to a point of considerable importance, as appears to me, in the elucidation of the habits and character of this ancient being. Many of his elaborations have been a puzzle to me, because of this repeated commingling of the attributes of weapons and flayers or skin-dressers in individual specimens. It has frequently been difficult to decide whether an object were a flayer or a weapon. I have among my grouped " weapons " specimens which might quite as legitimately have been placed with these "flayers." I have come to the conclusion that that ancient man was so equally a domesticated and hunting and slaying animal that his weapon was often a domestic implement as well ; that

Fig. 182.

such were at times deliberately so fabricated as to serve the two purposes. Our Fig. 182, for instance, was perfectly suitable for the hand as a flayer; it was equally suitable for the hand as a weapon, and as such was quite formidable. If hafted it was a splendid and terrific one. This was found in an ancient gravel-bed above the shoulders of the Whitadder Valley in 1901.

At the end of 1906, with some other matter in view, the late Rev. Osmond Fisher kindly sent me for consultation a volume of *The Geologist* for the year 1861. In the said volume a passage occurs which so curiously and affirmatively corroborates my view of these Scottish and the English finds that, in justice to the writer and to myself, I cannot refrain from quoting the same. Considering that the passage was written nearly half a century ago, I judge it to be most interesting and opportune; I am delighted to quote it *in extenso*. The passage was written by the editor of *The Geologist* himself, and his remarks were made in reference to an article in the magazine upon some flint implements which had been found by Mr. Jas. Wyatt at Bedford :—

The specimen from Bedford, of which we figure both aspects [I have sketchily copied one, Fig. 183] is an example of the smaller kind of large flint implements, generally regarded as spear-heads, or as hatchets; but without asserting them not to have been used for one or other of such purposes, we would point out, that while the one side or edge from *c* to *d* is finely chipped out, the other is not so, for its entire length : the portion *a* to *b* being either split off flat, as in the present example, or left unworked, presenting the natural surface of the flint. . . . If these implements be held in the hand, this flat part will fit against the palm, generally of the right hand; but some will be held easily only in the left. The suggestion we would make from this is, whether they may not have been used in the hand as flaying-knives to strip off the skins of the great beasts slain with the larger spears or with flake arrows ? We do not wish even to insist on this suggestion, but we are the rather actuated to make it, as very little effort seems as yet to have been made to compare the adaptations of these ancient weapons to the nature and character of the operations which they were required to perform. To compare the fossil implements with those in use by the savage tribes of the present day, or with those in human graves, is right enough, but it is only one sort of comparison. The savage peoples of the present time have no such gigantic beasts as the mammoth and its now fossil congeners to contend with—the African chase of the elephant only being the nearest approach—nor had those of the "grave" period; and it seems only right that we should therefore pass beyond the bounds of mere comparison in our study of these fossil implements, and endeavour to make out and understand the necessary modifications of the weapons employed in the pursuit and slaughter of the great beasts; as well as in their own domestic operations of that primitive race by whom the flint implements were manufactured and used. The very association of particular *kinds* of animals with the worked flints, and the manner of their association in deposits, which are really undisturbed and have not been subjected to torrential action, should be the stepping-stones to the right path of inductive

(B 987)

Z

Fig. 186 is the third of these Colchester high-level puzzles. It is more weapon-like than either of the foregoing, and is a modified nodule. *a* is the natural surface; the large facet *b* is wholly sculptured out. Along the margin *c* the edge has been elaborated on both sides, the underside most conspicuously. It might have been weapon, flayer, or chopper. I rather believe it to be an illustration of a pre-glacial chopper. It is, like the two preceding, glaciated, and all three show the striæ upon the artificial surfaces.

I give one example from among

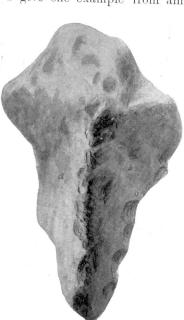

Fig. 186.

Fig. 187.

my Scottish Palæolithic weapons as a further illustration of this kind of puzzle. It is a fine specimen of the flayer, if it be such, and an equally fine weapon (Fig. 187). The whole outline suggests the whilom flayer or knife or chopper, with an excellent hand-grasp. There is a cleverly produced and well-marked edge to the right of the drawing, and to the left a straight flat back as opposing the edge. With all this, if held in the hand, and especially if hafted, it would still be a formidable weapon. It is of black basalt, is highly rolled, and is from the Forth shore.

Figs. 188 and 189 will give us an idea of the variety of form which these weapon-like flayers assume. A whole volume might be illustrated with these alone. I need not, I imagine, dilate upon them ; they must be accepted as further samples. One is from the Forth, and the other from the Ayrshire coast.

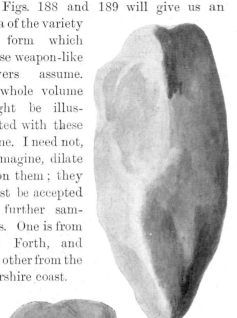

Fig. 188.   Fig. 189.

Dr. A. H. Keane has kindly called my attention to certain very similar forms from the Fayum, Egypt, as collected and described by Mr. H. W. Seton-Karr and illustrated in the *Report of the United States National Museum* for 1904 (see Pl. 6 in that publication, Nos. 124, 127, 128, and 129). They are wonderfully like many of these British Palæolithic forms but smaller : they rarely apparently exceed 3 inches in length.

The following (Fig. 190), which is a type of which I have found some few in the Forth and other areas, is marvellously like the Fayum specimens. This is formed from a tabular piece of dolomite limestone (those from Egypt of chert or flint). It is 7 inches in length, and gives, I believe, indication of glaciation, and is a shore specimen.

Fig. 190.

hacking edge. They are both Forth specimens, the one from the bed of the Esk and the other from the estuary shore.

In Figs. 193 and 194 we have, I think, corroboration of the last two being choppers, for though they are essentially of the same build their edge margins have more the expression of being intended for chopping. This, taken with their length, one being 9½ and the other 9 inches, gives them a decidedly chopper-like aspect rather than that of the flayer. I find no smoothing evidence of labour upon these larger specimens generally, which is, with many of the smaller, a highly characteristic feature. Both these specimens are also of quartzite.

In Figs. 195 and 196 (one specimen) we have something like a further puzzle. There can be no doubt whatever about its being an artefact, wholly sculptured out from a larger mass, the only question being as to what was the intention of its elaborator. It has a somewhat club-like look; but it can hardly have been intended for such a weapon, since if held by the thinner end more than one sharp edge—speaking of it before it was water-rolled—would have had to be grasped. Were it hafted in any way it would be a terrific weapon, but its general expression is not that of a weapon. Could it have been a flayer? The only difficulty here is, I think, its size— it is 10½ inches long and weighs 3 lbs. 3 oz. It has a well-defined edge a, which is opposed to a rounded back b, and a characteristic hand-grasp c. It possesses also the phenomenal feature of the flayers (or skin-dressers?) in that the facet a in the right-hand figure is distinctly smoothed by the usual (suggested) labour. It would have made, and it may have been, an excellent chopper; but mere chopping would not have so smoothed the one side by preference. It looks as though it had been used as a flayer of the larger mammals, and it goes well in that capacity with the greater weapons which we have seen; but, again, the hand that used it must have been unusually powerful—but size, let us remember, is not either in the mammal or insect world a criterion of strength. A gorilla is, according to repute, some few times stronger than a modern man, notwithstanding the fact that the latter is of finer build than the said member of the Simiadæ. Ancient man may have been from force of habit much stronger than we. This specimen has greatly interested me; it is of the same material, dolomite limestone, as the fine glaciated weapon Fig. 88, and was found on the Forth shore. And it also exhibits what I take to be evidence of glaciation.

If we turn back to Fig. 34 we have an object which none could doubt, both from its form and elaboration, to be a weapon. I have deliberately placed it among the weapons. It was skilfully sculptured

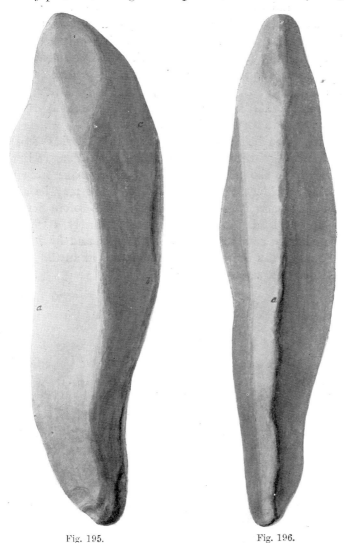

Fig. 195.   Fig. 196.

out from a cylindrical nodule, the whole of the work conducing to the narrow end, which is obviously and laboriously pointed. In the hand it is decidedly a weapon. Yet the whole of the large facet— the lighter shaded in the figure—has been, not *ground* flat and smooth, but so smoothed that its surface can only be compared with the more used surfaces of the mullers or skin-curers. It has interested me greatly, because the smoothing is more pronounced than is usual in the flayers, and the smoothing in this instance is just as strongly indicated at the butt-end as toward the point. It cannot owe that artificial aspect to flaying. It can, I imagine, only have been so produced by its having been used as the mullers and curers were used. Yet it is unquestionably a weapon. I procured this (flint) specimen from the actual gravel-pit at Mitcham. I have, however, found several other similar weapons which exhibit that same peculiarity. If we turn to Fig. 66 we have another which exhibits that feature. The facet above the break on the left side of the figure is thus artificially smoothed; and this is the more striking and interesting from the fact that that specimen came from *in situ* boulder-clay by Almond-side, Perth. The break may be of glacial origin, in which case the smoothing was effected before the ice-foot's presence in the land. It was, I believe, distinctly a weapon : the smoothing in any case could not have been caused by its use as a flayer. These relics are still puzzles, but are meanwhile the more interesting on that account.

CHAPTER XIV

Handles

In the use of his domestic implements Palæolithic man had a great conception of the utility of a *handle*. This is strikingly exemplified in the Scottish relics. It is also clearly shown by such research as I have been able to prosecute in the English gravels.

The actual handle is a most common feature, which is shown to have been obtained in a great variety of ways. The hand-grasp, as we have styled it, was essentially a handle which was designed and intentionally so elaborated. But the hand-grasp was in all the foregoing such a real part of the body of the implements, that its being such was not at all apparent, except through a comparative study of accumulated specimens. We are now coming to certain implements in which the handle part, the designed and actual handle, is so conspicuous a feature that that attribute alone of the said implements stamps them as of human origin.

This aspect of my search has been perhaps the most fascinating of all its varied phases of interest. It was intensely interesting, for instance, to find in some (Scottish) deposits, which had yielded up diverse objects that satisfied myself as to their human origin, but which would not readily be convincing to others, a fabrication with so well-designed and sculptured-out a handle that there was no denying its expression and evidence of intention. Or when, after finding such things in Scotland, I go down to southern England and (through laborious effort) find the handles with as strong assertion of deliberate intention and elaboration as is shown in the North, gratification and delight enhance one's ordinary interest. I trust that my readers will find in what follows some, at least, of the fascinating interest this phase of the quest has had for me.

But where handles begin and the mere hand-grasp ends, it is difficult to say or to show. If I produce a flayer of the foregoing Palæolithic-weapon type, and show that the old figure of the primitive weapon has been sacrificed to the notion that the hand would have a better hold by striking away a portion of the broad butt, which conception was carried out, I am inclined to view such instance as a first step to the elaboration of a *bona fide* handle, *i.e.* a portion of any implement so designed and elaborated as to fit well

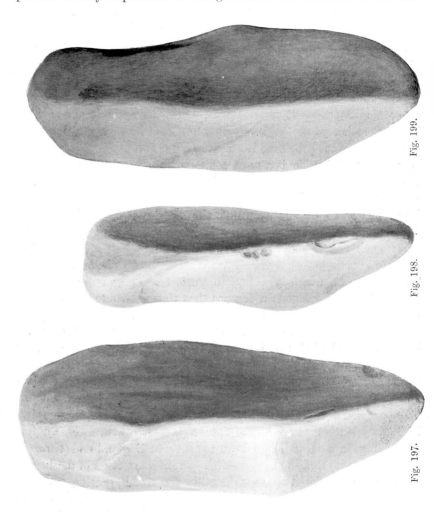

Fig. 199.

Fig. 198.

Fig. 197.

a clasping hand, as against a precarious grasp by the thumb and fingers, the condition of the hand-grasps in the foregoing.

Fig. 197, a large, admirably sculptured-out specimen of dolomite limestone, is an example. It is distinctly weapon-like—has a fine edge along the margin of the dark facet in the drawing, and the same from the point to some distance along the other well-balanced margin, which balance is destroyed by a large piece having been struck away from the broad butt-end at the place of the usual hand-grasp, with the evident intention of giving the hand a firmer hold. The effect in the hand is all that could be desired; the thumb comes over the middle ridge, and the ball of the thumb fits into the concave facet seen at the butt; which facet, with other elaboration at that end, so far completed a designed handle. The stone might have been a weapon, but there is the tell-tale smoothing toward the point of the broad unbroken facet of the underside. Another " hall-mark," as we might denominate this feature.

In Fig. 198 we have a more than usually interesting specimen in the fact that I picked it out of *in situ* boulder-clay (Forth), and it exhibits some glacial striæ. It is also of dolomite limestone, is still weapon-like in form,—its butt, is however, no longer broad and heavy, like that of a weapon, but is much more like a handle; and this handle was elaborated in the act of its fabrication, and not by striking away certain parts as an after-thought.

Fig. 199 is another of identical style of elaboration as Fig. 197, and also of identical style in the manner of the handle, viz. by a portion being struck away from one side of the butt; this also has a broad under-facet without a mid-ridge, and was doubtless a flayer or chopper. It is of quartzite, and is from the shore at the extreme mouth of the Forth estuary. It fits the hand excellently.

It is certainly interesting to myself, and will doubtless be so to my readers, that, just as I found corroborative instances of the *sectional* flayers in the English gravels, so I found exactly comparable illustrations of these Palæolithic-weapon forms, with parts broken away in order to produce something like a handle, in those same southern deposits.

Fig. 200 is an admirable instance of this. It is a replica, so far as flint would permit of its being so, of the fine northern specimen

Fig. 200.

Fig. 197. It was elaborated entirely upon the lines of the Palæolithic weapon. It is identical in the result in almost every feature of the above-described Scottish implement—its edge along the right-hand margin, its partial development of the edge from the point on the left, its sculptured point end, and the piece taken away for the convenience of the hand. The underside is flat, as in the foregoing example, and gives decided evidence of use in the usual way, notwith-standing the fact of its having been highly patinated, *i.e.* decomposed upon the surface, so that it looks like a coarse chert. Its normal condition was a glistering flint. It must have been exposed for ages upon the surface of the land before it found its way into the river-gravels. It is from the low-level bed at Mitcham, Surrey.

The portion struck away from the top left-hand of this figure (Fig. 200) left a broadish, flat hand-grasp. It is interesting to find that this flat surface has also been used exactly as the facets of the two "puzzles" with which the last chapter closes.

Fig. 201 is another of the corroborations from the Palæolithic gravels of England. It was also fabricated on the lines of a weapon ; being a massive exterior flake from

Fig. 201.   Fig. 202.

a large nodule, the underside is mainly the natural exterior surface. It was further elaborated, as is seen upon the face shown, and then a large portion was struck clean away, and the handle (*a*) is the result. I believe that this also shows the effect of labour upon the facet (*b*). It is from a high-level pit at Croydon.

Fig. 202 is a very interesting specimen, because while its elaborator still proceeded in his work as though a weapon was intended, a flayer was certainly in his mind; for the handle is not so much the result of breaking a piece from a weapon form (although it was so broken) as of actual design and elaboration. It (the handle) shows not only upon the face seen, but especially on the side not shown in the drawing, that it was sculptured out in the fabrication as part and parcel of the whole. Let us notice the decided way in which the handle projects to the right beyond the trend of the margin line of that side.

This is worth a study; just as it was a study of a Palæolithic man how he could elaborate a flayer with a handle out of a flattish flint nodule. There is sufficient of the exterior surface of the original nodule still left on the underside to show how admirably he succeeded in achieving what he aimed at.

Though Fig. 203 is more of a flake than 202, there is the same intentional handle. Advantage is taken here of a natural hollow, a "pit-of-percussion" probably, and that may also have been intentional. I have seen other cases of advantage being thus taken of such accidents

Fig. 203.

Fig. 204.

—if they were such. They gave great purchase to the hand in their use as flayers or knives.

If we take the difference of material and the consequent different mode of work adopted in Scotland into consideration, Fig. 204 is identical in form and elaboration with Fig. 202 immediately preceding. The handle was designed and fabricated with the implement—it projects from the regular line like the foregoing at a marked angle.

The underside, as usual, is flat—the product of one skilful stroke, in the production of which a bulb-of-percussion, not altogether absent

Fig. 205.   Fig. 206.   Fig. 207.

in fabrications from the Scottish rocks, is quite pronounced. It is from the Clyde estuary shore, and is of quartzite.

Fig. 208.

In Figs. 205 to 207 we have an interesting series of three smaller relics of similar weapon-like aspect in which the handles were elaborated with their fabrication. They are from the English gravels, and show clearly the groping for the handle. One is from the higher-level gravels of Croydon, the other two from low-lying beds at Mitcham.

Fig. 208 is another a good bit larger, but, as will be seen, is of the same type. I would point out that this and some others of the English flints show as conclusively the effect of manual labour as do many of the Scottish specimens.

Where we have found "flayers" and "knives" of any particular type it is my experience we may look for implements of larger calibre and of the same general build; for if we assume the flayers and knives to have been required for the opening and skinning of the carcasses of animals, larger implements would be required for the greater mammals, in cutting them up, or for detaching such limbs as might be desired. I have found examples of the same type, choppers or knives, of much larger proportions. I do not mean to suggest that other more advanced forms were not in use—we have taken a type, and are following it as far as that particular form will take us.

Fig. 209.   Fig. 210.

Figs. 209 and 210 may have been flayers or choppers. While their handles are very conspicuous and exaggerated, the body of the implement is still of the weapon shape, with the mid-rib so characteristic of the Scottish elaborations—weapons, knives, and flayers. The former of these is from the Forth shore, the latter from an ancient delta-deposit at Aberdeen.

In Figs. 211 and 212 we have two remarkable specimens,

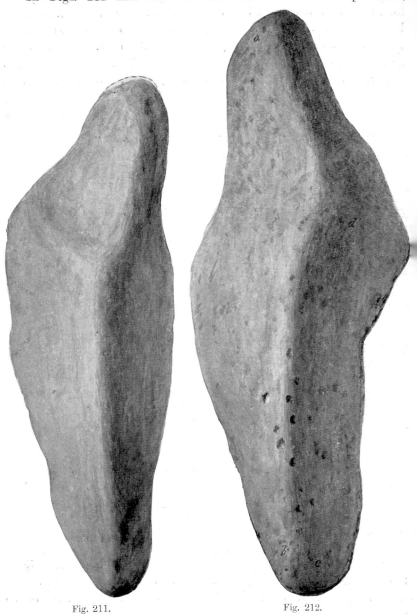

Fig. 211.   Fig. 212.

particularly as to size. I consider them both of the weapon type,
although the weapon form is not so pronounced—the mid-rib

perhaps maintaining it more than any other feature. What I would point to in both is the wonderful boldness of their elaboration. Both are the result of most clever masterly flaking. Their undersides are individually the result of one detachment. The upper faces—shown in the drawings—except immediately at the handle end, are the result (in each) of two splendid flakings. This is most characteristically seen in Fig. 212. From the extreme end of the handle, on the left side of figure, to the point end, the facet is the result of one detached flake, as from *a* to *b*, and from *c* to *d*, of another single flake. What excellent knives such flakes must have been. Let us call to mind the illustration of the Bushman and the similarly produced flake, and what he did with it ere he threw it away! These must have been magnificent choppers or knives; but their handles, both, are primitive conceptions, and not a vast improvement upon the mere hand-grasps. We shall ere long see the conception of the handle modified, and the handles wonderfully improved. But none could ever be fabricated with more skill than is this of Fig. 212. An edgewise view would have shown what a cleverly produced implement it is. It is $12\frac{1}{4}$ inches, and that of Fig. 211 $10\frac{3}{4}$ inches in length. The former was brought up from the bed of the Clyde estuary, West Kilbride, by seaweed (1894); the latter is from an ancient river-bed of the Allan, about 100 feet above its present level, between Dunblane and Bridge of Allan (1895).

From this point I find myself so entirely environed by handles, and these of such a multiplicity of form, that I hardly know in which direction to follow. We are now considering what we may call the *deflected* handle—this will lead us on a good bit farther. There is the *perpendicular* handle, and that will lead us in quite a different direction, and will finally leave us in the presence of implements of a design and aspect totally different from these we are now considering. The *horizontal*, the *saw* and *bulb*, the *notch*, the *concave*, and a few other names might be invented to designate the various aspects of handles.

Perhaps we had better go on till our deflected handle is exhausted, and then return to another starting-point, which would perhaps be actually the ideal and proper plan of their study, since their distribution and occurrence, so far as I can show, point to their having been elaborated and used to a great extent side by side; our running back in order to start afresh is perhaps intuitively a thoroughly Palæolithic method.

Figs. 213 and 214 give us an interesting relic, as having occurred among the débris of the presumed Palæolithic workshop at Dalmuir, Clyde. It is in form what has been described as a "winged" javelin or spear-head, but the highly smoothed flat underside showed it to have been used as a flayer. From its peculiar form it could scarcely have been used for any other purpose; the high smoothing produced, which was most obvious, seems to determine that. The drawings were made years ago. I fear the object itself is among my irretrievably lost good things. The "wing" had been in part broken away.

Fig. 213.   Fig. 214.

While we are still studying the deflected handle, let us mark that in our future illustrations of the same the figure and the elaboration of a weapon-like body is discarded or lost. It was (probably) found that a broad *flat* surface as well as a cutting or flaying edge was a desired feature. In any wise, flat chopper and knife surfaces, *i.e.* as flat as possible, are now alone associated with the deflected handle.

But here is immediately a case of harking back, so far as the handle is concerned, for this is the result of a piece being simply broken away. Yet it (Fig. 215) is an excellent specimen of what we may call a newer type. It was cleverly sculptured out with the view to two flat faces in place of the old weapon form, and these faces were well produced, with lateral edges for the flaying purpose, which purpose is on both faces shown (toward the point) to have been extensively carried out, and yet the handle is of the most primitive character. It is from the Ayrshire coast (1894). It has at first sight quite an accidental look about it; and so, for that matter, had most of the specimens we have already discussed — *at first sight!* It, like many others, demanded thought and patience. It is a rugged - looking flake - like stone, of some size, *i.e.* 8½ inches in length. It has a well-defined but accidental-looking handle. I soon realised, however, that there is hardly any part of its whole surface that is accidental. It is as deliberate a fabrication as

any that can be adduced. But it is an unconventional emergency kind of specimen.

In Fig. 216 we have an object that may be taken as a transition between the weapon and the

Fig. 215.

actual chopper forms. It is of basalt, is a Clyde-shore specimen, and shows the effect of labour toward the point end of the facet indicated distinctly.

If we now study the four Figs. 217 to 220, we shall observe great similarity in style and form; the two former are Scottish, the two latter flint, and English. The English specimens have both been roughly but cleverly produced from flint nodules, which nodules, as I have before pointed out, are always most erratic in form. These are cases in point—their fabricators were in an emergency. The only means at hand of procuring a knife, or hatchet, or flayer, were, say, two or three flint nodules. The only one

Fig. 216.

gravels and both in 1904. The Scottish forms are of dolomite lime-stone from the Forth estuary shore.

The groping for a handle and the attempt to make one is seen in a Scottish specimen (Fig. 221), which is nearly 8½ inches long, and

massive, and must have demanded a powerful wrist and strong grip in its use. Yet this shows as distinctly and emphatically as any specimen which I possess the artificial smoothing by use to which one has so often to refer. This *use* is most evident at the point end, and also less conspicuously on the corresponding position of the other side, while it is not indicated at the handle end. It occurred in the bed of the river Whitadder, Duns (1901).

We now come to what we may accept, so far as my experience has gone, as the highest attainment of Palæolithic man in these sculptured-out *deflected* handles. The most important examples are Scottish, but this may, and, I believe, does arise solely from my limited research among the English gravels. We are not, however, without evidence of the use of what may for our purpose be styled superior handles, but, as we shall see, circum-

Fig. 221.

stances led, in the flint areas, to the use of a superior sort of handle, which was not so much a sculpturing out as the adaptation of certain accidental features to that purpose. Let us to our present consideration.

In Figs. 222, 223, and 224 we have a group representing what I have suggested as the highest attainment in these sculptured-out deflected handles. I do not say they are the best actually made by this man, but are a representative group of what such a conception of the handle brought about.

In Fig. 222 we have an excellent specimen which has been wholly sculptured out, handle and all, from a mass of trap. The cutting or flaying edge and the broad back opposing it, and of course the broad facets, *and* the handle were cleverly produced, the whole being part and parcel of one conception. The handle is a fine piece of work. Both the large facets give, I believe, evidence of actual

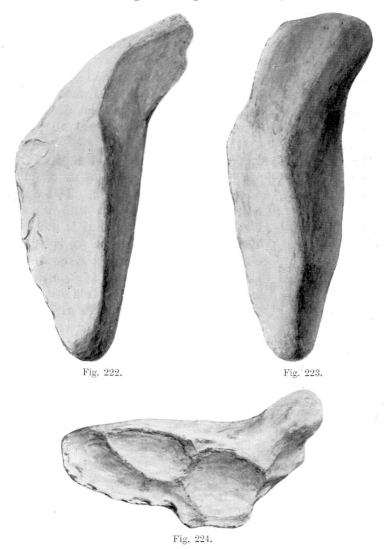

Fig. 222.   Fig. 223.

Fig. 224.

labour in the use of the implement. The specimen is highly interesting as having been found in an ancient deposit in the Whitadder Valley, Duns (1901), which yielded, as has been seen, several other interesting finds.

In Fig. 223 is presented a yet more clever piece of intentional sculpture, which was also found in an ancient delta-deposit, Musselburgh, as far back as 1883. It must, however, even there have been "derived," for it was water-rolled before it found its last resting-place. Its most striking feature is, however, the very definite way in which it shows that it has been elaborately used. The lighter-tinted facet shown is smoothed most perfectly by some flaying (or skin-dressing ?) process, as is also the flat underside. The handle end exhibits very little of this effect; it is, as usual, most noticeable toward the point. The handle can be seen without description to be an excellent piece of work. This suggests glacial striæ, but not conclusively.

Fig. 224 is one of identical form from the English gravels. But while this, in design, in figure, in the development of an edge and a broad " back," and in the deflection of the handle, is a replica

of the foregoing, the care with which the flint operator had to proceed is well shown. The whole aspect of the face (a) is the result of several distinct flakings, whereas in the foregoing Scottish specimens the corresponding face was achieved by one bold stroke. The reason of this more cautious work in the flint example is apparent in the fact of the broad back (b) being the natural surface of a nodule, which points to imperative limitations in the freedom of his work. Any attempt to produce a facet correspondingly bold and smooth with the Scottish work would probably have destroyed the prospect of any useful implement whatever being produced. This is what I mean by the *necessitated* dilettanteism of the flint regions, as compared with much bolder work in Scotland. I have before tried to make that clear in this volume, but this seems an excellent opportunity for driving the point home.

It is a matter of the deepest interest to have found so identical a fabrication in the English gravels, especially as my investigations

Fig. 225.

South were always hurried and brief; we shall further find that certain peculiarities of the flint nodule induced a fashion in the matter of handles that it was impossible to adopt in Scotland, but of this more anon. Our present specimen (Fig. 224) is from the Mitcham gravels, so often referred to.

Fig. 225 is another excellent illustration of these Scottish flayers. It is of dolomite limestone. Its underside is the result of one bold conchoidal fracture; the face shown indicates the style of its elabora-

Fig. 226.   Fig. 227.

tion. This also exhibits, in a less degree than Fig. 223, the result of use. It is from the shore at Prestwick (1897).

It was interesting to find many implements in the collection of Egyptian forms obtained by Mr. H. W. Seton-Karr now in the Kelvingrove Museum, Glasgow, whose chief feature is the deflected handle, which was in construction, in mode, and fashion identical with the method of production of these Scottish forms, the only difference being due to the peculiarities of the material from which they were fabricated, viz. chert or flint. The similarity in form is

Fig. 228.

very evident (see Figs. 226 and 227). They were produced in a rough-and-ready sort of way, just as were produced certain specimens, as we have seen, which the English gravels have yielded. Yet they are masterly productions, with excellent cutting or flaying edges, and

Curator of the N
for his kindness a broadish back,—the drawings will give a better idea of them than
other drawings fro any description. It will be seen that the handles were sculptured
It may be int out from the mass with the implements.
"coups de poing" The handle in Fig. 226 is much more pronounced than in Fig. 227.
Karr puts it—wi These are, except as to certain recent breaks, in perfect condition—
as evidential of every stroke of the fabricator as on the day on which
they were made.

They present no feature by which their possible age could be
even suggested. But I exhibit them as showing that the Scottish
and English relics have their counterparts in other areas of the
world ; and if we may draw an inference, it is, that as they were
found actually upon the same continent on which a Bushman only
"the other day" produced a flaked knife from a stone with which to
cut up an animal, age need not be considered here, but only the fact
of identical forms and modes of elaboration. Fig. 228 is a further
magnificent specimen in the same collection.

I glean from an incidental reference to Egyptian *weapons* by
Mr. Seton-Karr that the finds in the Kelvingrove
Museum are from the neighbourhood of the flint-
mines in the Eastern Desert, that these "coups
de poing" (the weapons) or "drift" implements
are only found in that vicinity.[1] Mr. Seton-Karr
evidently considers them to be Palæolithic.

But let us suppose that objects of the frail
character of these Egyptian implements (speaking
of the knife-like ones) had been once upon a time
made in Scotland, and made in the rugged fashion
of these Egyptian specimens, of the common rocks
of the country. All that I can suggest is that
ninety-nine out of every hundred, and possibly nine
hundred and ninety-nine out of every thousand,

drawing of an excel would be unrecognisable to-day. It is possible, and
It is, I think, much I think very probable, that I have discarded many
edged butt, its flatn a flaky accidental-looking relic in my search, owing
thin, suggest to me to my then want of experience, and therefore of
—not so much "co appreciative power.

Fig. 229.

broad ends were us For instance, since I made the above drawings
certain Palæolithic I have found one or two flake-like implements in Scotland, which
Of this more anon.

1 "Flint Implements of the Fayum, Egypt," *Report United States National Museum,*
1906, p. 748.

It is also interesting to come across the following in the above-referred-to statement by Mr. Seton-Karr: "It is indeed probable that peculiar types discovered in different parts of the world have been evolved through the local material. For example, in the Palæolithic workshops in the Madras Province of India, which I discovered with the help of Mr. Bruce Foote and Mr. Macleod, the

Fig. 232.   Fig. 233.

material in the shape of quartzite nodules is suitable for that type of implement." The result of my long experience is, and this I have often emphatically repeated, that types are characterised by the nature of the rock from which they are made—are characterised by local conditions. Mr. Seton-Karr's view upon this point has long been my own.

The circular cavity in the centre of the weapon (Fig. 230) is the natural result of a dissolved-out organic (fossil) form. The weapon

may, however, have been designedly fabricated with the view to that
cavity; it may have aided security in the mounting. It is impossible
for weapons with a sharp edge all round to have been used effectively
unmounted. I have met with other instances of natural cavities being
studiedly retained in the fabrication of forms, for some more or less
obvious purpose.

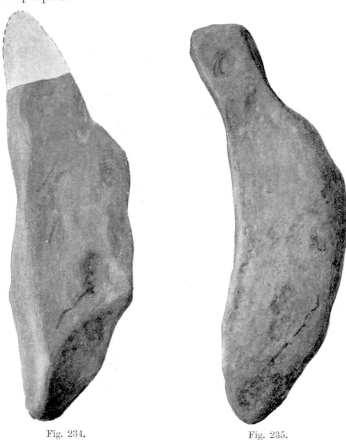

Fig. 234.   Fig. 235.

If we now make a more general study of Figs. 231 to 250
inclusive, we shall observe some few variations in the way in which
the deflected handle has been brought about in the actual elaboration
of the implements. While it would prolong this present chapter to
tediousness to elucidate every form, there are several to which I ought
briefly to refer.

Fig. 231 is characterised by its great simplicity; it is a thin
naturally tabulate piece, which has been simply shaped into its

present form. It could have been none other than a flayer. It is Scottish.

Figs. 232 to 235 inclusive are various Scottish examples, which

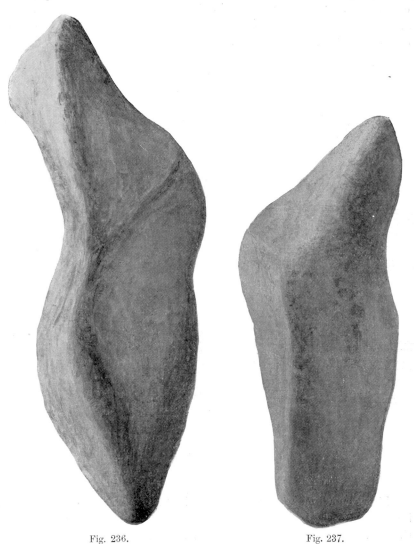

Fig. 236.   Fig. 237.

may, I think, have been choppers or knives rather than flayers. Figs. 236 and 237 are eccentric in form, the former a chopper probably, the latter very serviceable as a flayer.   Fig. 238 is an excellently contrived flayer (?) from gravels at Dartford, Kent, which Mr. W.

M. Newton most kindly forwarded to me for inspection. I have made this drawing and that of another specimen from the same enthusiastic investigator, to which we shall also refer. Fig. 239 is a Scottish example of the same general design and form.

Figs. 240 and 241 are excellent Scottish specimens with more pronounced, more serviceable, handles. The former is from the shore, Clyde (Troon). It is hardly appreciably water-worn; was brought ashore by seaweed. It fits the hand admirably; is of

Fig. 238.　　　　　　　　　　Fig. 239.

dolomite limestone. The latter, of almost identical form, is highly rolled, and has a special interest in having occurred in an ancient delta-deposit (Barbush Hill), Dunblane, which hill stands upon boulder-clay, and is about 100 feet above the present river (the Allan), which river at this spot is some 150 feet above sea-level. It is of a pseudo-granitic-like rock. It is not necessary to say how well it fitted the hand. Both these, I think, were choppers; in their forms they have almost a modern aspect.

Fig. 242, the handle end of an implement, is of most excellent workmanship. It is of (a much-decayed) dolomite limestone; was probably, when perfect, of fine form. It was originally struck from a mass against the planes of bedding which are perpendicular to its length. It naturally snapped across by a plane of bedding. All its skilful elaboration is against any possible lines of cleavage or natural fractures. It is just as it came in from the deep sea (Forth), and has received no modern rolling.

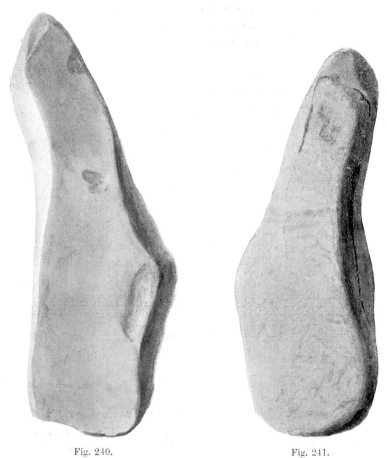

Fig. 240.　　　　　　　　　　　　　Fig. 241.

Figs. 243 to 246 are a group of small English flints, two from the low-level gravel-pit at Mitcham, Surrey, and two from higher-lying gravel at Croydon.

Figs. 247 to 250 are another group of Scottish examples, almost as small as the foregoing, which have been obtained from river-beds, or the estuary shores of Clyde and Forth; they are all fabrications from the ironstone-band, and are in a peroxidised condition.

This feature of "handles" is so pronounced, as we have already seen and will see further exemplified, that it is marvellous that it has not long ago attracted the attention of investigators. To have

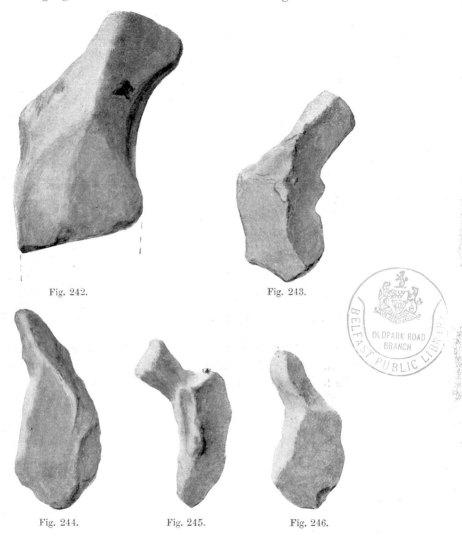

Fig. 242.

Fig. 243.

Fig. 244.

Fig. 245.

Fig. 246.

missed so unmistakable and undeniable a factor of evidence for a human intervention seems to me proof of the inadequacy of the old method of investigation, or rather of the lack of actual (*i.e. personal*) investigation. There has been, even where personal research went beyond the mere "collecting" through the gravel-diggers, so much a

looking with a negative mind and negative eyes, that both eyes
and mind were practically blind to all possible factors of evidence,
save a certain narrowly devised and jealously guarded line, from

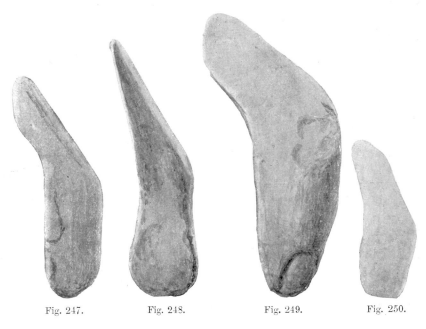

Fig. 247.   Fig. 248.   Fig. 249.   Fig. 250.

which, as has been seen, investigators so schooled seemed incapable
of breaking away. To be wise beforehand is thoroughly human, but
it is the following of a hard-trodden path to ignorance.

CHAPTER XV

Natural Handles—The Man among the Flints

LET us try to picture Palæolithic man among the flints. There were only flints, only stones, which he could command, and which appealed to him in all the mineral world when the necessity for effort and contrivance took him beyond the scope of his own active hands. What his own hands or a further aid by animals' bones and clubs of wood could not do, he sometime or other learned that the weight and hardness of flint, with the attributes of points and edges, could do in a wonderful fashion. The point of a nodule, which nodule was naturally often of a flattish pear-shape, and would at the broad end fit the hand without a modifying stroke, one day opened the eyes and mind of the man to the use of his haches. And if at any time such spontaneous weapon came into contact with another in offence or defence, either or both were more or less flaked by the concussion, or mayhap splintered into fragments. In which latter event the hand which grasped the splintered weapon would, as I know from experience, of a surety be cut; and then the mind was further opened to the ease with which edged tools were to be obtained from such flint nodules—knives, the merest flakes, with edges already there, as sharp as razors.

The flints were all nodules. Never a square block or tabular bedded mass, but nodules of all conceivable and inconceivable forms, minus any ruling shape, erratic, shapeless, so far as any form could be anticipated. There were natural clubs, natural haches, natural knives, flayers and choppers, where a nodule had by any possible accident become fractured. In the natural clubs there was a hand-grasp, which was often a *bona fide* handle, *i.e.* as good as though fashioned with intent. In the natural haches, and I have specimens which show clearly that there were such, the butt was already naturally provided and of such proportions that no elaboration could give the hand a better grasp. Handles were already there; and the man could never have made one step toward his present attainments had he failed to see and to utilise them.

We have already seen in our study of the curers or mullers, that Palæolithic man widely appreciated the value of a natural process or excrescence in a nodule, and adapted the same to his purpose. We shall now see that he chose and elaborated his nodules so as to take advantage of the ever-varying form, and produced his knives and flayers and hatchets with handles, that were as in anticipation part and parcel of the nodules, and suggested such and such to the fabricator. In a word, the handles, more or less natural, are in multitudes of his relics the conspicuous feature ; another undeniable " hall-mark " which only claims to be recognised to be conclusive of his intervention and handiwork. In many instances which have been discovered, even the butt-ends of weapons are handles as essentially as the handle of a dagger is such to-day. The nodule with a natural hand-grasp at one end and a point at the other was chosen, and with that intent. I found several such specimens in the Somme Valley in 1883. I have since found others in the Palæolithic gravels of England, and several of flint on the coast along the south-west corner of Scotland. These were true " coups de poing." I have, however, a series of flat flint nodules, which are naturally " almond "-shaped, and show at least in more than one instance that they were

Fig. 251.

intentionally modified to be used probably as weapons. They are the origin, as I conceive them to be, of the typical haches, both in form and style of elaboration ; for when the æsthetic surface-flaking came into vogue, these had only to be treated tenderly, and flaked but " skin-deep," to be of the best type-form, and illustrative of the more refined work and skill of that Palæolithic man. But what we have now in hand are his domestic forms ; and these will show us the true Palæolithic man, his capacity, his arts and contrivances, in a way that his weapons of offence could never have suggested. Let us turn to them.

In Fig. 251 we have a domestic implement of very pronounced design—a flayer, it seems, since the mark of labour is, I believe, clear upon it, especially upon the broad flat under-facet not shown. It was, of course, possibly also a whilom knife, but, as is evidenced, was used as a flayer. Its design was, as is also apparent, based upon the presence in the nodule at the now handle end of a process or excrescence, which became with certain modifications the actual handle.

In the elaboration the greater part of the original nodule was skilfully struck away : this first produced the broad, flat underside, while a further bold stroke produced the facet *b*, which gave the operating edge to the right of *b* ; other strokes produced the smaller facets at the base of the figure and the thing was complete. The handle as it is now presented was already there : *a* and *a* is the exterior surface of the nodule, the incurved line which forms a neck being natural to the original. This is a deflected handle, the deflection depending upon the natural circumstance of the stone. As a flayer it suits the hand admirably. It is from the low-level Mitcham pit.

In Fig. 252 we have an instance of the whole nodule being, with very little modification, adapted as a handled implement. The chief

feature is the handle ; and this was doubt-less the great attraction to Palæolithic man. It is itself as long as the broader flaying (?) portion of the implement ; which broader portion was, naturally, a flattened oval, reduced, however, to a more usable condition by (as is seen in the drawing) a large surface-flake having been struck from it, while in the corresponding position of the side not shown a circular flake was removed. It was never an elegant speci-men, but it doubtless served the intended purpose. What it lacked in efficiency in the body the operator gained in the purchase which the excellence of the natural handle gave him. There is abundant evidence of intentional elaboration about it ; and the underside of the handle (not shown) was cleverly modified to suit the hand. It is from a pit at Norbury. After using such

Fig. 252.

a natural handle, little more than instinct would suffice to dictate a similar one in the user's next fabrication.

Fig. 253 was fabricated from a cylindrical but oddly bent nodule.

The great inducement was doubtless the handle *a*, which existed naturally in the nodule form—the facet *a*, for the whole length of the figure, and a considerable part of the handle's underside, is the natural surface. The other long facet seen in the drawing and the underside of the broader end have been sculptured out. The great indentation forming the neck is natural to the nodule, and undoubtedly suggested the handle to the fabricator.

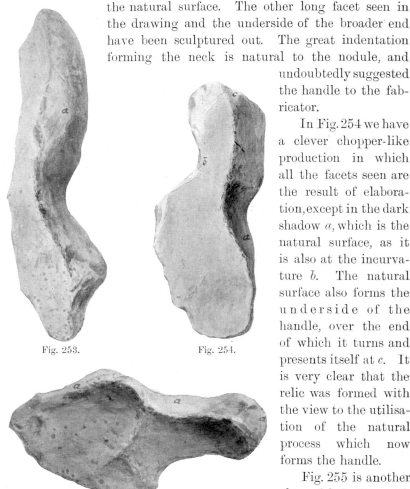

Fig. 253.   Fig. 254.

Fig. 255.

In Fig. 254 we have a clever chopper-like production in which all the facets seen are the result of elaboration, except in the dark shadow *a*, which is the natural surface, as it is also at the incurvature *b*. The natural surface also forms the underside of the handle, over the end of which it turns and presents itself at *c*. It is very clear that the relic was formed with the view to the utilisation of the natural process which now forms the handle.

Fig. 255 is another clever fabrication with the purpose of producing an implement with a handle. The suggestion of this handle was already there before the fabrication was begun, as is clearly shown by the present position of such exterior of the nodule as is left along the facet *a a a*.

All the above might have been knives or flayers, or both. They all have a well-defined edge and an opposing broad or broadish back, and an excellent serviceable handle.

One of the most romantic pieces of modern research is that in which Mr. Worthington G. Smith not only discovered but elucidated the contents of a Palæolithic floor (at Caddington, Bedfordshire). The romance lay not more in the discovery than in the splendidly patient and laborious way in which the contents of the "floor" were collected—every specimen and flake possible. And when collected— the work of several years—flake and implement were arranged, com-pared, and finally in many cases fitted together; flake to flake, often to a considerable number, fitted again upon weapon and implement, from which they had been struck unknown thousands of years ago. This is no less than a wonderful achievement; as wonderful almost as the story which the achievement unfolds. The Palæolithic floor referred to is, as I understand it, *pre-glacial*. Mr. W. G. Smith believes the ancient man to be early *post-glacial*; but it seems to me that the numerous sections which he gives of the positions of the relics of this ancient man show that he did his work on the sites illustrated, before the last inception of ice : or certainly before the ice reached the area of that ancient man's habitat.[1] The relics occur in such a way as to show that they received quiet—most quiet burial. The most delicate flakes were not moved from the spots upon which they fell as the ancient men worked. Artificially accumulated heaps of flint nodules ready for the fabricator remained as they were piled together in that remote past.

These ancient land-surfaces are buried under finely constituted clays and silts, such as only the quietest of waters could have deposited —possibly the incipient floodings from a river which was supplied at such times with argillaceous matter—was it the early inception of the ice which gave the supply of clay to the flood-waters ? Was the clay deposit or "drift" the result of whilom dammed-up waters—a glacial lake ? It was something equivalent to this ; but I incline to the river-side floodings ; since the waters of an ice-bound lake must have given some evidence in erratically scattered stones which are not mentioned as occurring. But whatever the origin of the deposit which buried the ancient man's habitat, that deposit is now covered with ice-contorted "drift," and itself in places shows that it, too, was disturbed by the ponderous ice-foot, *i.e.* by movement and pressure from above. No human relics and no deposits which were overridden

[1] *Man the Primeval Savage*, chap. iv.

by that ice could have been made and laid down in times subsequent to that ice's inception. The old land-surfaces were at least *inter-* and possibly *pre-*glacial.

I have been particular in describing so much, because one or two of the fabricated implements from those old land-surfaces, which are from four to seven feet beneath the present surface, are deeply interesting in our present study of Palæolithic man's appreciation of a *natural* handle.

Among the relics which Mr. Worthington G. Smith so wonderfully rescued, with the chippings from the long-hidden workshop, and restored, are several, but one in particular that will interest us. Upon pp. 146 and 147 (*Man the Primeval Savage*) Mr. Smith gives illustrations of an implement, two of which show the varying sides of the same as it was found, and two the differing sides of the flint nodule from which the fabrication was made; by the recovery and skilful application of numerous flakes, the nodule itself is restored to

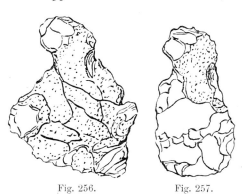

Fig. 256.　　　　　Fig. 257.

One-fourth natural size.

almost its actual condition before the remote human worker took it in hand. I trust that I shall be pardoned by the author for making and using outlines of two of his masterly drawings (see Figs. 256 and 257). In the former drawing we have a typically normal flint nodule whose most striking feature is a pronounced protuberance.

In the latter the expansions of the nodule have been largely chipped or flaked away; but the protuberance is left almost intact, and the result is a chopper-shaped flayer, knife, or hatchet. It is a fine illustration of the actual procedure of a Palæolithic man; who having found a nodule with a suggestive excrescence, elaborates a handled implement therefrom. To the end of time no better illustration will ever be found. It is indeed a question whether another investigator will ever be endowed with so fine a spirit of research as to accomplish such a feat. It is as though we actually saw the implement made by that ancient man; which, once completed, we stoop down, pick up the débris, and put all together again.

This is, I think, the finest of all Mr. W. G. Smith's restorations : he has pieced on to the fabrication, so far as I can count in the drawings—and eight drawings of this are given in the pages referred to and the two following—close upon thirty flakes. But let us notice that Mr. Smith is inclined to consider it an unfinished specimen, a weapon in "an initial stage," although he does see that it *might* have been what I am now claiming for it. It was not only a domestic implement, in form and size, it was a finished and an unusually excellent one ; and when we realise that it is 6¼ inches in length, the handle assumes greater importance. The author speaks of it as follows :—

> All the lower part of the implement was finished in Palæolithic times, but the upper or point end was apparently left incomplete. It is, however, just possible that the implement may have been designed for use as a chopping tool, the lower part and sides, as seen in the illustrations, having been intended for use in cutting or chopping, and the upper part designed for use as a kind of handle. If so, the tool may have been a rude chopper or cutting club, and is complete (pp. 148 and 149).

There is a further reference to "chopping tools" in the said volume. Upon p. 230 is a drawing of what must have been a fine example of a very primitive idea of a chopper. It is of half-moon shape, the cord of the bow being a broad back—a hand-grasp, such as we have seen ; the bow being a cutting or chopping edge. The example is 13 inches in length, and weighs 2 lbs. 3½ oz. But there is no further reference to the adaptation and use of handles : the work is as usual an exposition of the Palæolithic haches, *i.e.* weapons alone.

Some years ago my friend Mr. W. M. Newton, an enthusiastic investigator, sent to me for inspection a box of rough flints, almost every one of which was in my opinion a human fabrication. Among this group was a roughly but cleverly fabricated large hache, which was distinctly glaciated. But what most attracted my notice was a knife-like implement which was the less obviously such because certain cherty portions had been dissolved out along its edge. I greatly regret that I did not make a drawing of the same before the group was returned to London. I have, however, made an out-line which conveys my impression of the specimen (Fig. 258). It was a very fine thing, but had a rugged look, and to many eyes doubtless would appear to be a natural and accidental production ; but it was certainly anything but accidental. If looked at as it should be, *i.e.* as it was before its cherty portions were dissolved out, it was an unusually clever fabrication. It was about 9 inches in length, with a naturally formed but modified handle. It was probably suggested much as the foregoing (Fig. 253) was suggested, by the natural form of the nodule. If these two are compared, say, as knives, it will be seen that though there is a great difference in their general expression, the one being of fine modern-like form, in the actual result they are identical—the handle end, the cutting edge, and the turned-up point.

From further inquiry it seems that this specimen cannot now be found: Mr. Newton, however, most kindly sent me photographs of another chopper-like implement, which are reproduced as Figs. 259 and 260. Although very unlike the missing knife, it is very like the foregoing specimen of the great restoration by Mr. W. G. Smith. In one of the photos (Fig. 260) it is clear that the neck of the object is, in part at least, the natural conformation of the original nodule: in a word, the handle was already there before the making of the implement was begun. It is the story over again of Fig. 257.

Fig. 258.

Since I received the photographs from Mr. Newton he has generously lent me two other specimens, before referred to, of which one has been discussed, the other I introduce here (Fig. 261). This is also a specimen whose handle was suggested by the natural conformation of the nodule from which it was made. The incurved shaded facet *a* is the natural exterior surface of the nodule;

Fig. 259.   Fig. 260.

all the rest is sculptured out. But that part alone shows that the neck of the now handle was the feature of the original nodule which induced the fabrication of the implement.

This adaptation of natural handles is a more than thrice-repeated story : it is the story of every specimen in this chapter, which, though a short one, is to the writer more suggestive, more full of the actual vision of that ancient man than any other chapter in this book. Let us realise that every object in these few pages tells a definite story; *i.e.* tells its story by a datum line of one or other recognised Palæolithic deposits, and not by the indefinite " occurrence " of most of my Scottish finds—on ocean shore or in river-bed. These English and French examples are distinctly Palæolithic in their occurrence.

It was thus Palæolithic man who discovered and developed the use of the handle. It was he who conceived the forms of our modern knife and chopper. He not only made and used them, he varied their form according to current mode and fashion ; in accordance often with changing choice of varied rock material, or from mere whim or fancy. But he it was who handed down to us the conception and character of many of our now domestic and manipulating tools.

We have caught a glance of a great fact in this chapter ; we shall be enlightened yet more as we proceed.

Fig. 261.

The specimen (Fig. 261) may have been a knife; but that it was largely used as a flayer is evidenced decidedly by the worn facets *b* and that of the flat underside (not shown) as the point end is neared. In accordance with many of the foregoing illustrations, this evidence of *use* is not so marked at the handle as at the point end. It is a beautiful specimen, of fine figure and of clever elaboration.

Mr. Newton's specimens were obtained by himself from a pit or pits at Dartford, Kent, from which beds he has also obtained typical Palæolithic haches. My own specimens in this chapter were obtained from gravel from the Mitcham (Surrey) pit, or from actual pits at Norbury and Croydon. As is indicated, Mr. W. G. Smith's specimen is from Caddington (Bedfordshire).

By a search among my flints I have discovered three further specimens which illustrate our present argument. My large collection, mainly Scottish, is housed under trying circumstances, and specimens get out of sight. I have just made drawings of these three, which are all

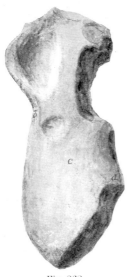

Fig. 262.

from the low-level pit at Mitcham; the first (Fig. 262) follows wonderfully well upon the photographs sent by Mr. Newton (Figs. 259 and 260), and upon Mr. G. Smith's Palæolithic floor specimen (Figs. 256 and 257), as also upon Fig. 255. It is more particularly, at least in outline, like that of Mr. Newton's photographs. But while the former may have been a knife, a study of this latter (Fig. 262), and especially an examination of the specimen itself, shows that it never could have been a knife. It might have been even a good knife when, in the making, it was struck off from a larger mass or the nodule simply split into two portions — there *was* an edge certainly around the lower shaded portion, but the fabricator did not want an edge sharp enough to cut; so he deliberately and cleverly manipulated that whilom edge into an almost rounded condition. This intention is clearly seen in the specimen. It is a flayer: I cannot conceive what else it could have been.

It tells the same story as the others: the incurvature (*b*) is almost as it was in the untouched nodule. The whole of the face (*c*) is the original exterior. How much of the dark shaded portion of the neck, the great bay to the right, is the actual result of sculpturing away it is impossible to say; but the suggestion of the handle was there, in the nodule in the natural indentation at *b*. It is worth while perhaps to consider this for a moment in conjunction with Mr. W. G. Smith's suggestion of his specimen being unfinished. It is in appearance much more unfinished: yet the elaborator carefully gave the finishing touches to it, when he reduced the whilom cutting edge to a mere flaying condition. It is a finished flayer.

I think Mr. W. G. Smith's suggested story of that ancient and now buried Palæolithic valley floor very interesting: let me give it:—

As I have said, I incline to the belief that the whilom habitat of that ancient fabricator was beside a river—a pre-glacial river. It was a place of encampment; probably a temporary dwelling-place. If it were such river-side floor it was grass-grown, nay, it was more; since all the plants in creation had free play in those days, it was jungle and possibly a tangle: there Palæolithic man encamped. He got flints from the river-bed—there he could also watch for his quarry to come down to drink. Weapons and knives and flayers were needed; these his relics show that he made, and the débris show that he made them there. Thus domestic and other forms were found in association with the débris of their fabrication; their dwelling-place was also their workshop.

Did he carry his weapons and domestic implements about with him? It is scarcely credible that he did: he had no pockets—I venture to assume as much; and if he had *I* know the weariness entailed by pockets full of stones over miles of trackless country. No, by design or accident flayers and other implements were left behind, and were all soon hidden away by the undergrowth. The rains descended and the floods came; the river sent out its waters on to the river-side lands, where the quiet flood had time to drop down even to the very finest its suspended earthy matter; and so, when Palæolithic man returned, if he ever did, to the same spot, he found no trace of his former occupation; for the river-flood deposits and vegetable growth had blotted out all his former works, but he was ready, without a thought of the past, to perform the same acts again.

In the next two specimens (Figs. 263 and 264) we have great similarity with each other in form, this having depended entirely upon the natural suggestion of the handles. The handles are both what might be called straight, and for the size of the implements are large. Both the handles to some extent have been sculptured out with the bodies of the implements from the original mass. In Fig. 263 the natural exterior of the flint still entirely surrounds the handle,

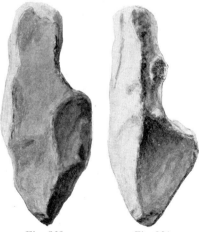

Fig. 263.　　　　Fig. 264.

except on the flaked facet shown: in a word, the handle itself was there, as in other instances, only a large flake was struck from it. In

Fig. 264 the part of the handle to the right of the figure above the expanded lower portion is the unaffected exterior of the nodule; and this exterior surface forms also the greater part of the side not seen.

Though these specimens are small—both just under 4½ inches in length—the principle of the utilisation of natural excrescences of the nodules as handles is as well indicated in them as in larger specimens. The flint nodule, as I have before pointed out, always imposed restrictions upon the fabricator. And, in the matter of the handle, while the handle itself was suggested, its style was entirely governed by the exigencies of the nodule. These two last are cases in point; the protuberances being approximately straight, the handles could not be other than straight. Our next chapter brings us back into this northern region, where circumstances induce various other modifications and phases of Palæo man's work, some of which will come as a surprise to us.

As a collateral point, it may interest some to learn that the protuberances of the flint nodules, which attracted the interest and finally exercised the intelligence and the fabricating powers of ancient man, are not accidents in the true sense of that word, but are the result of design, with which man had nothing whatever to do; of design in Nature. The flint forms are largely the present representatives of whilom living creatures, of living chalices; of beautiful cup-like animals with graceful downward stems, that expanded into a root-like hold at the base. These were sponges, or their first cousins : much more ancient living forms than man can claim to be, inhabiting the old deep-sea floors upon which the present "chalk" was accumulating.

These forms, Ragadinia, Chenendopera, Jereica, with their related animals of to-day, and a good many forms of the plant world, had and still have the power of secreting silex in their organisms. In the days of the Upper Cretaceous rocks these sponges accumulated their flint *spicula* in layers or beds in the chalk, the then bottom of the sea : layer upon layer, as the chalk was built up. This flint, by a natural law of affinity, became massed around the sponge or other organisms; and by the aid of chemical and possibly electrical and other forces became concentrated solid masses—at times, of the actual form still of the ancient chalices, whose stems were the quondam protuberances from the nodules, and are now the handles of long-ago elaborated implements. Often the nodules are masses or bundles of the old sponge forms, *i.e.* such masses were the primary attractive forces to the *spicula* and possibly also to the deposition of silex in solution. In any case the sponge forms can often be made out, and a fractured flint will at times present in its matrix their skeleton structures. So the handles discovered by primitive man were suggested to him by the fact that they had been stems or handles to some of Nature's beautiful cups, and their very root-holds give to-day a swelling termination to the said protuberances which gives such handles the excellent hand-grasp. Invert Fig. 256, it still has the sponge form.

Let us also notice that the expansions of the ancient living cups are now often represented in the expanded blades of knife and chopper, as they are doubtless also exhibited in the broad butt-ends of many a hache. Thus design in Nature has been caught up and utilised by man.

I have, it will be remembered, pointed to several instances of the adaptation of the natural handles in the discussion of the skin-curers from the English gravels (see Figs. 145, 146, 147, 148); in one or two instances the actual sponge form is very evident.

CHAPTER XVI

Handles : A Great Achievement

" There is no new thing under the sun."

WE have seen that Palæolithic man was skilled not only in the fabrication of various implements, as necessity demanded, but in the making of implements with handles. We have seen (Chapter XIV.) that this fashioning of handles is a pronounced feature among the presumed Palæolithic relics from Scotland. It is so far a feature among the northern relics that I was induced thereby to make renewed investigation in the English Palæolithic gravels, with the view to corroborating—if it were possible—the said handled implements of North Britain.

It has been seen in Chapters XIV. and XV. that wonderful corroboration was obtained from the southern gravels ; that though on the whole the search resulted in inferior specimens, full illustration of Palæolithic man's appreciation of the handle was found ; the inferiority being due not so much to a want of conception of the utility of the handle, or of ability to produce the same, as to the more intractable nature of the flint itself.

We have seen in our continuation of the argument of handles in Chapter XV. that handles were largely if not actually originally suggested to Palæolithic man by natural handle-like excrescences of the flint nodules ; that the ancient man so frequently followed the suggestion and retained the form of these natural excrescences, that we may style them " natural " handles without exaggeration.

The ancient man may, before he arrived at the flint areas, have been accustomed to the making of handled implements ; in which case the natural excrescences of the flint nodules would not have first suggested the handle, but such excrescences would naturally have been chosen. But inasmuch as the flint forms in instances where the natural handle has not been utilised are exceedingly poor productions, it does not look as though he had brought the custom of elaborating handles into the flint areas, but had learned it there.

But suppose that after he had sojourned in the flint areas he made his way into Scotland, we should expect him to imitate, in a country where such natural handles are not to be found, the forms which they had induced him to make in those flint areas. We have seen how the Scottish forms were actually corroborated in the English gravels; which would naturally be the case if the style of elaboration was brought from the South into Scotland, and there, so far as the material permitted, adapted in the Scottish fabrications.

The Scottish rocks actually permitted better-things to be made ; for the attributes of the flints were against the more successful elaboration of bolder forms except through slow and laborious processes, while the northern rocks often possessed such attributes as to offer scope for more successful (emergency ?) work, and this greater success was decidedly attained. We have noticed in the last chapter that the better-formed English domestic implements are those which resulted from the direct use or adaptation of the natural handle. The forms made in England at the suggestion of and by the passive aid of the natural handles, were imitated in Scotland ; but before we proceed with our Scottish forms, I should like to point out a striking coincidence in the form of certain Egyptian relics, which I have traced from figures in a publication of the " Egyptian Exploration Fund," and some of the Scottish things (see Figs. 265 to 268). The two former are Scottish, and are both formed of dolomite limestone ; the two latter are Egyptian; and are of flint or chert. Except in the material, the forms are practically the same. The Scottish specimens are water-worn and possibly aided in their rounded condition by decomposition. The Egyptian forms are literally as they left their fabricators' hands.

As a mere coincidence their similarity of form is interesting, but it may mean much more than the mere coincidence. Some are doubtless ready to suggest that it was quite natural for these ancient men to make implements that would resemble each other in their forms, whether made in, say, Egypt, France, or Britain. I do not, however, conceive it to be natural for men far apart, without a model mentally or otherwise retained, to make implements of identical form. It is not an easy thing, and certainly not a natural attribute of man, to make any *new* form. And when striking similarity of form appears, even though the oceans may now separate the similar objects, there is an *a priori* assumption that they had in some remote era a common origin in some type or some " accident," such as the natural handles, allied with the natural forms of nodules suggested.

Fig. 265.

Fig. 266.

Fig. 267.

Fig. 268.

If we compare these Egyptian and Scottish forms (Figs. 265 to 268) with Figs. 254 and 255, in the last chapter, we shall see the family likeness of the handles to which I refer. These last are from the English flints.

Let us further consider Scottish specimens which possess handles, and are, as *I* consider, strongly reminiscent of the natural handles in the better flint examples, and equally suggestive of certain Egyptian forms.

Fig. 269 suggests the English flints of the natural handle type plus the greater freedom of elaboration in Scotland referred to. It is of fine figure, with a cleverly induced blade-like expansion; but

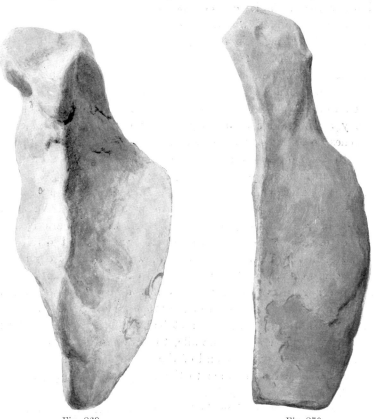

Fig. 269.   Fig. 270.

the handle is strongly suggestive of the indefiniteness and limitations of the flint nodule. Indeed, an examination of the object itself reveals the fact that the handle was suggested in the original stone, before the elaboration was begun. The facet (*a*) and the projecting portion of the handle above (*b*) are the original surface of the stone; all the rest has been boldly and cleverly fractured out. It is of dolomite limestone, and is a Forth-shore specimen. It may have been originally what it suggests, a fine knife ; but distinct evidence shows it to have been actually used as a flayer. Its underside is flat, and the handle, when viewed upon the knife-like edge, is distinctly laterally deflected.

Another of the Scottish specimens—once upon a time a fine knife or chopper (Fig. 270)—is formed from what is technically known as "ironstone-band," a well-known association of the "Coal-measures" and other rocks. This material is in its pristine state generally a grey and brittle rock, which gives sharp edges in fracture. These attributes of brittleness, hardness, and sharp edges made it a useful rock to Palæolithic man.

I particularly mention its pristine condition, because in that state its constitution is so full of certain salts of iron that, when exposed to the atmosphere or in water, it undergoes drastic changes. Its grey bright colour becomes yellow or red ; by chemical change it becomes, so to put it, "mellowed" upon the surface ; which surface is apt to flake off in filmy sheets or flakes, an eighth or even a quarter of an inch in thickness, according to the extent of decomposition. These exterior flakings, red or yellow or brown, or approaching black, are, when pulverised by Nature or human contrivance, the "ochres" of the house-painter and the artist. They are hydrated peroxides of iron with clay—an impure iron rust. I dwell upon this matter in view of what is to follow ; we shall repeatedly have to refer to this material, and our specimens exhibit peculiarities which some of my readers would perhaps not understand without the foregoing attempted exposition of the properties of this rock.

But this knife (Fig. 270) cannot be said, except perhaps for the bulbous termination of the handle, to be reminiscent of the flint forms. But in the squared end of the blade and general outline it bears considerable resemblance to the Egyptian examples, Figs. 267 and 268.

But let us study another Scottish example which seems to me to be entirely reminiscent of the English specimens, with their natural flint-nodule handles (see Figs. 271 and 272). This is quite a gem as a fabrication, is still of beautiful form, even though it was fabricated from the ironstone-band, has exteriorly undergone decomposition, and has lost one or more thin films from the greater part of its surface. Its original surface is seen to the left of the handle at *a*. While this strongly suggests the flint fabrications with the handles, in line with certain other productions from the

Scottish rocks, a greater freedom of treatment is distinctly evident. The rugged flint outlines and surfaces have given place to finer flowing lines, and what one may style refined surfaces. The more flowing lines are even seen in the less carefully elaborated Scottish examples (Figs. 265 and 266), which are compared with the Egyptian specimens.

The drawings (Figs. 271 and 272) give a far better idea of the

Fig. 271.   Fig. 272.

beauty of this specimen, and the skill with which it was fashioned, than any words could convey.

I cannot, however, declare, as I can with the handled elaborations from the flint gravels in England, that this is Palæolithic, since it was washed up from beneath the waves of the Forth estuary. It has an extremely ancient appearance, is exteriorly greatly decomposed, and is of a dark iron-rust colour. I can say nothing more about its age, except that it is associated with certain unquestionably Palæolithic forms in my collection, which were all brought up from the deep sea within the Forth estuary. I have, however, found similarly fabricated iron-band stones along the Clyde estuary, and in various parts of Scotland; sometimes, but more rarely, in deposits, and even in boulder-clay. I do not mean that I have found boulder-clay elaborations of such good form, or with such handles, but that undoubted implements formed of the same material occur in that deposit.

But let us try to see that, while the natural handles of the flint areas aided and abetted and possibly instigated the use of a handle, the excrescences of the flints, and the forms of the nodules themselves, imposed limitations which possibly and even probably retarded development in the mode and style of the handled implements. The man of the flint areas could not get beyond the limited capacity of the nodule; and while he was governed in his ideas of the handle by the form and capacity of the natural excrescences, his conceptions were, so to put it, hide-bound; it was not easy to break away from habit and tradition, combined with the circumstance of the material from which he elaborated his implements.

It actually, so far as my experience of the flints has gone, appears to have been so; for while among the flints I find a variety of cunning contrivances to adapt the implement to the hand of the operator, I do not find any bold deviation from the lines of the naturally suggested handles; and when bolder things are attempted, such as large choppers and flayers, the idea of the handle is almost lost in the indefiniteness of the intention in the mind of the elaborator.

But in the Scottish things the reverse of this is evident; for, though I find in North Britain domestic forms which are perfectly analogous to those of the Palæolithic gravels of southern England, they have a bolder aspect; and they are immediately surrounded with objects of a still bolder conception, with a greater variety of adaptation to the demand of circumstance.

It is only natural that the man, having conceived the advantage of the natural handle, as in England, should in Scotland, where he is thrown upon his own powers of sculpturing out such handle—the natural excrescences being no longer at hand—in the very effort to produce the same, vary his results according to the nature and capacity of the stones which he fashioned; which variations were ever a new suggestion to him that ultimately resulted in a great differentiation of form in his implements. There is extraordinary evidence of all that I am now suggesting in what follows in the elucidation of the Scottish objects, and this greater variation, greater boldness, and greater success in the style of work will be best seen in the individual descriptions and illustrations. But while I show

how much more was attained in what I believe to be Palæolithic
times in Scotland, I would not have my
readers understand that Palæolithic man
of the flint areas was without *corresponding implements* ; he had them and used
them, but they are almost unrecognis-
ably poor as productions, compared with
the northern forms, although similarly
poor productions occur among them also.
Palæolithic man in North Britain achieved
with great skill and freedom what the
man of the flint regions was ever feeling
after, and only tentatively arrived at.
Much the same story is told, as I believe
I have pointed out, in the fabrication of
the Scottish Palæolithic haches as compared with those of the South.

If we now study Fig. 273, we shall
be struck by the great contrast between
the ruggedness of this, and the beauty
and refinement of the last (Figs. 271 and
272). In a sense it is a harking back
to introduce this specimen here ; for, as
is seen, the handle is the result of simply
striking away a part of the handle end,
and not of elaboration. The specimen is,
however, an excellent illustration of the
greater freedom with which the Scottish
elaborator could work. I believe the
ancient man was instigated to the elaboration of this whilom fine chopper by the
natural curve shown in the broad back.
The large facet shown, and the corresponding underside, were sculptured out.
It is doubtful whether the portion along
the dark-shaded edge is a sculptured surface. In any case the specimen is boldly
produced, and must have been a highly

Fig. 273.

effective hatchet ; or, as a possible weapon, it would have been a
terrible one. It is 13 inches in length, and weighs several pounds.

It is a Forth-shore specimen (1896). Seaweed was still attached, which had helped to bring it ashore.

In Figs. 274 and 275 we have another illustration of the splendid capacity of the ancient fabricator, when the rocks offered scope for its exercise. The drawings at once show what a fine hatchet this is. Its admirable handle, and the free fine intention expressed in it, are very evident. Yet there is little work in the sense of elaboration about it; it is the result of a skilful selection of a stone, a boulder probably, from which a large flake a foot at least long was cleverly struck. This massive flake was then split again through its whole length—as clever a stroke as can well be conceived—which produced the broad flat back along the line to the left of Fig. 274, the width of which is seen in the edgewise view (Fig.

Fig. 274.   Fig. 275.

275). The broad face of Fig. 274 is the natural and original surface of the boulder, except about the handle, where some further elabora-

much as i
rounded by
 I parti
because th
such lentic
had, where
curred, a
of utilising
because the
ing, or cho
already the
ally a conve
in such n
fracturing
domestic o
ments. V
further illu
This specin
ever, have
much more
out from a
ticular in for
side, the sha
278, is sugge
ing been bo
its somewhat
choidal surf:
out, more es
face shown i
flat. In any
men exhibits
in the genera
the almost n
of the hand
stone itself
ancient look.
on the Forth :
 In Fig. 27
more than us
identical form

tion was effected, although, as this older surface was already much
chemically altered, but in no sense rotten, even the handle elaboration
partakes of the older aspect. The
under face shown to the right of the
edge of Fig. 275 is the sculptured-out
work, with, of course, the broad back.
This, an exceptionally fine specimen,
is $11\frac{3}{4}$ inches in length ; with it a large
carcass could still be cut up.

A feature of this specimen is still a
puzzle to me. I noticed first upon its
original and more decayed surface
several bold scores or scars, which run
more or less in line with the length
of the implement ; they are so placed
that they could not have been done
in using it as a hatchet or weapon.
I therefore concluded that they are
glacial scorings, and that the ancient
man had fabricated his implement
from a glaciated boulder. But the
puzzle is still there, for the larger
fabricated face is distinctly scored also.
If these are glacial scorings it is most
striking in such an object. There is
an absence of the small finer characteristic striæ, and the stone has escaped
in a wonderful manner from the usual
"fretting," if it be glaciated. Stones are,
however, often distinctly glaciated, and
still are perfect in form. I am, however, inclined to be cautious in assuming the glaciation of this example. It
is a Tay-shore specimen (near Dundee),
1884. It is of dolomite limestone.

In Fig. 276 we have another
admirable chopper, of what one might
call an up-to-date aspect. It is now, however, rotten and dis-
reputable-looking. It was formed of a very impure ironstone-band,
i.e. there is a good deal of argillaceous and carbonaceous matter

Fig. 276.

ironstone-band, and was wholly sculptured out from an amorphous mass, it was found in an ancient deposit in the Whitadder Valley —the Millburn deposit before referred to as yielding one or two striking Palæolithic weapons. Though the handle and outline are very like Fig. 277, there is no suggestion of a naturally lenticular mass in this. It has not (now), and perhaps never had, so good an edge as the last; but this kind of rock becomes rounded by chemical change, and this the more rapidly in a thin edge — the material being more exposed than, say, in a squared form; and a quondam edge may have (as I suspect here) wholly disappeared. This is one of the more rare instances of the occurrence of a handled chopper-like form in a Scottish deposit in association with undoubted Palæolithic weapons.

Fig. 281.

Fig. 280 is suggestive of the last in its general form. It is, I believe, a wholly sculptured-out example from a basaltic rock from which crystals have dissolved, so that it has a semi-spongy and most ancient look. It is, I believe, *most* ancient — it has lost part of its under surface (not shown), and part of the handle, which loss is indicated. It has, I believe, now its original outline, although the blade may have been wider; the whole is an excellent conception, and the form of the handle is particularly fine. This is from the Ayrshire coast, 1897.

In Fig. 281 we have a remarkable specimen. It is remarkable in its figure, which, without the suggested restorations which I have appended, is what we have spoken of as an up-to-date, quite modern form. With the suggested restoration, for which the implement itself gives warrant, its modern aspect is perfect. I am, however, coming to the conclusion that what we call an up - to - date form is so ancient in origin that we may well hesitate to suggest even an approximate estimate of its age. That is, in any case, best left undefined at present, so far as I am concerned. I only know that these forms are often most ancient—not only by their condition, but at times by their geological occurrence. And another fact presents itself in a startling way to myself as I remember that I have never found, during all these years, one specimen which has in any sense a modern look *except in form*. All are invariably most ancient in appearance. I leave this phenomenon to be digested by my readers. This particular specimen is of a grey granitic rock. It is considerably rolled, and parts of its surface have disappeared. As indicated, part of the finely contrived handle is lost, and the point end is also gone. It is a North Berwick, Forth-shore specimen.

I have another specimen almost identical in form from the shore, mouth of the Tay estuary, which is dated 1880. It is somewhat smaller than the foregoing, and has also lost its point end. It is of a (now) honeycombed basaltic rock.

" Handle " and " point " ends of these domestic forms, just as in the case of the Palæolithic weapons, are not uncommon.

I could give illustrations of some few of these, but one must suffice here, which is of a roughly broken-off blade end.

What Fig. 282 may have been like it is impossible to say for certain, but the portion shown in the drawing suggests that it is part of a very finely designed and executed implement. It is, as usual, most ancient in appearance. It is from the shore near Oban.

As is fitting at the close of this chapter we come to the most remarkable specimen of all, Fig. 283. This is a marvellously clever elaboration. It is wholly a sculptured-out implement. The flaking-out of the blade, which itself is a bold, daring conception, is magnificent work on both faces ; the

Fig. 282.

underside is also flat, but exhibits more actual elaboration. The cutting edge is still in perfect condition, except that it is rounded (water-rolled). There is a broadish bevelled "back" below the margin *a*, along what looks only like an edge in the drawing. It is therefore not so weak at the point end as might be imagined.

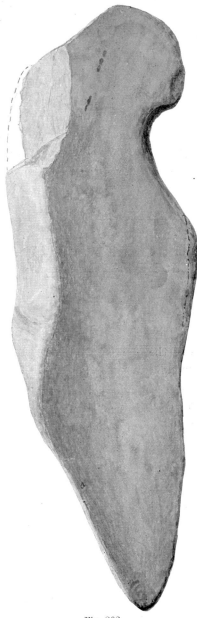

Fig. 283.

As is seen, a fragment has recently come away from the handle end above *a*, and the loss of this has quite spoilt the hand-grasp. The damage was done by the rough shore waves, which had begun to break it up. It is for its size a thinnish specimen — is just under 12½ inches in length, and might soon have been broken beyond recognition, although as a rule stones are not broken up, but only rounded on the shore. Its comparatively slender build, however, and its fairly rotten condition, exposed it to easy destruction. Some seaweed was still attached to it, showing that it had but recently come ashore. How long it had lain at the bottom of the Forth estuary it is impossible to suggest; and how it got there in an undamaged state is of course a problem. It may be Neolithic. Its shape, like some of the preceding, suggests what we consider recent forms; but so do some of the finds from the actual Palæo-lithic gravels of England. While the handle of this is like, or suggestive of, a modern *saw* handle, it equally recalls certain of the flint-nodule handles, and was produced probably by lateral strokes delivered from right and left. While the surface is finely honeycombed, it has not so actually ancient an appearance as some of the foregoing. It is of a variety of trap.

APPENDIX TO CHAPTER XVI

It was my intention to give a further chapter upon the morphology of " choppers." I have of late years discovered that these forms are to be found in places much more commonly than one could have imagined possible ; and I had intended fully to illustrate the various forms of these choppers, but a brief glance at a limited number of samples must suffice. There are so many more of this particular form of relic in my collection than I had imagined before beginning this study, that to get a broader view of them I find it necessary to be less particular as to details. Several further typical forms will be suggestive, and will help us to understand what a marvellously well-written history is revealed to us by these chopper forms alone.

I would lay stress upon a pronounced feature, which is a very natural one, and very informing. We all, I presume, understand that implements which were elaborated as choppers from stone, and especially when handles have been added, would be very liable to fracture anywhere between the grasp of the hand and the heavier part of the operative blade. This is the feature. Fully half of these said choppers are either detached blades or detached handles. They doubtless often broke in actual use exactly as we should expect them to break, that is, nearer, as a rule, to the base of the handle than towards the point end of the blade. Blade ends are more common than handles ; that is to say, they are (naturally) more easily recognised than a handle or a fragment of it.

These implements have intensely interested me. Some were sculptured out against the planes of deposition, in certain quartzites and dolomite limestones. These have naturally broken clean across in some plane of deposition ; others through planes of prismatic or other cleavage ; while many have fractured against the natural strength and compactness of the rock, and present equivalent ruggedness in the break. Every one of these elaborations is a graphic chapter in its form and intention, and often in the condition in which it has come down to us.

To return to more primitive styles, here is an implement of excellent design and skilful work, but of eccentric form (Figs. 284 and 285). When I discovered it on the shore near North Berwick seventeen years ago, I concluded that it was a weapon, a Palæolithic hache. It is, as much greater experience has shown, a double-edged chopper. I have no doubt of that, though it would also have been a terrible weapon. It is still perfect, except for the pronounced disposition to break up into fragments, as seen in the drawings. Its edges were cleverly produced, and though it has only what may be called a bulbous hand-grasp (best

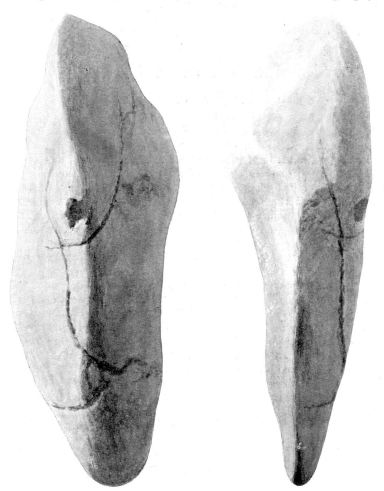

Fig. 284.   Fig. 285.

seen at the upper end of Fig. 285), it would, but for its liability to break, still be a most effective implement for the division of a carcass or for any chopping operation. The longer edge to the right of Fig. 284 was the more usable, though both edges would still be highly effective. It is, I believe, a decayed dolomite limestone, is $9\frac{1}{2}$ inches in length, and weighs several pounds.

Fig. 286 is a fine production, with a handle rather suggested than

Fig. 286.

worked out. It, however, speaks clearly for itself as a serviceable chopper. It is exactly one foot in length, and is of basalt.

Figs. 287 and 288 show a very fine blade end of a chopper once provided with a handle. It is an Ayrshire-coast specimen, found in 1897. It was, however, one that could by no possible reasoning be taken for anything but what I now assert it to be. I presume it once had a handle, somewhat as suggested in Fig. 287. It broke exactly as

Fig. 287.   Fig. 288.

one would have expected it to break. It has been much rolled since that destructive event; the specimen, however, clearly shows how it broke; it is otherwise in perfect form. I believe it to be of ironstone-band, in which much less iron than usual is present. It is decayed, *i.e.* peroxidised, but in slight manner. I have quite a series of portions of blades of this excellent type. Its present length is within a small

Fig. 289.   Fig. 290.

fraction of 9 inches.   With a handle it was a splendid example ; but this portion of it is very weighty; no wonder it broke. I cannot of course declare that the break was not the result of some natural accident, but it suggests having been broken in use.

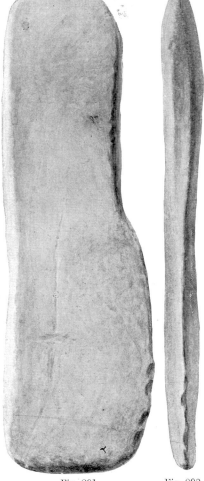

Of all the domestic implements that have come into my hands none strike me as being in design and skill and free workmanship more masterly than that of Figs. 289 and 290. It is of a basaltic rock, has been (anciently) highly rolled, but is, except that it is much decayed, almost perfect. Its fine straight edge, sharp when first formed, with the weighty

Fig. 291.   Fig. 292.

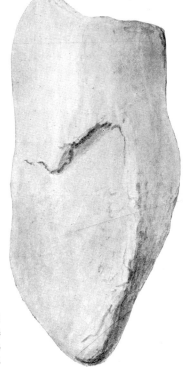

Fig. 293.

broad back and the cleverly executed and bilaterally expanded handle, made it a most formidable weapon or a most effective domestic implement. It is a Clyde-estuary specimen (near Troon), 1896. It had evidently but recently been brought from the deep sea. It was among a huge mass of seaweed which had come ashore during a violent storm. It is over 1 foot in length, and of most antiquated aspect.

The specimen of Figs. 291 and 292 is of a different type altogether. It is of the ironstone-band and highly peroxidised; so much has it been transformed by chemical change that I believe it to have lost a more or less thick film from its whole surface. It was originally thicker in body than it now is. It may have been fashioned from a naturally tabular piece of that rock, or it may have been a large flake struck from a mass and then shaped; we cannot tell. But we can tell, by taking it into the hand, what an effective knife or chopper it once was. It has still a sharp edge, which with the excellent handle, and its weight,—the material is almost as heavy as iron—would make it still a very useful weapon or domestic implement. It is interesting as having occurred in a gravel deposit, a "raised beach," below The Butlaw, Forth. The apparent cross-like figure upon it is merely the result of chemical decomposition.

Fig. 293 is one of the detached

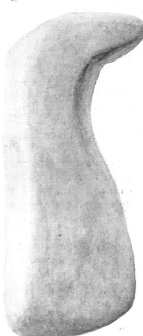

Fig. 294.   Fig. 295.

blades. It is of a trap rock, and a Forth-estuary shore specimen. It speaks clearly for itself.

I take Fig. 294 to be a detached handle, and if so it is a remarkable specimen, though by no means unique in the sense of being an isolated form. It bears the character of several of the flint examples which we have studied where the natural processes of the nodules suggested the elaboration. It was formed with the same intention and style of work as the handle of the fine knife or chopper with which the last chapter (XVI.) closes, though the form is different. Two further similarly produced handles will immediately follow. But let us consider the present one.

It suggests a very fine fabrication ; the blade of such a handle ought to have been surpassingly good. An examination shows, in my view, that the body of the blade was roughly detached, possibly in use. That detachment occurred ages ago ; there is now no apparent difference in age between the fractured end and the rest of the surface of the figure, as there naturally would not now be if it were broken in actual use. I said the break took place ages ago, because after that fracture the stone was much rolled by river or marine action, and after the rolling it lay somewhere, probably in the bed of the estuary (Forth), till it became decomposed and elaborately honeycombed by crystals having been dissolved out. It is of some species of trap with quartz veins. It has a most venerable look.

Fig. 295 is a very similar specimen, and is also, I believe, a detached handle ; but the detachment arose in a different way. There is, I think, clear evidence that the detachment took place long after the thing was fabricated and used. Its underside is flat, with such aspect as to show it to be the result of a natural fracture ; it is a good deal more recent than any of the surface shown in the drawing. Its more ancient surface is excessively rolled, the underside being also water-worn, but to much less extent. It seems to me to have been the handle end of a whilom fine chopper, and through some natural accident to have parted from the main mass in a plane of bedding or cleavage.

If we doubt these last two being detached handles we have only to look at the next specimen, Fig. 296, to see that such a supposition is no mere fancy. For here we have a still tangible chopper, with a handle of the same type though of inferior form. It was, however, probably once of better form than it now is. It is, as is apparent, much dilapidated, and was certainly broader in the blade and possibly longer than at present. In any case it is an excellent and an illuminative specimen ; it occurred on the shore at the mouth of the Dee, Aberdeen (1896). It is of a decayed but still hard and brittle quartzite, and is antique enough in aspect and dilapidated enough to have gone through the glacial mill. There is, however, no real evidence that such was the case.

We have doubtless noticed a resemblance to " birds' " heads in this group of handles, notably in Fig. 294. My friend Mr. W. M. Newton, who has devoted much time to this question of designed animal forms in Palæolithic relics, says that such forms were attempted figures of various contemporary animals. I see no reason why they should not have been such ; with the marvellous art-productions which these same peoples left in caves on the Continent, and in other parts of the world (Egypt, for instance), and these last of flint or chert, it seems to me that we ought to expect to find evidence of such artistic efforts in their relics wherever found, and especially in connection with the elaboration of their domestic forms.

One of the most interesting of all the choppers which I have found anywhere I came upon in a pit at Farnham, Surrey, so recently as September 1907. It comes in here not inappropriately as I happen to be writing these lines. It would, however, have come into the section dealing with "natural handles" more appropriately, seeing that more

TH
bee
as
in
wo
the
bo1
of
as
wo

I
bo
ne
sk
th
tre
m;
th
w(

m;
if
or
pe
in
ti(
at
a1
h;
d(
a1

Fig. 296.

Fig. 297.

than three-fourths of the surface of the handle in this specimen is the natural unaffected exterior of the original nodule, while almost the whole of the rest of the implement has been sculptured out. It was fabricated from a cylindrical nodule which was characterised by a natural protuberance, and this, with slight modification, forms the handle.

It comes in well in this place from the point of view that, if we consider

Pacific Ocean clubs and weapons, when I was attracted by some made from hard wood, which, both in size and shape, as to the blade, —the handles were more developed—were practically identical with this. What suggested this form, and at places so far apart? I naturally thought, "they are *scapular* in shape," and the murder was out, *i.e.* it was out by suggestion. They were possible reflections of a whilom use of scapulas as weapons, or domestic implements, or for both purposes.

This Scottish specimen, both in the flat and edgewise (Figs. 298 and 299), is strongly suggestive of the shoulder-blade of a large mammal; I think the handle end particularly so; it seems to reflect the peculiarities of the articulated (jointed) end of that particular bone. One does not vouch that it is so, but the drawings will, I imagine, convey that impression to the reader. It is boldly produced from a probably tabulate mass of dolomite limestone. It is produced in the plane of its bedding; but none of its facets are in that exact plane, but are all struck away more or less diagonally across the bedding; it is in no sense an accident, but is a case of an almost wholly sculptured-out specimen.

I have since found several others of almost identical form in Scotland, but being too indefinite as to their elaboration, they were discarded. I have, however, other specimens which are highly suggestive of such imitative origin, and which are undoubted fabrications.

In general expression, and again particularly at the handle end, Figs. 300 and 301 are highly suggestive of the blade-bone of some mammal,—the sculpture of the "handle" is so very like the articulated end of a scapula, and the blade and the edgewise view add to this suggestion. As there were animals and animals, so there were various models in the scapulas in use. There is evidence of various forms of scapulas being copied. They are triangular and sub-quadrilateral, as they varied in mammals; narrow and sabre-shaped, as in birds. The present specimen is much smaller than the foregoing, being but 8½ inches in length; the model for the same would probably be that of quite a different animal from that of the foregoing, and modifications naturally came in in the making. In any case this was a hand chopper or flayer—there is, I believe, evidence of its having been used in the latter capacity; and, as the edge is still perfect except as rounded by rolling (see Fig. 301), it was hardly used as a chopper, but might have been a knife. The cleverly deflected handle gives splendid purchase in the hand, in whatever

especia
exposes
is neve

capacity it was used.   Its fabrication was most skilled work.   It is entirely sculptured out from a mass, and was a piece of real sculpture as we now understand that word.

It is more than usually interesting and valuable, because of its *occurrence*.   It is not a shore find, but an ancient delta-deposit

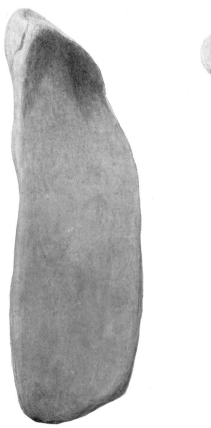 

Fig. 300.   Fig. 301.

specimen.   It is from Barbush Hill, near Dunblane—a hill of sand with seams of gravel, before referred to.

deterio
chippin
become
to the
specime

This example, with several large rubbing-stones, had been thrown out by the workmen among material too coarse for the purpose for which the gravel was wanted.

The summit of Barbush Hill is somewhere about 300 feet above sea-level, and nearly 100 feet above the river Allan, which runs a compact hard rock of a dark blue-grey colour, they are now on the surface chalky and approaching white. This illustrates the nature and origin of several interesting fabrications, apparently of *chalk*, which I found in the subsoil—*boulder-clay*—when the foundations of the Parsonage here were dug. The drawings of this show what an admirably clever production it is.

Figs. 304 and 305 is another example, a knife or flayer which

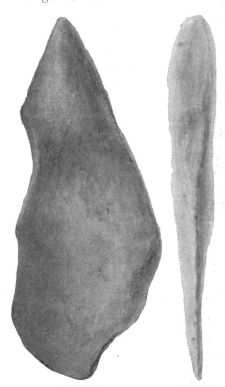

came ashore near where the immediately foregoing was found. It is of the same material, but much smaller, and is also scapular-like in form. So, and I think in a remark-able degree, is Fig. 269, if we turn back to it.

Some other finds of a differ-ent type, but of suggestively scapular-like form, have for some years attracted my attention. These are segments (generally) from lenticular ironstone or limestone nodules. They are, roughly speaking, scapular in shape, have often a designed handle or hand - grasp, are nearly always so formed as to utilise the natural edge of the lenticular mass. In a word, they are merely broken out rather than *sculptured* out,

Fig. 304.   Fig. 305.

but clever and efficient im-plements all the same. This is a case once more of the ancient man taking advantage of a natural accident in rock-forms. And for this very reason, *i.e.* of the natural "accident" and ancient man having come together and produced certain results, a modern man (myself) makes the mistake of discarding for a good many years all such examples, because of their decidedly *natural* conformation, at least in part; whereas, as he now knows from experience, had he treasured the discarded items, their cumulative evidence would have been long ago overwhelming of man's intentional intervention. I

I have discarded a considerable number, but for several years past some have been kept, though none of them are illustrated.

In Figs. 306 and 307 we have another elaboration which is remarkably scapular-like, with the same articulate joint-like handle. It is

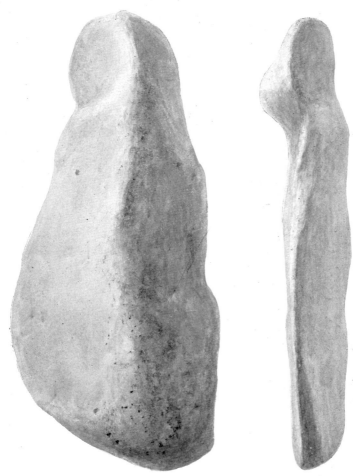

Fig. 306.   Fig. 307.

a larger specimen than either of the three preceding, being just upon 9¾ inches in length and 4½ in greatest breadth. But for its rotten condition and rounded edges, it would still be a most effective chopper. It tells the same story as so many of the other finds of similar form, viz. that it was considerably water-worn ages ago; since which time it has been decomposed and honeycombed under as the striation is there, it shows that its glaciation took place after it acquired its present form.

I believe that it is a clever human fabrication, that it was a fan-shaped scapular-like implement, that it was pre- (or inter-) glacial in origin, and that it received its glaciation entirely after its present form was given to it. That it was "fretted" in the usual way at various places all around its margin is seen, the frettings having all a fresher look than the unfretted general surface.

By the kindness of the discoverer I have this fine specimen now before me, and have produced the drawings from it. Mr. M. B. Cotsworth, York, a well-known and enthusiastic scientist, was, as he tells me, walking along the seashore at Sewerby, Yorkshire, when he noticed the handle end of the implement protruding from *in situ* boulder-clay. With some difficulty it was extracted from that deposit and carried home. I am deeply indebted to Mr. Cotsworth for the loan of so highly interesting and, as I conceive, magnificent a specimen of pre-glacial man's handiwork.

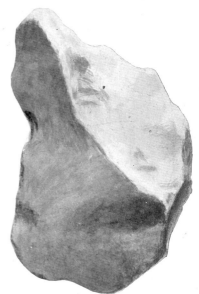

Fig. 310.　　　　　　　　　　　　　　　　Fig. 311.

Mr. Cotsworth expressed it as his opinion that the large lateral portions had been removed from the original nodule by the fabricator carefully chipping out the intended lines of detachment as grooves, which, when struck, naturally broke along the lines of induced weakness. There is actually some suggestion of this in the specimen.

Once more we may transport ourselves to the English Palæolithic gravels, with the view of corroborating these northern scapular-like implements. That I have not much to show on this head is, I presume, the result more of the want of opportunity to search for the evidence than that examples do not occur. I have one at least, and that so remarkably like a scapula that it looks in the specimen, and in the drawings (Figs. 310 and 311), more as though it were a fossil blade-bone than a fabrication from a flint nodule. It must speak for itself as to its presumed imitative figure. It was probably a flayer by intention; it could scarcely have been a knife, and is not large enough to have been an effective chopper. It is a skilful production, is from a high-level gravel-pit at Croydon, and is 5¾ inches in length. I obtained it in 1905.

Another phase of this study of possibly imitative forms has lately been suggested to me by several specimens from the shores of the Forth. The first, shown in Figs. 312 and 313, is, on the face of it, a chopper or knife; in its day perhaps both. It was cleverly sculptured out bodily from a mass of quartzite. Its handle end is most peculiar, being irregular and apparently without design; yet there is a good deal of pronounced intention in it. For instance, the lateral deflection seen in the edge view

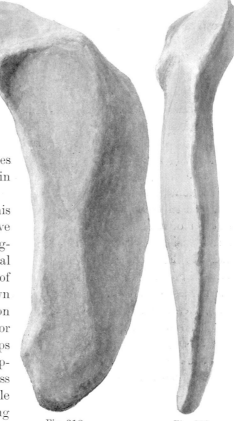

Fig. 312.   Fig. 313.

(Fig. 313) gives the hand a firm grasp, while the raised part with shadow under the deflection to the left of the handle end of Fig. 312 is an admirable lever for the thumb; the whole is well designed, but why of such a peculiar form? I am speaking now more particularly of the handle end. The blade is chopper-like, but the scimitar - like curve to the handle end, and the eccentricity of form in the handle itself, are striking, and decidedly peculiar.

If Fig. 312 be now viewed with the implement placed horizontally and the handle end curving up to the right, the whole thing is very like the lower jaw of a mammal, the alveolar ridge—teeth-socket ridge—being the line along the top or back of the blade, while the handle end is marvellously suggestive of the natural and articulated end of such lower jaw.

It *may* be an accidental imitation; in any case it is a finely conceived and well-sculptured chopper, that would, we cannot doubt, have done as good service in the hands of Samson as the historic ass's jaw-bone. It is, in a straight line, $8\frac{3}{4}$ inches long. It was washed in from the bed of the Forth estuary.

Another of these suggestive fabrications, discovered in 1906, is shown in Fig. 314. It is a striking specimen in more than one way—in its fine chopper-like aspect, so far as the blade itself is concerned, its excellent handle, and the peculiarity of the upturned nose or head. In this case, as seems to me, we have once more an almost real imitation of a mammal jaw, modified for adaptation to actual use. In this instance, what we may call the chin (the incisor) end of the maxilla is the handle, in place of the articulated end; and this has been well adapted to the hand by the sculpturing out of a piece from its under-edge. If this be such an imitation of actual jaw imple-ments, then the upturned nose or head is again a reminiscence of the articulation of the natural jaw.

If we regard the upturned nose of this specimen as the articulated end, we have a most jaw-like object; and if we restore the chin end with the incisor teeth, the whole thing is resolved into a perfect jaw. In the whole figure the lower mandible of a mammal is, in my opinion, graphically represented to us.

If we now bear in mind the peculiar curve of the "articulated" ends of the two foregoing specimens, and particularly of Fig. 312, and then turn to the figures of the Egyptian forms (226 and 227), and then to the two Scottish forms (222 and 223) and to the example from the Palæolithic English gravels (224), we shall see at least a suggestion that the "deflected" handles were the natural reminiscence of the articulated ends of the original weapon and chopper and flayer, all combined in one, of which the jaws of animals were a natural and

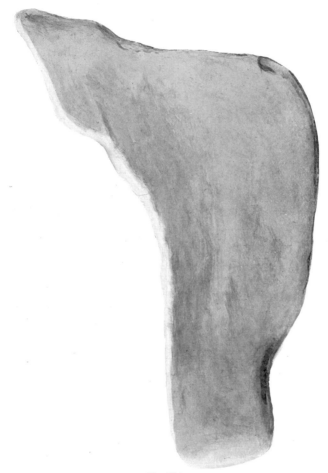

Fig. 314.

never-failing supply. In Figs. 233 and 234, and in others, we have also remarkably jaw-like forms.

One further instance will complete this study of the possible imitative origin of most interesting forms (see Figs. 315 and 316). This specimen of a thin but cleverly produced chopper is of such build that in the hand it suggests a large rib of, say, one of the great mammals. It is a wholly sculptured-out example; it was not naturally tabulate, but is so by intention. It has obviously been broken, since its elaboration, at the handle end, where I have suggested the extension. If that end were unbroken, it would be still more like a rib. But once again, the character of these as human productions is not one whit affected, whether they be these suggested imitations or not; they are equally human work.

As though to place beyond cavil the imitative nature of these forms, or to make the matter the profoundest of puzzles, a specimen in stone has come to hand so wonderfully like a scapula that several intelligent people have declared that it must be a fossil one, *i.e.* an actual scapula become petrified. But it is not a fossil in the sense of its ever having been anything " organic " ; it is a human fabrication from a compact close-grained fragment of the ironstone-band. It is peroxidised to such an extent that it is of a chocolate colour —it was a silver-grey when it was made—and in places it has lost a thin film of the peroxidised surface. Yet it is so perfect a copy of a scapula that I have never ceased to view and to handle it with a sense of something like astonishment.

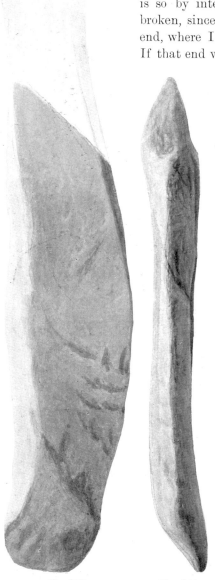

Fig. 315. Fig. 316.

The present chapter was so far complete when I lighted upon this specimen, but it has so aroused my interest as to necessitate some further remarks.

Will the reader examine the drawing (Fig. 317)? I cannot say that it is good as such, but I have scrupulously avoided exaggerating its main features, so as not to make it more like a scapula than the original actually is. Yet I think that any one, even though he may be a comparative anatomist, who may see this drawing, will at once conclude that it is an actual blade-bone of some mammal. If the very animal which a scapula of that particular build and pattern represented were specified it would not be surprising.

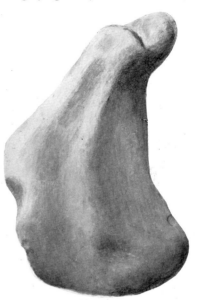

Fig. 317.

I lately (1907) spent a day or two in the National Museum, Dublin, where, owing to my interest in the present phase of the subject, I devoted much attention to the mammal and other animal departments.

If we turn to Fig. 318 (among the group of outline figures), we have there a hastily produced sketch of the scapula of the dugong, a marine animal, first cousin of the manatee and sea-cow, and a more distant relative of the seals, sea-lions, etc. I copied this from the actual skeleton simply because it happened to remind me of this last specimen. In an illustration in Milne Edwards's *Manual of Zoology*, I find a somewhat different drawing of the scapula of an animal of the same genus, but probably a different species (see Fig. 319). If we now compare Fig. 317 with these two, marking the difference between right and left scapulas, we shall see that that occupies in actual form a position between them. If this similarity is an accident, it amounts almost to a miracle.

But should some hyper-critic say, " The dugong group never lived so far north," I should say that it did in the warmer *Cyrena-fluminalis* period when Palæo man and the great mammalia were conspicuously present. In any case seals and sea-lions, the wolf, and

Fig. 332 is of the corresponding bone of the also extinct aepyornis of Madagascar.

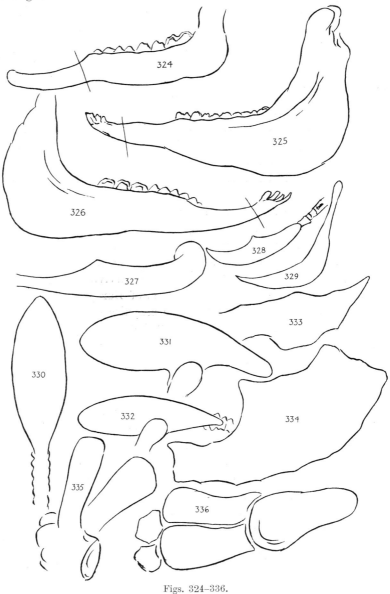

Figs. 324–336.

Turning back to Fig. 312, and viewing it in the position of Fig. 324, with which it should be compared, let us imagine the portion of

of the horn of the Ir
sketched.   Here is
viz. that bones need
in recognisable cond
a cave, associated wi
that they would ne
vincing enough und

Fig. 3

except in rough
larger of these is r
Another curiou
man made of bone
polished bones, *i.*
found somewhere
where; they show
been carried on w
The four Figs.

the figure to the left of the diagonal line (in Fig. 324) to be broken away, and we shall have practically identical forms; and if we imagine the teeth to be removed from the latter, the forms become still more alike ; or if imaginary teeth be placed in the corresponding " alveolar ridge " of the former, who would not imagine that to be a drawing of an imperfect mammal jaw ?   Fig. 324 is of the inferior maxilla of the extinct Irish elk.

If we now turn to Fig. 314, and compare it with Fig. 325, which is a drawing of the lower jaw of a horse, and if we remove the teeth from the latter, and once more detach the part to the left of the diagonal line, we find that we have a very fair model for 314, the handle end being in this case the chin end.   The horse, or his immediate ancestor, was certainly the coeval of Palæolithic man, and of course through all time since.   If, once more, we place imaginary teeth along the ridge of Fig. 314 and add the " chin " end, we get almost a perfect lower jaw of one of our heavier-built horses.   Fig. 326 is that of a camel, which is here placed with that of the horse to show that the ancient man had that particular form of osseous weapon or implement under his eyes wherever he went, in the camel where the horse was absent, and conversely.

I may be thought fanciful, but it is worth while to compare the appended outlines of some modern implements or weapons with the foregoing.   Compare, for example, the form of Fig. 327 with the whole figure of Fig. 324, and if that is only a chance resemblance it is a striking one, and one that has curious aspects ; for instance, the turned-up rounded end is a mere ornament, and is not necessary to the effectiveness of the implement.   It is an Egyptian (bronze) knife from a mummy case.   The lower line is the cutting edge; the curves in the back that meet in an elevated point look to me like survivals of the alveolar ridge—teeth-socket ridge—with the full extension of the jaw as in, say, Fig. 324.   Imagine teeth along the line in Fig. 327 from the raised point to the incurved end, and Fig. 324 is practically repeated.

Fig. 328 was among Chinese " implements of war and chase " in the Dublin Museum.   And Fig. 329 is a wooden club, a " nulla-nulla," from Queensland, Australia.

These three last all seem to me to owe their present forms to the once universal use of the lower mandibles of animals as weapons or domestic implements.   It is well known that bones were used, as I have suggested, in the past.   I was interested in two objects which were exhibited in the said Museum with other human relics from

Fig. 345 is a Scottish specimen which I found in an ancient river-deposit in the Crieff and Comrie railway-cutting before referred to, in 1892. It is of dolomite limestone, which is decomposed and bleached upon the surface into a semi-chalky condition. It is decidedly of the form of a Palæolithic weapon; but it is clear, when the specimen is in the hand, that it is the broad and not the point end which has received most careful elaboration. The point end is very unfinished and possibly has received damage, although, if it were mounted, it might be effective enough as a weapon; but that does not explain why the butt-end was bevelled off to something approaching an edge, and carefully rounded. This rounded butt-end was a puzzle to me for some years, though I accepted the find as a Palæolithic weapon.

But Fig. 346 was a greater puzzle still, and for a much longer time. That example was found in 1883 at Edmonton—the Edmonton of "John Gilpin" fame. It was among coarse (sifted) gravel, from some unknown pit; and again I conceived it to be a Palæolithic weapon. It was at once perceptible that the point—the operating

end (presumably)—was not well placed; and once more I was struck by the fact that the butt-end had had considerable labour bestowed upon it, apparently for the same reason that the butt of the foregoing had been so treated, viz. to bevel that end and to nicely round it; an item of that end has been broken out since its elaboration. It is bevelled off, but not to a cutting edge; it was excellently rounded. Why, once again, was the butt— if it were a Palæolithic weapon—more carefully elaborated than the point, and why the evident bevelling at the butt?

Fig. 347 is another Scottish specimen, which I found in 1889 in a high-level ancient river-deposit. This also I conceived to have been intentionally a Palæolithic weapon.

At that time, let us notice, I was ready to recognise such forms wherever found as Palæo weapons, i.e. things to be used at their point ends, provided they showed sufficient artificial elaboration, and were sufficiently stout in build to warrant such assumption. Many

Fig. 347.

that it
Neolithi
the forr
valuable
of a por
hand ; l
faces to
of this
lying de
was one
land, its
thirty-fi
In
same for
actual u
The imp
that the
In F
form.
like at
bold flal
possibly
from, I
Dunblar
Fig.
ridge in
edge at
point en
Palæolit
I believe
In its p
broad er
be held
i.e. by a
handle,
below tl
specimer
delta de
interesti
In F

a specimen of similar form was doubtless overlooked or discarded because of the too frail aspect of such finds, while this greater frailness is now seen to be their common and intended attribute.

But at length it became evident that many of these forms had been fabricated *specially with the view to the broad end*; and the supposed operating point end was only an indifferently elaborated handle or hand-grasp. *The presumed butt-end was the operating end.* They were flayers, as I take it, and were so bevelled and rounded, yet withal kept blunt, that skins should not be torn nor cut in the flaying. This is their story, which having once been grasped, is corroborated by finds on almost every hand: in English gravels, in Scottish deposits, and by many specimens from estuary and marine shores.

They will best tell their own history by the medium of such typical

Fig. 348.   Fig. 349.

examples as I have drawn. I have sought to give representative and illustrative specimens, which I will endeavour to describe. These

Neolithic axe form. It is of a fine-grained (Aberdeen) granitic rock, and was found in high-level river-gravels, *i.e.* about 30 feet above sea-level at Aberdeen, in 1896. This is in its *occurrence* also an unusually interesting find; it is also considerably rolled.

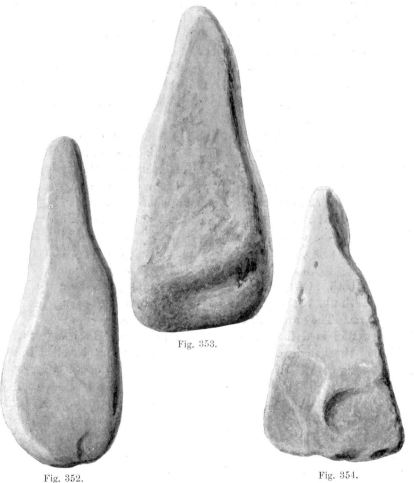

Fig. 353.

Fig. 352.

Fig. 354.

Fig. 354 is another, a Forth-shore specimen, which is decidedly axe-shape at the broad end; and there can be, further, no doubt as to which end of the implement was intended for use. The bevelling with the view to the broad edge, though roughly done, is expressive of deliberate intention.

Before we proceed further with our study of the development of this form in Scotland, let us see what corroboration of this occurs in the Palæolithic gravels in England.

In Fig. 355 we have in flint very much a duplicate in form, in the mode of elaboration, and certainly in the evident intention that the broad end was to be used, of Fig. 350. The handle end is as evidently a handle. There is the difference only of the more indefinite outline and the less clear surfaces characteristic of flint. This is a specimen from the low-level pit at Mitcham, Surrey. Let us remember that we have seen in our flints the ancient scapular-shaped

Fig. 355.   Fig. 356.

knives and flayers; we are starting with that recognisable use of the *broader end*, the attainment of which led up to the form and use of the Neolithic axe.

With this in view we have in Fig. 356 an actual scapular shape, with still something like a reminiscence of the articulated end; which I think we also have in the flint form from Edmonton (Fig. 346). This present specimen may in outline suggest a Palæolithic weapon, though the butt is quite shell-like in its thinness, and the point end was obviously intended for the hand. It was cleverly flaked from a largish nodule, and afterward shaped upon the face shown; the other face is entirely the exterior (natural) surface of the nodule. The whole is a fine example of deliberate intention.

I have been somewhat particular in describing this example because of its occurrence, which is not in the least indefinite, but points to a most ancient origin. I found it in the high-level pit at Colchester (1902), by which position I conclude the said gravel-deposit to be immediately post-glacial. It will be remembered that I found in this pit some 23 per cent of the items to be glaciated.

In Fig. 357 we have a most interesting specimen. It was

sculptured out from a nodule so completely that not a vestige of the original surface is to be seen. Its underside is one boldly obtained surface. The face shown has obviously been fabricated with the view to the use of the broad end, which is bevelled off and squared. It is deeply iron-stained, and has been fretted as though by pressure movement : it looks like the ice-fretting so commonly seen in certain of the Scottish forms. Its appearance is most ancient, in accordance with its occurrence, which was also in the Colchester high-level pit, where the immediately preceding was found. It is chisel-like, and I here confess that I was astonished to find two such forms in so ancient and unequivocal a position.

Fig. 357.

That even in that ancient (Colchester) position the stones represent different ages is clear from the condition of these two finds. In this last we have undoubtedly evidence of a "derived" specimen, which must have been ancient, very ancient, even when it was derived by that deposit from some other source. If the deposit were immediately post-glacial this example could scarcely come under that designation, since the ordinary stones of the said gravel are almost unstained, and altogether much more modern-looking than this, as is also the case with its fellow-occupant of that deposit (Fig. 356).

If we compare these last two finds with each other, the strange inference will be, that the one most elaborately sculptured out (Fig. 357) and most suggestive of the ultimate Neolithic forms is by far the more ancient (in appearance) of the two.

We have an interesting specimen in Fig. 32, if we turn back to it, among the weapons. This is in general aspect considerably like an ordinary Palæolithic weapon. As perhaps has been stated already, some specimens partake so much of the character of both the square-ended (domestic ?) forms and the Palæolithic weapon, that I think it may be assumed that some were actually used in the one and the other capacity as occasion demanded. Certainly some of the weapons, or those I have considered such, were used when they offered such facets as could be used for such purpose as "rubbing stones," as well as weapons.

This specimen (Fig. 32) is on the face of it so like a weapon that I have figured it as possibly such among the Palæolithic weapons proper. But the more I have studied these forms as they have come to hand, the plainer becomes the intention of their fabrication, not as weapons so much as broad-ended flayers, or some such implements. The point end of this never was, I believe, brought to a point; the sides of that end were so flaked as to suggest a handle more than a point. Further, the whole design is tabulate, and it thins out slightly toward the broad end, whereas weapons proper thicken often excessively in that direction; and this is further bevelled at the broad end, where it is squared with considerable care and intention. I take it actually to be designedly a handled flayer, and not a weapon. Again, there is something particularly striking about the appearance of this implement. It is deeply iron-stained, worn, and battered-looking, and is one of the most ancient flints in appearance that I possess. It was found by myself in the low-level pit at Mitcham, and is evidently much more ancient than the common facies of the pit stones. It is unquestionably a derived specimen, and had a venerable history before it found its way into that Mitcham bed.

We have now reached the fact that forms which anticipate the Neolithic polished axes and were used as (probably) knives, certainly as flayers, and possibly as axes at their broader ends, are found in ancient Scottish and English deposits, and particularly upon certain coast shores of Scotland, where they have mostly been picked up. As long as I assumed that the Neolithic axe form was peculiar to the Neolithic period, it was always a profound puzzle to me to imagine how Neolithic man became possessed of a weapon which was the actual antithesis to that of Palæolithic man. I have in vain tried to understand how the broad edge came in and the point went out. I concluded that Neolithic man was of an origin so far different from that of Palæolithic man that he had, from some unknown accident, or from some natural model, started with that form of weapon which the latter man had never used. I could not realise the remotest possibility of the typical Palæolithic weapon ever having become the axe of Neolithic man, and I do not think it could ever have become that type of implement, as it certainly never did, *as a weapon*; but might have become such an implement if its broad end were ever used for domestic purposes. But the forms which we have been studying have, so far as we have seen, attained such shape that any further development must lead directly into the Neolithic axe. Let us see several of the Scottish examples which seem to me to have actually acquired the Neolithic axe form.

In Fig. 358 we have an excellent illustration of a specimen which

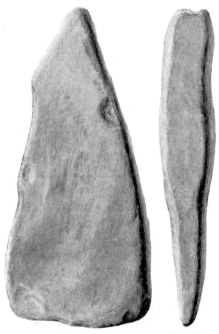

is not only axe-shape, but is at the broad end bevelled on both its faces to produce the axe-like edge, which is seen in the side view, Fig. 359.

This, I believe, belonged to high-lying river-gravels upon a plateau-like level above the flanks of the Whitadder Valley, near Duns. It lay with highly rolled gravel on an exposed bank, and was not found *in situ*: it also is rolled appreciably. It is of dolomite limestone.

Fig. 360 is another which, while it is of a good axe-like form, shows that it could never have been used as a chopper, for the reason that its broad end is abruptly truncated or

Fig. 358.   Fig. 359.   squared. But an edge to the

left of the broad end shows that it was intended to be used, as it doubtless was, as a cutting or scraping, or more probably flaying, instrument. In flaying, if the skin is to be preserved, it only needs to be lifted, so to put it, from the carcass—lifted or forced, but not cut away. Hence many of these flayers (?) exhibit no trace of an actual edge, and some, as I have already shown, are thick and truncated at the operating end. Nothing is more clearly shown than the care that was taken by Palæolithic man that skins should not be cut.   This has been apparent all along the domestic line, both

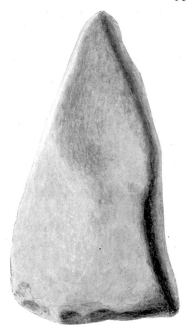

Fig. 360.

in the Scottish and English imple-ments.   And this, coupled with the several extraordinary and varied series of presumed flaying elaborations, which we shall discuss with the common occurrence of the equally presumed skin - curing specimens before described, points to the ancient man as a great hunter and flayer of animals, and a dresser of skins.   This last is also of dolomite limestone, and is a Forth-shore specimen.

In Fig. 361 we have a much more striking specimen, which was, I believe, a true axe.   It is finely expanded at the broad end, which was brought to

a whilom sharp edge, and would do effective chopping even now. It was originally wholly sculp-tured out.   Its rounded appear-ance may be in part the result of rolling, but is, I think, more due to decomposition.   It is an ironstone specimen, is now of a deep rusty-red colour, and is, save for the altered surface, much what it was when it left the hands of its fabricator.   It looks like a specimen intended to be mounted, and actually seems designed for some sort of socket rather than for the hand. It might of course have been equally a knife.   It is a Forth-shore specimen.

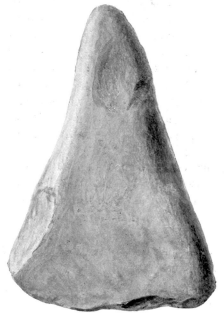

Fig. 361.

Let us notice the bell-like expansion of the broad end, and the fact that the elegantly rounded edge has been spoiled by certain chippings—possibly through use.

This (361) takes us well up to the beautiful though not perfect form of the Neolithic battle-axe (Fig. 362). It is startlingly like a

bona fide Neolithic weapon ; but it is not polished, nor is there any sign of polishing about it. Neither is there any suggestion of its actual flaying use, nor does the handle end suggest that it was intended for a socket-holder, but for the hand. Yet it is a beautiful specimen, that obviously owes its entire form to a skilful sculptor. Its two greater faces were marvellously well produced, and on both faces they are alike bevelled at the broad end to the beautiful curve shown in the drawing. It has a very antiquated look, since all its facets are pitted with the cavities of dissolved-out crystals ; it is of a basaltic rock, and with the other two immediately preceding was brought in from the depths of the Forth estuary by the

Fig. 362.

usual aid of seaweed. The specimen could, with a little trimming about the handle end, be now polished into a refined and typical Neolithic hatchet. Yet I believe it to be, with the rest of the Scottish and the English forms, purely Palæolithic. This only shows what we have seen in other forms, viz. that the Scottish elaborator, freed from the intractability and limitations of the flint nodules, produced finer forms with bolder, freer work.

CHAPTER XIX

Neolithic Forms in Palæolithic Times (*continued*)

In the preceding chapter our review of suggestive Palæo-Neolithic forms took us through so enormous a period (or periods) of time that it is impossible to take Neolithic man back into such remote epochs, or indeed much beyond the ill-defined closing section of the Stone Ages. So far as my own feeling goes, all the relics reviewed are Palæolithic; but inasmuch as the more I know of these relics and of their occurrence the more convinced I become that there is no possible divisional line between the times of Palæolithic and Neolithic man, and that, therefore, I cannot dogmatise in such connection, I leave it an open question. All that I am sure of is that forms which we have hitherto associated solely with Neolithic man are the common property of Palæolithic man through long ages, and that in the ultimate stages of those primitive times such forms gradually assumed a refined and polished aspect. I may have seemed to rush through the preceding chapter, but my aim was to point briefly to the one striking feature of our present argument.

In attempting so much I have doubtless, beyond mere assertion, demonstrated very little. As how could it be otherwise with a few pages of printed matter, a few illustrations at my disposal on the one hand, and a well-nigh limitless history of humanity on the other? I could but hope to give an idea which should be supported by certain data from actual relics, whose existence and character are conveyed in the illustrations.

If we turn to Figs. 363 to 369 inclusive, we have forms which, when scattered among countless stones upon a sea or estuary shore, or in a river-bed, or among gravel or earths in a pit, or upon an outcropping exposure, would even by the trained observer be ignored as assumed natural forms. Many are of what I should call simpler forms than these illustrated, and would therefore be considered all the more natural; they are at times flaky and tabular, with right-angled sides and ends, which are so much like fragments of naturally broken-up rock that they attract no attention. And yet they are intentional productions, or natural productions which have been more or less modified to suit the hand of a human operator. Others have such gently flowing outline, *i.e.* are elongated ovals, especially when, as is frequently the case, they have been highly rolled by river or marine action or both, that one is apt to look upon them as carelessly as we look upon the chippings in a stone-mason's yard. Yet both the chippings from the mason's mallet and these simple, natural-looking forms are human work, or of human modification.

In the illustrations which I have given there is considerable

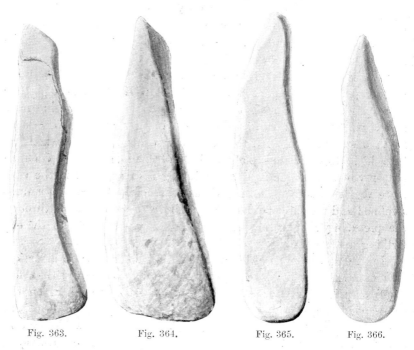

Fig. 363.   Fig. 364.   Fig. 365.   Fig. 366.

evidence of design and intention, a handle end and an operating end in every case: a bevelled edge generally, though by no means always, at the broad end; which edge may indicate a whilom knife, or flayer, or scraper, or chopper, or weapon. We can only guess as to their long-lost uses, though some of them, just as with other forms which we have studied, tell a tale of their actual use in their smoothed or abraded surfaces.

All the illustrations given (Figs. 363 to 369) are of Scottish relics, and the foregoing remarks refer to them alone; for a brief space further let us keep to them.

When these Scottish forms are collected and arranged, and certain features pointed out, the cumulative evidence of design is unassailable; many of the individual examples, when handled and studied, are evident enough in themselves to assert a human origin. Let us look at Figs. 370, 371, and 372. These have evidently been sculptured into their present form; of that there can be no doubt.

Fig. 368.

Fig. 367.   Fig. 369.

The first (Fig. 370) is a shore specimen of limestone. Fig. 371 is a Forth-shore specimen, and is formed from the ironstone-band. The last (Fig. 372) is from the bed of the Whitadder River near Duns, and is a semi-crystalline quartzite.

If we carefully study Figs. 373, 375, and 377, with their accompanying side views, we can have no hesitation in admitting them to be intentional forms. But the forms themselves are such that, when admission is made of their human fabrication, they are, and, I confess, naturally enough, declared to be Neolithic.

They are of so-called Neolithic form; but there is an entire absence of polishing, hence there is a standing question which is never answered, and "unfinished" states seem to be conditions of particular interest to some, simply because an *a priori* opinion has

Fig. 370.   Fig. 371.   Fig. 372.

decided that the relics *ought* to possess such and such attributes, and in not possessing them they fall short of an "orthodox" standard. A Neolithic implement of this type should be polished, that is the standard. If we recognise an unpolished one, many of us are so constrained in our mind that we can give no room for its possible earlier advent into being, *e.g.* in Palæolithic times, or for the possibility of the Neolithic man himself not always having polished them, and so we describe them as "unfinished" Neolithic axes. In my recent visit to the Dublin Museum (1907), I found a series of forms which are similar to these we are now considering (from Cushendall, Co. Antrim), and are described as "ready for grinding," *i.e.* for polishing. The polishing process was obviously a later

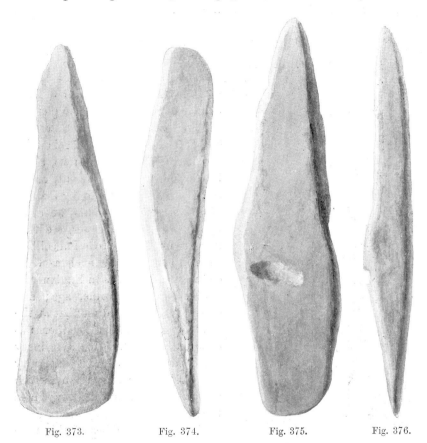

Fig. 373.   Fig. 374.   Fig. 375.   Fig. 376.

development, an æsthetic outcome of the secular use of such forms. This narrow conception of the typical Neolithic form is exactly on a par with that which only admitted the fine Somme-Valley weapon types as evidence of Palæolithic man. No man ever began his elaboration work with either the one or the other refined forms.

But let us look at our illustrations again, and particularly the last three; they are all highly suggestive of the Neolithic polished (narrower) chisel-like forms. Are they Neolithic? Some are certainly not; although of this particular form in Scotland the large majority might be of any age, seeing that they carry no evidence more definite than seashore or river-bed can give. There is, however, some indication of their greater antiquity than Neolithic times in the occurrence of Fig. 364, which was found in the Dalmuir deposit before referred to; of Fig. 365, which came from a high-lying and ancient river-bed at Dunblane; and of Fig. 373, which occurred in a similar deposit in the same place.

This question of whether they are Palæolithic or Neolithic need not here greatly concern us, since, if we follow our argument, as we are endeavouring to do, by a study of what has been found, we shall, before our chapter closes, see that they are more likely to be Palæolithic than Neolithic, inasmuch as their common equivalents in England are distinctly of the former age; and events have so aided me that at the last moment, and altogether unexpectedly, more extraordinary evidence of their great antiquity was yielded to me in Ireland, which evidence will form a striking finale to this work.

Fig. 377.   Fig. 378.

The Scottish relics of this type run through ever-varying changes, just as they run through an enormous space in time. Some are small—so small as to make one wonder what purpose they could have served. Some are large—large enough to have been murderous weapons, mounted or in the hand, clubs or choppers. Some are sharpedged at the broad end, with flat and squared or oval lines to the figure. Some are designedly so blunt and squared at the broad end, large and small alike, that it is a puzzle with myself for what purpose

they could have been designed, except perhaps (the larger) as clubs
or bone-crushers.

I have given several illustrations (see Figs. 379 to 382 inclusive);
the first three of these are large and well worthy of careful description : I could illustrate a whole volume with such examples alone, but
my space is well-nigh exhausted. They are all sharp-edged at the

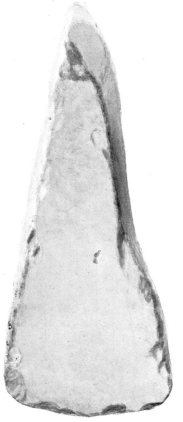

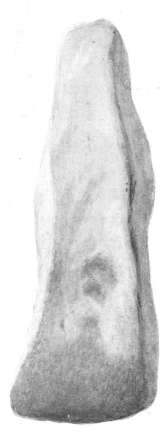

Fig. 379.   Fig. 380.

broad end, and speak clearly for themselves. The last of the four
(Fig. 382) shows the effect of decomposition, and also shows how
a core merely of an ancient implement may be, and sometimes is,
all that is left; the core is seen partly exposed—this last is of the
ironstone-band.

But if we take two such specimens as Figs. 383 and 384, we find
them clumsy and heavy in build and in the handling; nor had they

ever more than what one might call a flaying edge at the broad end.
Some are actually intentionally and cleverly squared at that end.   In
support of our argument of possible origins for such forms, let us
fall back upon a suggestive illustration.

I believe I have mentioned that, as a young man, I spent some
years in collecting, among other fossil forms, the osseous remains of
the great Reptilia or Sauridæ of the Upper Cretaceous rocks of East

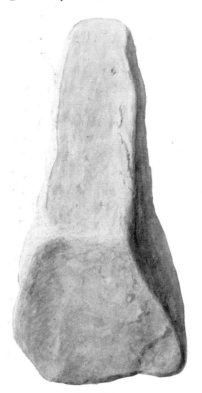
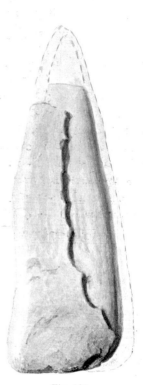

Fig. 381.   Fig. 382.

Anglia.   In collecting these Scottish human fabrications I have many
a time remarked to myself, "femur of Ichthyosaurus": "humerus
of Plesiosaurus"; or "*ulna*," or "*radius*," or "*phalange*," of this or
that now extinct animal.   These forms strongly reminded me of
them; and here my reader readily finds a crux.   "Oh, come now," he
says, "Palæolithic man did not borrow his forms from the Mesozoic
epoch!"   No, he did not!   But the ancient saurians have left
their relatives behind them, and these are with us to-day; and

I much the same types of bones are still about us, as they have
u ever been.

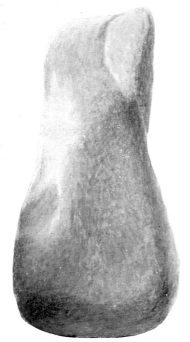

Fig. 383.   Fig. 384.

I turn to the note-book of my visit to the Dublin Museum and
find two or three highly interesting and suggestive drawings—Figs.

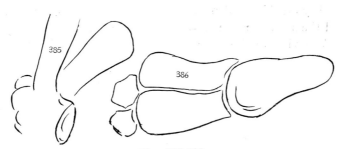

Figs. 385–386.

385 and 386. The latter of these represents the humerus, ulna,
and radius, etc., of a porpoise; the former certain natural processes
(projections) of the vertebræ of the bottlenose whale.

Just as in the Scottish forms, in these also there are many variations, such as we ought to expect; for these things neither represent a single generation of men nor a passing fashion in the form of implement; they represent untold generations, possibly successive peoples, and great physical changes in the areas of their occupation.

See Figs. 394 to 399, which are modifications of the same idea,

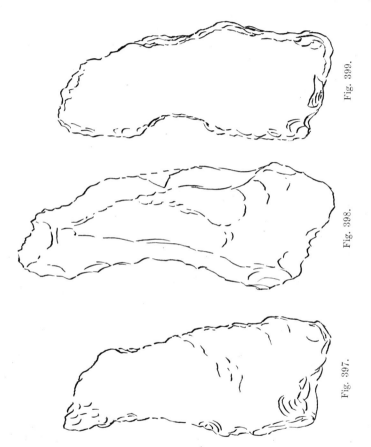

Fig. 399.

Fig. 398.

Fig. 397.

showing a handle and a broad operating end. The first of these is from the high-level gravels, Farnham, the two latter from the low-level pit at Mitcham.

But let us see whether the English gravels yield illustrations of the Scottish finds represented by Figs. 363 to 369, which may or may not have originated from the use of the vertebral processes, as in Fig. 385.

At first sight we should perhaps see no resemblance to possible bone precursors, or to the Scottish forms (Figs. 363 to 369) and others (English) which we have seen in Figs. 394 to 399. Indeed, we often see very little of the actual nature and attributes of anything "at first sight." As an illustration : when in 1883 I collected the specimens, Figs. 398 and 410, from the high-level gravels of Hildersham, Cambridgeshire (Sedgwick's "coarse gravel of the hills"), I did so because I conceived both to have been fabricated with a view to the point ends as possible spear-heads. Now, by the force of the cumulative evidence of the assumed points being more often than not quite pointless, by the often striking curve to right or left of the whilom presumed point end, by the often peculiar design of that end, and by the endless evidence of the intention, and the actually shown effects of the use of the broad end, they are indicated as not for use at the point—not weapons, but probably domestic implements. Having reached this result, we have but to allow for the now recognised intractability of the average flint nodule, to see in such Figs. as 397 to 399 replicas of such common Scottish examples as are given by way of general illustration in Figs. 363 to 369. Let us endeavour to put this in a clearer light. In Figs. 400 to 405 we have flint forms that are, as I conceive, due to design and intention, broad-ended implements perfectly comparable with these Scottish specimens. They have all been elaborated with considerable skill from larger masses of flint; yet their forms are so much more rugged and suggestive of accident than the Scottish items, that I am ready to admit that possibly without the aid of the more easily demonstrated Scottish series, I should not have recognised them as intentionally broad-ended forms. But here they are, and such forms are scattered through the gravels of the South, and only need the investigator to become a big and momentous chapter in that ancient man's history.

Let us examine these six individually. Fig. 400 is from a low-level pit at Ashe (Surrey). In section it gives a triangle, and was elaborated from a nodule, the underside being its exterior surface. Fig. 401 is a more interesting specimen. It is a tabular piece of flint, three-fourths of an inch in thickness, which was struck out of a larger mass, *i.e.* was intentionally made tabulate. It was carefully and elaborately squared at the sides, and the handle end is designedly chipped into a recognisable handle. Its broader operating end has been badly fretted, and the specimen is *distinctly glaciated*. It came from the high-level Colchester pit from which several other more than usually interesting elaborations were obtained; some of these were also glaciated. Fig. 402 is a Farnham specimen, which

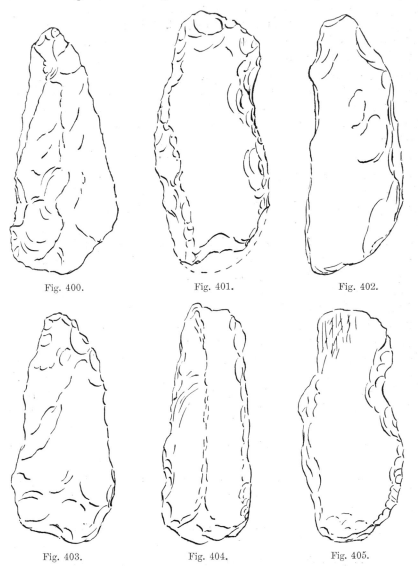

Fig. 400.   Fig. 401.   Fig. 402.

Fig. 403.   Fig. 404.   Fig. 405.

was also struck out from a mass much as the foregoing, but it is thinner and exhibits less elaboration. Fig. 403 is, so to put it, a purposely thinned flattish nodule. This upper side is altogether worked out, while the under is almost entirely the natural surface. Fig. 404 is decidedly a clever piece of work. The exterior of a cylindrical nodule was skilfully flaked away, leaving an implement of five almost smooth longitudinal facets, of which only one exhibits the original surface—a fine intention boldly carried out.

Fig. 405 is a section from a nodule, with a broadish back, formed by the original nodule's surface, reminding us of the previously studied side-edged *sections* with the pointed end and a handgrasp. But here is a definite handle and a broader end, though there is something like an edge opposed to the broad-backed side. This is the more interesting because the side shown, and particularly toward the broad end, is smoothed in the most marked manner; it seems almost to have been actually ground in some operation. The opposite facet, which is less flat, is not so smoothed. It is from the Mitcham low-level pits.

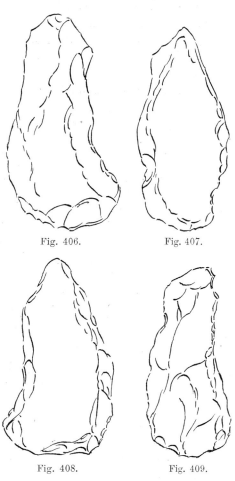

Fig. 406.   Fig. 407.

Fig. 408.   Fig. 409.

In Figs. 406 to 409 we have a continuance of the same forms, with such modifications as the flint nodules themselves impose. I need not dwell upon them. Fig. 406 is from low-lying gravel at Waterbeach, Cambridgeshire (1883); one is from Mitcham, and one from Croydon (1904). Fig. 408 was dredged from the bed of the Thames at Datchet (1904), and is otherwise interesting. It was cleverly produced from a nodule, the underside being a wholly and finely flaked surface; the upper, that shown, is mainly the natural surface, but it was skilfully elaborated all around the broad end and along the sides. From this point of view alone the specimen is interesting; its design and intention are striking; but additional interest lies in the fact of its being *distinctly and undoubtedly glaciated* upon the finely flaked under-surface. Its occurrence in the river-bed gives no clue to or suggestion of age, but of this aspect the glacial striation is a graphic and eloquent factor. It suggests even Eolithic times, for it is of a deep chocolate colour. Yet it is designed with a handle and a broad operating end : in a word, it was a distinct anticipation of Neolithic forms in some most remote era.

In Figs. 410 to 412 we have repetitions of the same forms. I

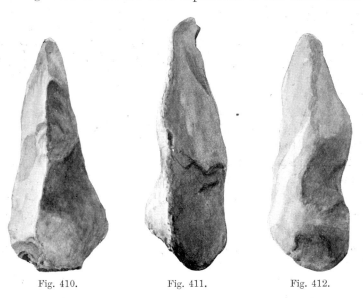

Fig. 410.   Fig. 411.   Fig. 412.

am trying to give my readers the force of cumulative evidence, but let us notice that while Figs. 410 and 412 might well be accepted as roughly produced javelin-heads, Fig. 411 could never have been designed for any such purpose. The nose-like termination of the point end, with the notch or catch, was a designed and intentionally elaborated handle, as experience has shown, the point ends of the others were also.

In Figs. 413 and 414 we have the true intention clearly before us. There can be no suggestion of a point being aimed at at the narrow end, but unquestionably a handle ; and the chisel-like broad ends are undoubtedly replicas of the broad-ended implements of Scotland, so far as the flints lent themselves to that form; and while they are of the Neolithic type, they are distinctly Palæolithic in their occurrence. Fig. 413 is from the low-level pits at Mitcham, Fig. 414 from high-level gravels at Croydon.

In Figs. 415 to 423 we have an interesting series of small examples, the longest of which is 3½ and the smaller about 2½ inches in length. All these, except the last two, are from the Palæolithic English gravels; the last two are rough outlines of specimens which I saw in the Dublin Museum; they are actually smaller than the English-gravel specimens. They are described as "adze-heads" from North America, and they are

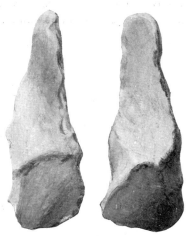

Fig. 413.   Fig. 414.

supposed to be comparatively recent. Whatever their age, it is deeply interesting to find counterparts of these small Palæolithic productions in America. I have always thought the term "adze-

Fig. 415.   Fig. 416.   Fig. 417.

heads" somewhat absurd for such things. It would be at least absurd to apply such a term to the similar forms from the ancient gravels of the British Isles, although I am unable to point to a definite purpose for their use.

We have so far missed what one might call heroic examples of this Palæo-Neo type, such as we have seen characterise the presumed

edge. The handle.end was, as I have said, snapped off, probably ages after its use. It was a clean break, the result, I imagine, of a downward pressure. It cannot have been broken in use, unless long afterward somebody happened to find and use it. This suggestion is not impossible, but it would be a pure assumption to assert this in order to get it broken. It is almost $1\frac{1}{2}$ inches through its thickest part, and the said fracture was produced by great force.

In Fig. 426 the loss of the handle-end occurred certainly long after the implement had been used, the use itself being clearly indicated. In my opinion the last two, although I can find no indication of glaciation upon them, are indicative of the crushing power of ice; I believe them to have passed through a glaciation. We shall, in the next chapter, see that this is more than a possibility.

And now comes the one regret of my Surrey investigation of the year 1907. It is this—I actually found a perfect specimen of this type, and of heroic size, in a pit which the workmen called the "Six Bells" pit, at Farnham. I found it at the end of a long day. I had been to the higher-level pits on the south side of Farnham, and then to the north-east side to this "Six Bells" site. I was tired, and this last find being large, I felt that I could not add it to what I had already to carry; so I did what I had often done before, left it for another day's visit. The next visit was three days after; when lo! the whole of a great gravel heap had been carted away, and the specimen was gone. That is my one regret. It was not far short of a foot in length, and so far as my memory serves me —and its form was deeply impressed on my mind—Fig. 427 will convey a fairly correct idea of it. Our next chapter will make it evident that such examples ought to be expected in the Palæolithic gravels.

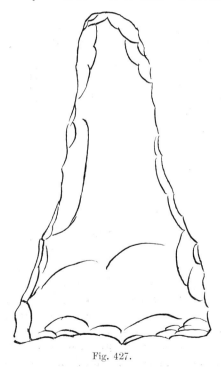

Fig. 427.

Nothing could be more striking than the fact of the common occurrence of these forms, practically the whole world over, *i.e.* not of the æsthetically shaped and polished, but of less æsthetic forms without the polishing, which suggests the use of such items through undreamed-of ages. A world-wide appreciation of the same style and form must mean their use through an illimitable period of time, an assumption which is verified by their *occurrence* in the British Isles.

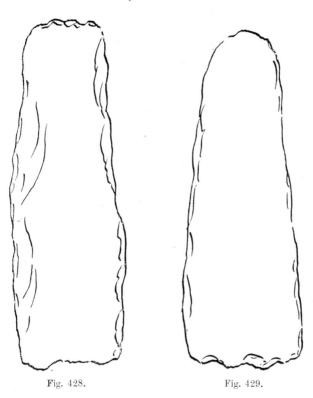

Fig. 428.   Fig. 429.

I made rough drawings in the Museum, Dublin, of three such specimens, of excellent form and workmanship, from Sweden, all formed from chert and unpolished. They are, of course, described as Neolithic. Two are shown in Figs. 428 and 429. I made also rough outline sketches of two from India, which are actual counterparts of the roughly made Scottish Palæo-Neo forms, and of, as we shall see, Irish forms, which, so far from being Neolithic, are unquestionably of glacial, *i.e.* of inter- or pre-glacial age. I have considered similar Scottish items to be of Palæolithic origin, any doubt on this head of their possible age being dispelled by the evidence from Hibernia.

The Indian specimens which I have reproduced (Figs. 430 and 431) are described as Neolithic; I do not contradict this, but they are of the roughest possible kind of work, and are not polished; their truest representatives in the British Isles can be traced directly into

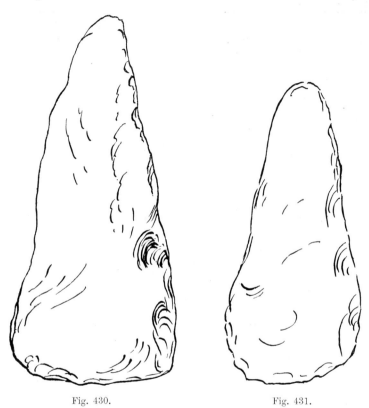

Fig. 430.   Fig. 431.

the glacial deposits. Under our present ideas about Palæolithic and Neolithic man, we naturally infer that all objects of this particular form are of Neolithic age. A greater misapprehension never existed.

Of these two Indian specimens, the first (Fig. 430) is about 9 inches in length and about 4 inches across its broad end. It is of a basaltic rock. The second, which is smaller, 6 inches in length, is of a more flaky rock, and is a replica of the more flaky objects from the bed of the Shannon before referred to.

I also made outline sketches in the Dublin Museum of New

Zealand examples, which are identical in form and style with many Scottish specimens, and, so far as I have seen, with Irish also; as they certainly are, too, with forms from the Palæolithic (flint) gravels of England.

These New Zealand specimens (Figs. 432 and 433) are large, one

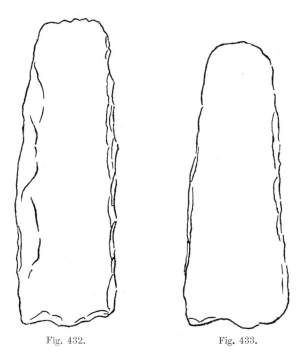

Fig. 432.   Fig. 433.

being a foot in length and the other 11 inches. They are roughly made and unpolished; and, being from that part of the world, may not only be Neolithic, but recent—the question is not material. They show the universality of this form, and are also another illustration of the anomalous fact of our ready acceptance of such implements from foreign lands, while we are unwilling to accept them as of human fabrication when found at home.

CHAPTER XX

Glacial Man in Hibernia

THERE may be little matter for a chapter on "Snakes in Ireland," but there is certainly matter for an almost endless chapter on Palæolithic man in Ireland, notwithstanding the general opinion that that ancient man never lived in that country.

I have been in Erin on four different occasions during the past nine years. On my first visit in 1899 I was, from what I saw, led to believe that there was in that country evidence of Palæolithic times; that there was such evidence as I had found in Scotland. I had the privilege of staying some few days with the well-known investigator into the history of ancient man, Mr. W. J. Knowles, at Ballymena, and I then saw that along the shore (from the Giant's Causeway to Portrush) flint elaborations of identical form and aspect with certain flints which I had found along the Ayrshire coast, and considered to be of Palæolithic origin, were washed in from the present floor of the Atlantic. On that occasion I neither found nor saw anything further corroborative of the Scottish finds.

In 1901 I was in the west of Ireland for several days at Ballysodare, Sligo, when, although my business there did not give scope for investigation, I obtained several examples that perfectly reflected the presumed Palæolithic character of the Scottish forms, and from that time I had longed for an opportunity to make further investigation in that country, but had given up all hope of the fulfilment of that desire, when circumstances paved the way for a visit. But that visit was attended by such remarkable and unlooked-for results, that it became memorable in connection with the whole subject of the present volume.

If I had desired, at the hands of Nature, the strongest proof of the correctness of my views concerning the vast antiquity of the Scottish forms and of their counterparts from the English deposits, I could not have anticipated anything more convincing than what lay before me on landing in the neighbourhood of Dublin. Within a few hours of my arrival I had discovered my opportunity, and for the greater part of a fortnight, in sunshine and rain alike, I spent most of my time in this quest. And, on my return North from Surrey, I secured several days further in the same neighbourhood.

Let me briefly point out the essence of the whole argument. Dublin is in part built upon a deposit of boulder-clay. That is the technical term, but it is there far from being a clay-deposit. While clays occur in it, it is much more a deposit of coarse gravels and sands and silts, which have largely disappeared in the area of the city itself, doubtless through the denuding agency of the Liffey for unknown ages. The deposit, however, is very pronounced in places, as on the north side of the tramway route between Sutton and Howth, and it was there that I first observed it.

I was on my way to Howth, but stopped short at Sutton, where, in a gravel-pit—a recent redeposition of the material of the said boulder-clay deposit—I found several very interesting relics; and along the shore at Sutton, among stones which, as I now believe, were also mainly derived from the same glacial gravels and sands, I found what were to me startling copies of the typical Scottish forms. But for the fact of a visit to Killiney Bay having been planned by my hostess the next day, I should probably have devoted my whole time to the deposit at Sutton, extended to Howth.

But Killiney Bay, south of and just outside Dublin Bay, offered such attractions that, had my visit extended to two months instead of two weeks, I should probably have spent the whole time and made the longest possible days in that delightful stretch of shore; and then I should have left undone much that could still be done in the matter of my quest.

A magnificent feature of that spot is the outcrop of grey granite which forms a sort of natural fortress at the south-eastern termination of Dublin Bay. Around to the south of this headland begins Killiney Bay, whose imposing sweep ends in another headland miles away, and this southern view is ennobled by two distant Etna-like peaks.

But a fine feature of the bay is the reappearance of the glacial deposit in the form of a cliff, which in places approaches 100 feet in height, and extends for several miles along the shore. At the north end this glacial deposit abuts, augmented in thickness, and folded and crumpled in the grandest manner, against the granite outcrop.

I approached the bay from the Dublin (the north) end, and had not been exploring a great while before I came upon one of our discussed "hall-marks"—one of the rubbing-stones (Fig. 436). On that same day my daughter, who knew as well what to look for as I myself, found what I have no doubt is a Palæolithic weapon

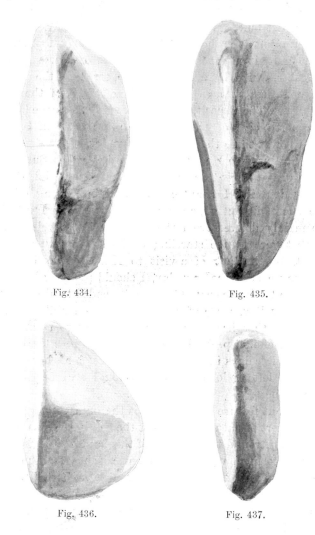

Fig. 434.   Fig. 435.

Fig. 436.   Fig. 437.

(Figs. 438 and 439). It is of quartzite, with quartz veins, and is in excellent condition, though highly rolled. It is of a common Somme-Valley type; and to recognise it the better, we have only to imagine it to have been formed from flint, and then in place of smooth facets, edges and angles and lines would, even though it had been equally rolled, have now indicated the original work. But I presume that we have learned our lesson by this time, and do not expect features that such an elaboration never possessed, or if it possessed, could not retain, and can recognise an object other than flint in its general form, and the expression of intention in its whole aspect. I am under the impression that this is the first Palæolithic weapon which has been recognised as such from Ireland. But whether such is the case, and the reader accepts this as an implement or no, it aroused my interest in the possibilities of Killiney Bay, and from that moment every possible hour was spent in the quest there.

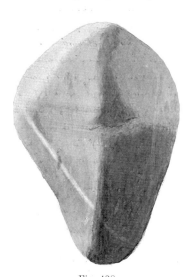 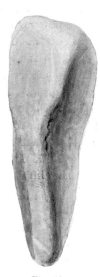

Fig. 438.   Fig. 439.

I discovered as I proceeded southward that the stones, which were sparsely scattered in the sand at the north end of the bay, increased in numbers; and then the fine cliff was reached, but darkness drove us, and the last train took us, hurriedly away.

Next morning I was down again early—this time landing from Killiney station, which brought me immediately to the finest portion of the cliff of the glacial deposit, where it rises to its highest, and the folding and crumpling is most conspicuous.

At the base of this cliff, i.e. beneath 70 or 80 feet of glacial deposit, I extracted from it several elaborations which, if those found on the previous day were of interest, were profoundly so. One was a well-fabricated rubbing-stone, with a fine "flat-iron" facet, which had been excellently shaped for the hand, and which is glaciated (Fig. 434). Another was a finely formed spear-head—I can give it no other name—which I had some difficulty in extracting from the matrix of that part of the cliff. In places the gravel and sands form unyielding masses of natural concrete; and this relic still retains some of the matrix firmly attached to it, the cement being a highly crystalline lime. A spear-tip from such a position is a surprise, but here it is. I have not made a drawing of it; had I not extracted it from the cliff myself I should have doubted its origin. I have, however, found excellent spear-points of identical form among the Scottish things and in the English gravels, but I have no space now for their discussion.

The whole of this day was devoted to the cliff—a risky proceeding, as seemed to me, since portions of the more yielding beds are always ready to fall, and the concrete-like beds break away in time by their own weight. Another find was at least equally interesting, and that was the broad end of one of the characteristic and cleverly wrought Palæo-Neo forms which were discussed in the last chapter. It is an almost exact duplicate of the cleverly elaborated flint from Farnham (Fig. 425). This broad end was inserted in a concrete portion of the cliff, its narrower broken end projecting from the matrix, as it was left exposed on a former fall of a mass. It was with difficulty released, and not without further damage; Fig. 441 is a drawing of it, in which I have tentatively suggested a restoration of the portion which was lost.

I have not space to dwell particularly upon every find, but I may remark that all these mentioned as coming directly from the cliff were already water-worn to an appreciable extent, showing that their origin goes farther back than the actual formation and crumpling of the cliff-deposit, which means that they are inter- or possibly pre-glacial. It was a profoundly impressive discovery, which ought to be carefully discussed; but we must now be satisfied with a general exhibition of finds and a summing-up of the whole result of that piece of work—of what I found actually in the cliff, and of what was found along the shore. The result seems to me to be almost indescribably far reaching; but let us proceed with our study in its whole aspect.

It must be realised by my reader that I approached that fine (Dublin) vantage-ground with forty years' experience in the field as my guide. What were to be found, if the things were there, I knew by heart. I had but to go and pick out, or pick up, what I had spent thirty-six years in Scotland in learning the meaning of. The things *were* there, and being there, I could no more miss seeing them than I could miss seeing the stars when the night sky is clear. In a sense, these stones are stars in the long dark night of man's origin and ascent in time.

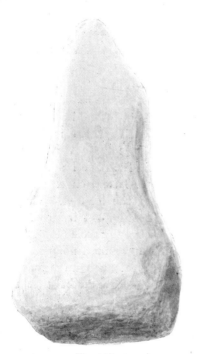

Fig. 440.   Fig. 441.

Let us see what the cliff actually yielded, for that gives us some index to the possible origin of the stones along the shore.

Three rubbing-stones, skin-curers, or whatever we may call them, were taken out of the matrix of the cliff. All three are of excellent form, with finely smoothed operating facets; which, placed among my Scottish series, would be indistinguishable in their typical features from them. They are all glaciated, two demonstrably so, the other —the largest—more slightly; but having come directly from the glacial deposit we recognise, and admit, the import of its striæ (Figs. 434, 435, and 437).

Alongside the tentatively restored broad-ended Palæo-Neo form is another from the actual cliff of the same type, but of rougher, less clever fabrication. Its broad end was this time projecting from the matrix, and I had not much difficulty in extracting it, for here the material was a friable silt. It is perfect, except that a fragment was broken from the side not shown, as is seen from the left lower corner in the drawing, by doubtless the last fall at that spot. It is a duplicate of many of the Scottish finds; and, as we must see for ourselves, these two (Figs. 440 and 441) are replicas exactly of the broken broad end from Farnham (Fig. 425). These have the same truncated broad end, which makes it a question as to their use. They may have been simply clubs, bone-breakers or otherwise, we cannot tell. It was just such objects as these which in Scotland reminded me of the femur and humerus of the ancient Saurians.

To many the four drawings (Figs. 442 to 445) would convey little expression of intention in their forms. But there is in all a deliberately intended handle. Three of the four are varying types of " flayers," such as we have already studied from Scotland, with the broad backs and an opposing operative lower lateral edge. The two upper have, as is seen, been fretted under the ice-foot. They all came from a more friable part of the cliff. Fig. 444 is, in size and style, so like those of the group from the Surrey gravels (Figs. 390 to 393) that had it been of flint there would have been no perceptible difference between them. This I consider as much an intentional production as the Surrey finds; and none can doubt that they are such.

All these last, and I think all the cliff stones, are water-worn, but to much less extent than the stones on the shore of to-day. They (the cliff stones) indicate, I believe, not marine, but river action. None of these last four show glacial striæ, which is possibly accounted for by their occurrence in a fine silty portion of the cliff. Stones from the coarser and concrete beds are more often striated.

But the most extraordinary of all the finds in the neighbourhood of Dublin remains to be noted, and that is, as I conceive it, one of the best examples of Palæolithic weapons that I have ever found. It is almost perfect in form, except for some presumable ice-fretting on one of its lateral edges, and the point is gone, probably by the same agency; it is also river-rolled. It is comparable with the

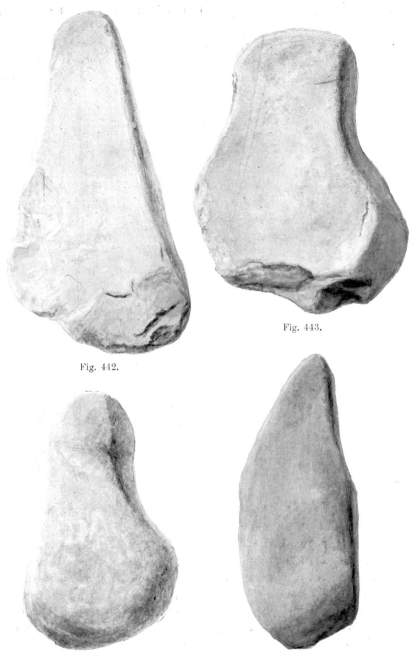

Fig. 442.

Fig. 443.

Fig. 444.

Fig. 445.

best of the Scottish haches, and brings to mind the better of the
fragmentary, highly glaciated specimens from the boulder-clay of the
Crieff railway cutting (1892). It is of the finest Somme-Valley type,

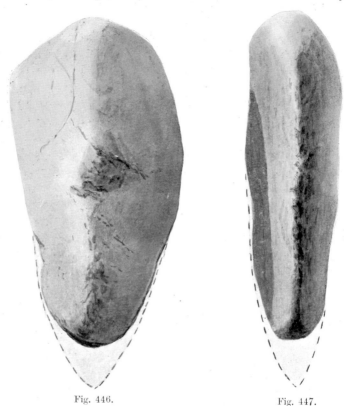

Fig. 446.   Fig. 447.

and were it of flint, would be an unusually excellent specimen (Figs.
446 and 447).

It is also an *in situ cliff specimen*. I had examined every
accessible foot of the cliff's face along the whole length of the bay
more than once, and had seen nothing like a typical hache when, as
a last extension of the opportunity, I followed exposures in a road
that has been cut through a low part of the cliff, a hundred yards or
so south of the little river whose mouth is in the centre of the bay.
Here I was somewhat puzzled by the fact that in the said road the
cliff had been dug into—for sand probably; I was only puzzled that
it should be so, when so much excellent shore sand lay within 50 feet
of the excavations. The material had been dug out from a depth of

about 4 feet below the level of the road—apparently to avoid the upper silts and to find better sand. In any case, the stones had been sifted from the excavated material and thrown up in heaps. This specimen occurred upon a heap that so overhung the larger excavation that as I touched the stones some fell into the pit whence they came. It is undoubtedly a cliff specimen, and is formed of the local granite. I have found various relics of granite in the Forth area, and one or two granite haches at Aberdeen. This one is now just under 7 inches in length, originally probably about 8 inches, and $3\frac{3}{4}$ inches at its widest. Its material would hardly allow it to show striæ unless they were actual grooves; it shows none. It was water-worn before it found its long repose in that glacial cliff. It was as unexpected a find as it is a treasure from that time-worn deposit, whose story of primitive man is yet to be opened page by page.

I have for many years been of opinion that the finest of all the Palæolithic weapons, whether of the Somme Valley or elsewhere, are of inter- or pre-glacial origin. The occurrence, therefore, of a finely formed Palæolithic hache in the Killiney Bay cliff was not in itself a surprise; the surprise lay in the fact of such typical forms not having been recognised before in Ireland. But that is only on a par with their wholly unrecognised presence in Scotland; and it were a miracle if they could be found commonly in South and North Britain as they have been, and not in Ireland. From what I have already seen, it is more than probable that Palæolithic man is as graphically represented in Hibernia as in any part of the world. Now for the shore items:—

That the stones along the shore near Dublin should be an epitome of the general finds of thirty-six years' investigation in Scotland was an *a priori* assumption; but I should not have deemed such an occurrence probable, nor should I have dared to anticipate such possibility in so restricted an area; that would have savoured of rashness and presumption. That the shores of Dublin and Killiney Bays do offer such epitome of the results of the prolonged Scottish search, and indeed of the results of the whole forty-odd years' work, is so clearly demonstrated that I presume the reader will see the fact for himself—not in my statements, but in the illustrations which accompany them.

While it is a matter of profound congratulation to myself that it is so, and that I was so fortunate as to be led to the spot as the closing words of this volume were being written, to see for myself how graphic the Dublin writing in this matter is, the very incident

certainly owe their origin in their present position to the denudation of the said glacial deposit. Some, a small proportion of them, are glaciated, as a much greater proportion may have been before they became so shore-worn. The glaciated specimens are of necessity from the boulder-clay deposit.

If we examine the group, Figs. 448 to 451, all from the shore of Killiney Bay, we have on the whole not a bad reflection of the group, Figs. 442 to 445, of the cliff examples. Three of the four are identical in material—a compact limestone—with those direct from the cliff deposit. The same stone was largely used in the fabrications of Scotland—particularly in the Forth area. They all have the same designed handle, and the same broad operative end or lateral edge. They are, as is natural, more rolled than the cliff specimens, but not to an extent sufficient to obliterate evidence of their elaboration; that is still quite clear. Fig. 449 is highly glaciated upon both of its broad facets, and is fretted to some extent along its thinner lateral edge. The two lower specimens have both lost part of their handle ends.

These two groups have, as is evident, a general resemblance to each other; Fig. 449 is, in design, distinctly a replica of Fig. 443, its main difference being that it is smaller. As this is glaciated and its counterpart was found actually in the cliff, they both doubtless claim that as their resting-place for many decades of thousands of years. The design of Figs. 450 and 444 is the same, though of somewhat differing build. A fragment of the handle end of Fig. 450 is gone. There is at least as much design in this shore group as in the cliff-obtained group; the cliff specimens are, however, the more striking, mainly because they are less water-worn, and such elaboration as they received is therefore more expressive of intention.

The very roundness of the group of six (Figs. 452 to 457) gives them, as seen upon the shore and scattered among other stones, a most natural and accidental look. Little evidence of elaboration remains, nothing in fact but the intention in form which the cumulative evidence of the designed handle end gives, and their broad operative end, continuously repeated, confirms. They are thus seen to be replicas of a multitude of the Scottish finds, and of the series which still shows all the original elaboration from the flint gravels of England. Fig. 453 is, let us note, a damaged and highly rolled replica of the two (Figs. 440 and 441) from the glacial deposit. If we take the three lower specimens of this group (Figs. 455 to 457) we have actually the general forms of the commoner Neolithic polished specimens. With

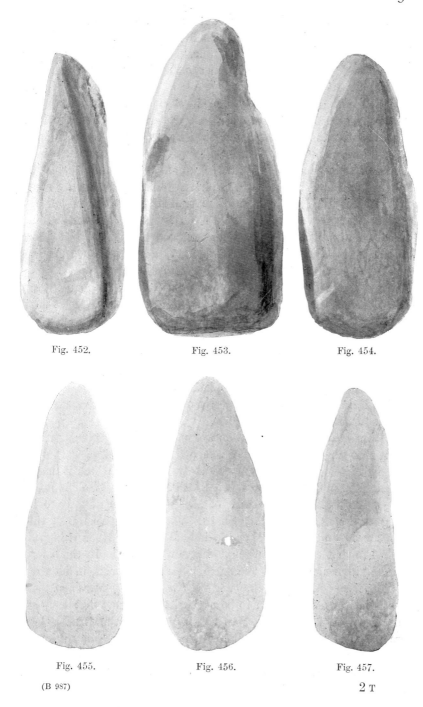

Fig. 452.   Fig. 453.   Fig. 454.

Fig. 455.   Fig. 456.   Fig. 457.

this in mind, I was greatly interested in a large series of perfectly identical forms in the Dublin Museum (before referred to), mainly of a porphyritic rock and lydian stone, which was collected as far back as 1843 to 1848, during the deepening of the river Shannon above Killaloe at that time.

This series embraces, *with* polished examples, a great many just such as the three of this group. Some are even much more flaky and natural-looking. How came they so long ago to have been recognised as human work, while similar specimens are to-day spurned under our feet as "natural" forms ? The answer is found in the fact of the polished and unpolished alike having been found in the river-bed together. The polished passed so gradually into the unpolished that there was no drawing the line between the two series, and so the sensible collector of that date accepted them all. And there they are still—a most interesting group, described of course as Neolithic, as justified by the polished specimens.

Now, while I do not wish to assert that Neolithic man always polished his weapons, which he probably did not, I consider it more than probable that many of the unpolished, flaky, slate-like examples of the said collection are of Palæolithic and possibly of glacial origin ; that they are the counterparts of those of the English gravels, and of the Scottish finds. I cannot, of course, prove this ; but the river— the Shannon—has no respect for polished or unpolished, for Neolithic or Palæolithic forms ; but irrespective of all age and circumstance, gathers and mixes them all together.

Another exhibit in that Museum shows certain specimens which indicate that they were rolled, river-carried, or wave-tossed Palæoliths before the Neolithic man attempted their polishing, which is merely an illustration of how history repeats itself. He, the Neolithic man, finding these highly rolled stones of the proper form already to his hand, gave the transforming touch to Palæolithic man's work ; they are thus verily and indeed Palæo-Neolithic weapons. Such things are described in that exhibit as "adapted natural forms." In the before-discussed "Shannon" group the same unpolished forms, in identical condition, were collected *as designed implements sixty years ago*.

Let whoever asserts them to be natural forms show that they are such. Let him find and show to us a spot in all the British Isles where porphyritic rocks, or lydian stone, or limestone, or quartzite, or any other rocks are deliberately breaking themselves up into these forms, and the whole scientific world will be indebted to him.

I have never found such a spot. I have never even seen a specimen that would be classed with these, that could be said to have received its form in recent times. Rolling by river or by sea does not make them natural forms, and such rolling and tossing certainly never produces them. They are not, and never were, natural forms; although even Neolithic man, who may have hunted along whilom shores of Killiney Bays for conveniently formed specimens, " ready for the grinding "! doubtless also imagined them to have been natural forms. We can scarcely conceive him to have been wiser than ourselves of the twentieth century A.D.

I may be pardoned for giving here a further Museum illustration in the matter of our quest, which shows, as I have already pointed out, that we often have an eye for things from abroad, while we fail to notice the existence of the same things at home, though they may be common enough.

The line-drawing (Fig. 458) is a sketchy copy of actual specimens in

Fig. 458.

the Dublin Museum, a " domestic " group from, I believe, Australasia. It comprises a large oval-shaped slab of sandstone trimmed into shape, with two mullers, or rubbing or grinding stones, lying upon it. One of these mullers or grinders was a highly rolled pebble, just as it had been picked up as suitable for the purpose; one of its facets is ground appreciably by use. The other may or may not be a split pebble—it may have been elaborated into its present form. I had such limited time at my disposal that my notes are of the scantiest. But this stone has a finely smoothed or ground underside. I have given a side view of it, and the two mullers are a modern instance of the use of just such relics as are conspicuously evidential of man through an enormous period of time, as such time is represented by boulder-clays in many parts of Scotland, and glacial and post-glacial deposits in the ancient gravels of England, and now in the boulder-clays of Ireland. They are ubiquitous in all the Pleistocene as well as in some more recent deposits. And they are just as evidently intentionally adapted, or altered, or wholly elaborated objects as are these Australasian modern instances, and they often equally exhibit the effects of industry. It is in my view one of the curiosities of science and of investigation, that we have been blind to what is so evident

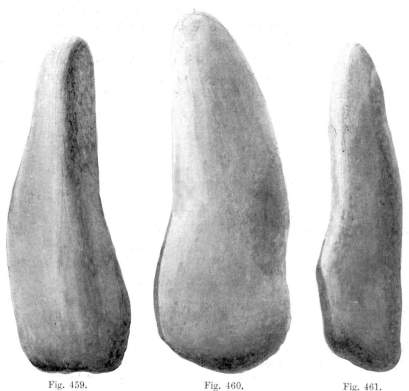

Fig. 459.   Fig. 460.   Fig. 461.

all around us. The slab of the above outline drawing is about 2 feet in length.

In Dr. A. H. Keane's work, *The World's Peoples*, p. 128, is an illustration of a group of Zulus (Natal) "grinding corn." One of the figures is using a flattish muller or grinder upon a thick heavy slab of stone. Such a comparatively refined people as the Zulus are still using a mode common in pre-glacial times,—whatever the use of the grinders the mode is the same.

In studying such a group as Figs. 459 to 461 we have to recognise

what the objects were, rather than what they now are. There is still
the original intention and design in each specimen—the handle and
the broad operative end; but all evidence of elaboration, all distinct
facets, all lines and edges, are lost in their highly rounded surfaces.
They are shore specimens (Killiney Bay), marine-rolled; and they

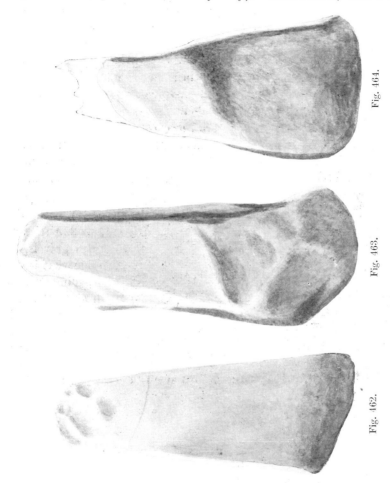

Fig. 464.

Fig. 463.

Fig. 462.

may or may not have come from the glacial cliff deposit. As a
convenient term I should denominate them "flayers"—they may
have been used in ways which we can never realise.

In Figs. 462 to 464, also from the shore, the two former from
Killiney Bay, the last from Sutton, we still see the actual elaboration.
These are more in the condition of the stones as they leave the great

but not sufficiently to hide the evidence that the whole thing was very skilfully elaborated from a parent mass. It is of limestone, a rock from which fine specimens from the Forth estuary are formed. It is 11 inches in length, and is from the shore, Killiney Bay. The drawing sufficiently illustrates it.

Fig. 470 is a chopper of a different type; I have several identical with it from Scotland. The blade ends of this type are often massive, yet of good form, as in this case; they are almost always minus the handle, the whilom presence of which is generally indicated by a conspicuous break of more recent aspect than the general surface of the implement. This specimen, which is an excellent one, shows clearly that it once possessed a well-defined, cleverly devised handle.

It is, as appears to me, perfectly natural that these heavy-bladed, slender-handled choppers should have come down to us mainly as blades only. The drawing, with the suggested handle, gives us an idea of what the form was; and if we realise that the broad back of this "blade" is from 2 to 2½ inches through, though the opposing edge is still appreciably chopper-like, we shall understand how liable handle and blade were to part company. This is from the shore at Sutton. It is not greatly rolled; but it is honeycombed with age upon the surface, and is bleached—a bleached limestone. Some of the Scottish examples exhibit a similarly bleached condition.

I am anxious to trace these chopper forms to the boulder-clays, whence, I believe, many have come. I have, without actually finding good *in situ* specimens, seen sufficient to warrant my belief in their origin at least in part in such glacial deposits. Their counterparts unquestionably occur among the Palæolithic gravels of England, and I now have before me a highly glaciated blade end, or what I take to be such, of a chopper form of the same type as this last, which I extracted from a "concrete" portion of the Killiney Bay cliff. It is roughly fretted, especially along the thick "back," and the handle is no more. The chopping edge is fairly intact. Fragments of the natural cement are still adhering to it. While it is not a typical specimen, it is, to myself, a highly interesting and suggestive one.

And the fan-shaped, scapula-like forms are also to be found along the shore. I found one of unusually excellent attributes. It is of fine form and perfect, except that it is slightly rolled. I have items like it in general expression from Scotland. It is of the same type as the fine glaciated specimen which Mr. M. B. Cotsworth found in the boulder-clay of the Yorkshire coast. The flint find which I so deeply regret having lost in the recent hunt at Farnham was of the same type. This particular specimen (Fig. 471) has a deflected handle, —in the drawing the handle end is turned upward. It is at least interesting to find that the scapula of the reindeer has a markedly truncated broad end identical in aspect with this implement in stone. The articulated end of the scapula has the lateral expansion which

Fig. 471.

could in stone be more easily imitated by such deflection in the handle.

It is at least interesting as a possible parallel in bone implements and actual stone fabrications. If these forms were weapons, they were actually double-pointed axes, the points, the angles of the broad end, being both the equivalents of a pointed axe. It was as a hand weapon a highly effective one. The broad edge could have been used as a chopper, but as there was seldom in these forms a lateral edge it

was for such purpose not the most effective contrivance. This is of
a green-stone, and may be a coarse variety of lydian stone. It is well-
nigh startling to find that in the Yorkshire glaciated specimen (Fig.
308), in this Dublin shore example, and others in my collection, we
have actual precursors in form of the infinitely more recent bronze
hatchets.

The last elaboration which the shore presented to my hunting is
shown in Figs. 472 and 473. It is, I think, a highly interesting specimen from this point of view, viz. that it shows us what we ought to
look for when Palæolithic man's weapons were formed of other material
than flint. It is of quartzite, which is permeated with innumerable

Fig. 472.　　　　　　　　　　　Fig. 473.

quartz veins, which veins, while the general matrix of the stone has
yielded more freely to the marine attrition, have shown greater
resistance and now stand out above the general surface. I have no
doubt that it was a well-formed Palæolithic hache. If we have the
power to picture a point upon the same, and to fill in certain present
irregularities in its surface—all distinct facets have disappeared in
its rounded condition—we shall have an excellent specimen of a
common Somme type. But I grant that upon any seashore in its
present condition, it would never have struck even myself as anything
but a natural form save for long experience and much corroborative
and illuminative evidence. But this shows us what we ought to

expect. A stone, though an actual weapon, will weather exactly as any other (natural) fragment.

I imagine the contents of the great glacial deposit under and around Dublin to represent pre-glacial river accumulations, river-"drifts" or delta-deposits, which the ice-foot simply gathered and mixed together and crushed up, introducing some of its ice-borne material in the process, while the deposit itself finally became a *moraine profonde* as the ponderous ice crept upon and overwhelmed it.

APPENDIX TO CHAPTER XX

"Survivals from the Palæolithic Age among Irish Neolithic Implements"

I was anxious to find the monograph with the above heading before the completion of the chapter upon "Glacial Man in Hibernia," since it was impossible to ignore such a paper, Dr. A. H. Keane having directed my attention to it. But I failed to find it till I applied to the author, Mr. W. J. Knowles, Ballymena, too late for notice in the said chapter. The monograph occurs in the *Trans. Royal Society Antiquaries, Ireland,* vol. for 1897, p. 1.

Mr. Knowles's paper is most interesting, the gist of which is that he arrives at the conclusion that there was no hiatus or great gap to break the continuity of Palæolithic into Neolithic man, notwithstanding the faith in the hiatus of such men as Mr. Boyd Dawkins, Sir John Evans, Sir H. H. Howarth, Dr. James Geikie, Sir Charles Lyell, and many others. This is the conclusion to which I have arrived, from data quite different from those upon which Mr. Knowles bases his conclusion. While he sees survivals of Palæolithic times in what he believes to be Neolithic productions, I show that the typical Neolithic forms, *i.e.* their more barbarous precursors, were in use long ages before Neolithic man appeared upon the scene. I trace these precursors of the characteristic (polished) Neolithic forms even into undoubted glacial deposits.

I was pleased to find Mr. Knowles in agreement with myself as to the vetoing of the assumed hiatus. But a study of Mr. Knowles's paper, and particularly of its accompanying illustrations, shows in my opinion that his whole argument is based upon an unwarranted assumption, viz. that all stone relics in Ireland are Neolithic, *i.e.* that no Palæolithic relics occur in Ireland. In my view his illustrations are (mainly) of actual Palæolithic productions.

While I admit that if there were no break in the continuity of the ancient man, Palæolithic weapon forms probably did survive into Neolithic times, but why should forms in Ireland, which correspond with "those of the cave-dwellers in the south of France of Palæolithic age," not equally be of Palæolithic age? If those of the "Moustier type" or of the "Solutrien type" are Palæolithic on the Continent, why are they of a more recent age when found in Ireland? If these forms occurred in undoubted association with polished forms and pottery, there would be justification for styling them Neolithic, but there is no suggestion of this. They have been found erratically scattered about the country, as at "the banks of the river Bann," "at Clough, Co. Antrim." One find certainly has a Neolithic aspect in its reported occurrence, viz. "in a bog" near Ballymena. But the *occurrence* of purchased specimens is often doubtful.

Figs. 3, 4, and 5, Pl. I. of Mr. Knowles's monograph, are of the general aspect of Palæolithic weapons from the flint gravels of England, and with the exception that the Scottish finds are not of flint, they are of the general aspect of what I consider to be Palæolithic weapons from Scotland. But Fig. 3 is of basalt, a rock of which many of the Scottish specimens are formed. Palæolithic forms were many and various, as they were bound to be, seeing that they range over so enormous a period of time, and possibly through succeeding peoples, who were still all Palæolithic.

It may be urged that if I object to "survivals" of Palæolithic times (*i.e.* Palæolithic *weapon* forms) occurring in the Neolithic age, it is equally legitimate for objections to be raised against the occurrence of Neolithic forms in Palæolithic times. May it clearly be understood that I do not deny even the probability of Palæolithic forms surviving into Neolithic times. My argument is that they *did* so survive in a different line, and became the recognised Neolithic forms. What I object to is the failing to give to the occurrence of Palæolithic forms its due significance. Unless Palæolithic forms, no matter where found, can be shown to be undoubtedly associated with actual Neolithic elaborations, they are *a priori* Palæolithic. On the assumption that Palæolithic man never existed in Ireland, there is no alternative to styling such Palæolithic forms "survivals" from Palæolithic times. But the assumption is a mere opinion that has in no sense the weight of a verification.

I have found, as has been shown, an excellent and undoubted Palæolithic weapon (of granite) in the glacial cliff of Killiney Bay, Dublin, and in the same deposit the said precursors of Neolithic forms. Palæolithic man certainly inhabited Ireland as continuously as he inhabited England and Scotland; the case is that of the insensible passage of one ancient people (Palæolithic) into the other (Neolithic), but where one ends and the other begins will never be clearly defined. There are data upon which we might trace Neolithic man into glacial times, and the same data would obviously take Palæolithic man into Neolithic times. I cannot, however, look upon a Palæolithic weapon from a glacial deposit as a possible "survival" into Neolithic times, any more than I can look upon Neolithic forms from the same deposit as of Neolithic age. We have been too narrow in our conceptions, too circumscribed by our own devisings of "types," and too certain in our definitions in matters of which we have had but a passing view.

CHAPTER XXI

Miscellanea

In searching among my numerous fabrications for certain Scottish fan-shaped specimens which I knew would duplicate the excellent Irish find (Fig. 471), and corroborate the lost Farnham and the Yorkshire boulder-clay specimen (Fig. 308), I not only found the examples referred to, but several others which have, as appears to me, so important a bearing upon what has been discussed that we cannot in justice to our present study forgo a consideration of them. And as one or two suggestive and important finds have been made while the matter of this volume has found shape, I cannot perhaps do better than add a chapter of *Miscellanea* as an appendix to the whole.

I have made a drawing of one of these Scottish fan-shaped implements (Fig. 474), the intention and work of which makes it a replica of the Killiney-Bay specimen. It is somewhat larger than that, being slightly longer in the handle, which is also reflected upward, as seen in the drawing. Though it looks in the drawing like a naturally tabular fragment, it was a wholly elaborated-out implement. Nor is it so flake-like a specimen as appears: it averages more than an inch in thickness, and at the handle end is 1½ inch through. It is a decayed quartzite from the Ayrshire coast, 1892. Other examples of this form might have been illustrated from my collection.

These forms recall the glaciated Yorkshire-coast specimen (Fig. 308). I may here point out that it would have been quite possible to illustrate a whole chapter with finds (Scottish) which, like the Yorkshire example, have been broken out from lenticular nodules (ironstone), some resembling that fine glaciated find, some being excellent anticipations of the Neolithic bronze hatchet. It was want of space alone that prevented this being done.

We have discussed "chopper" forms, some of which are of striking figure and of clever workmanship. Some are of almost gigantic build and of varied conceptions in outline, while some, and these not necessarily of more recent aspect, exhibit what we are inclined to consider our up-to-date notion of utility in handle and outline.

opposing broad back, the edges being to the right of both figures. They are all three in exactly the condition one might expect of such forms as had passed through the glacial mill. Most of my more perfect chopper specimens must, I imagine, be of post-glacial origin, but there is evidence of their actual occurrence in the boulder-clays; and some of my finds, which have commonly occurred as detached broad ends and occasionally handles, have possibly come from glacial deposits. This is a question of the greatest interest, for it seems to be a bridging over of profound periods of time by the graphic power of such a commonplace thing as a chopper, inasmuch as pre-glacial, or at the latest, inter-glacial man's view of the utility of such an implement hardly differed from what ours is to-day.

And still the wonder grew—

I had barely completed the foregoing in this appended chapter, when (in January 1908), after a big storm, I essayed a search over a good many miles of the Forth estuary shore. This hunt extended to altogether seven or eight excursions—the weather being mild and propitious; in two instances the result was deeply interesting.

There had come in from the deep sea, and lay stranded upon a great stretch of sand, a stone to which were attached straggling masses of seaweed, and upon which were bunches of barnacles. Such a newly stranded object seldom escapes inspection from myself should it come within sight. I turned it over; it was apparently too large and ungainly and "dirty" to be worth further inspection. With the seaweed and other attachments it weighed a good many pounds, and in its then condition was not an object one would care to carry. With several miles to walk, and railway as well, I did not look at it twice, but went on; I was, however, uneasy in my mind, from a sense that I had not done justice to it. So I turned back, under a strong impression that, in turning the object over, I had laid hold of a well-formed handle. It was an impression made upon and through the hand alone. I once again found and stripped it of its seaweed; it was then seen to be the most remarkable example of choppers that I have ever found.

As it was growing dark, I hid the relic in a bank, and in doing so forced it in among rough broken rock. The sequel will show how I regret having done so. Next day I brought the stone home and made a drawing of it (Fig. 477). It will at once be seen that it is a veritable chopper, with a finely sculptured-out handle, the whole being a wonderful piece of work.   It is 1 foot 10½ inches in length,

Fig. 477.

the blade 6 inches in width.   It is a magnificently. produced
(B 987)   2 x

implement—a terrible weapon or a highly efficient domestic hatchet. Its broad end is peculiar in form. It was a hatchet that would have crashed into the skull of even the mammoth, or have detached a limb from its carcass.

This specimen seems to have belonged to the age of the Great Mammalia. *It is glaciated!* If it be not striated, then the fine weapon (Figs. 88 and 89) is not glaciated; nor are some other implements glaciated which I have taken out from the actual boulder-clay in Scotland and from the Dublin glacial cliff, although they exhibit identical striation. I am the last in the world to desire to exaggerate any evidence. I am astonished at what this specimen seems to assert, viz. that it is of inter- or pre-glacial origin. I state what it implies to me.

Fig. 478.

In forcing this fine example into a crevice among rough rocks I scratched it barbarously, to my regret; but such scratches are quite different in character from the original striæ, and are easily detected.

This find is of the heavy ironstone-band. It had certainly long been embedded, and thus sheltered from the atmosphere, and I should say from water also; much of the boulder-clay is alike impermeable to air and to water. The condition of the specimen is such as to indicate that it was, before it was embedded, gently but decidedly river-rolled. As is evident in the drawing, it is in a rotten condition, but otherwise is wonderfully perfect.

Another result of this recent hunt is particularly interesting in connection with this heroic chopper and our study of glaciated chopper forms. It seems to me to be a snapped-off end of what must have been another magnificent implement, equally fine in the skill with which it was elaborated, and possibly also in its size, with the immediately preceding. Like the foregoing, it is formed from the ironstone-band, and was, as I conceive, the terminal blade end of the implement. It was of massive style, being 2 inches through at its "back"—to the left of Fig. 478 —and nearly 2 inches through where it has been snapped. It is 4 inches across the blade, which was brought to an excellent edge, and is incontrovertibly glaciated. I removed it from an outcrop of boulder-clay which I have visited many times during the past seven years, and from which I have taken (*in situ*) some few astonishingly interesting glaciated specimens. But for the suggestion of possibilities by the fine example, Fig. 477, I should hardly, I think, have ventured to describe this (Fig. 478), it being from the boulder-clay, as the point end of a fine chopper. I should have described it as the finished and intended form of a "flayer." I believe it to be what I suggest. It is becoming clear that if I fail to speak as to what is evident, the very stones will themselves cry out.

It will be noticed that in this specimen (Fig. 478) a portion has been (glacially?) fretted out from the blade. It is a break that might have resulted in *use*, but certainly not in use in its present form. Such a break could only have happened through the power lent by a handle, which, however, is missing; but that break I believe to have been the result of ice-fretting; the actual point was fretted away also.

Fig. 479 is another example from the same glacial deposit, which I obtained a year ago; this may also be the detached end of a chopper, though I think its present form was intentional. It is unquestionably an artefact, which I have placed among the flayers proper. It is also distinctly glaciated.

I have more than once been tempted to make the study of our ancient stone implements in collective petrological groups, and not, as we have done, in accordance with form. By collective petrological groups I mean groups of mainly one kind of rock from certain localities, which often exhibit a characteristic facies, "local" features,

Fig. 479.

which are highly suggestive and interesting. They may, as an
illustration, give us characters of certain more or less limited periods
of time—of peculiar fashions of those times which may have
characterised even different peoples, different peoples in different
ages, in accordance with particular forms of these ancient relics
that various localities are now yielding up. It was, as I think
from the evidence, the fashion at different times to use certain
rocks in preference to others—now it was ironstone, now quartzite,
now certain volcanic rocks, now dolomite limestone, and so on.
Such use of rocks was doubtless always more or less governed by
the prevailing petrology of localities, and by the accidental circumstance of the more free exposure of certain petrological groups. I
have been for some days selecting out of my collection, by way of
study, certain dolomite limestone forms mainly from central Scotland,
and of these the Forth estuary is the nucleus. That is, I have
brought together a representative group of dolomite limestone
fabrications, weapons, and domestic forms of all possible aspects.
The effect is most striking; so much so that it is clear they would lend
themselves to an interesting study on their own account; and perhaps
their highly suggestive attributes constitute the reason why, after
making drawings of several, I determined not to introduce them into
this present study. I have perforce omitted a good deal from this
volume that might have been written, and of this the present position
is an illustration; but this chapter of *Miscellanea* has given me an
opportunity of referring to them.

Certain members of this dolomite series have been used in
illustration of the forms we have discussed in previous chapters,
where they illuminated the common facies of the whole collection
of relics; but I would now point to certain features which belong
more to them as a dolomite group than to the whole series.

If, for instance, we take Figs. 480 to 482, which represent one
specimen, I may at once say that it is the only rock in Scotland
from which I have found this particular and characteristic form to
be made. This may be the result of the attributes of the particular
stone itself, its fracture being nearer that of flint than any other
Scottish rock. It gives conchoidal fractures with sharp edges and
lines, and these features it retains perfectly when not exposed to the
air, or to river or marine rolling, under which circumstances the
material soon loses the sharpness of lines, and except for mere outline, becomes expressionless. Bulbs-of-percussion are often seen

this in
percept
The
that w

upon this rock; there are several upon our specimen, which is fully illustrated in order to show the character and the style of its elaboration. Its whole aspect, work, and form are more suggestive of flint areas than of the usual style in Scotland.

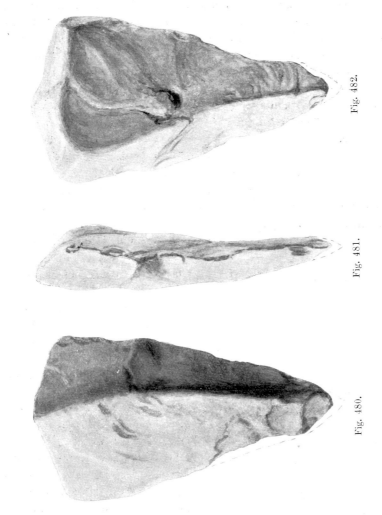

Fig. 482.

Fig. 481.

Fig. 480.

weapons
javelin-h
In F
this dolo
lithic we

If I had found only one example of this peculiar style and feature, we might look upon it as "an accident," as I have been assured by some experts that it is; but I have a series of this style and form, not to mention a large group with the same style of work, but of differing forms. I give illustrations of several others, so like

not a weapon. I myself experience a kind of disappointment in saying so; but I cannot be led by other than tangible evidence, which evidence is that but a short time before I came upon it the shore waves had broken from the broad end what must, I think, have been

Fig. 491.   Fig. 492.

a species of handle; and if so, the elaboration was either a large knife or a chopper, although the detached fragment for which I searched in vain may not have been so extensive as to mar its form as an actual weapon. I have another, a little smaller (this is $8\frac{1}{2}$ inches in length), of the same species of work. The fine *glaciated* weapon (Figs. 88 and 89) is of the same rock, and in general form is not unlike those

of the series which Figs. 480 to 490 represent; but this brings me
to a puzzling point, viz. that while that specimen and some others
of the same material are highly glaciated, as a rule these Forth area
dolomite limestone objects give no evidence and little suggestion
of glacial association. Most of them must, I think, be post-glacial,
although many of those from the Dublin glacial deposit are of this
or an allied limestone rock.

This dolomite group comprises a considerable variety of fabrications: hatchets of varying form; javelin-heads of excellent style,
some so small as to suggest arrows; and domestic implements—
mullers, choppers, flayers, knives, of which I could have given a
large series of illustrations. Some are suggestive of Neolithic forms;
but inasmuch as forms equally Neolithic in aspect occur in boulder-clay
and in the Palæolithic gravels of England, nothing as to age is exemplified thereby. Certain of these
dolomite forms are peculiar, spoon-
like and otherwise, suggesting
touches of a real domestic civilisation. I do not suggest the use of
" spoons," but am pointing to the

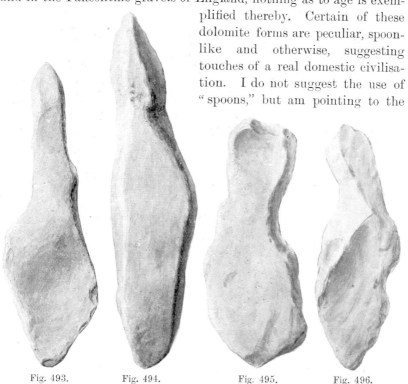

Fig. 493.   Fig. 494.   Fig. 495.   Fig. 496.

great variety of relics. As I have drawn specimens of these peculiar
objects, I here utilise them (Figs. 493 and 494), with their counterparts
from the English gravels, of course in flint (Figs. 495 and 496).

Counterparts of some of these Forth dolomite forms occur, as we

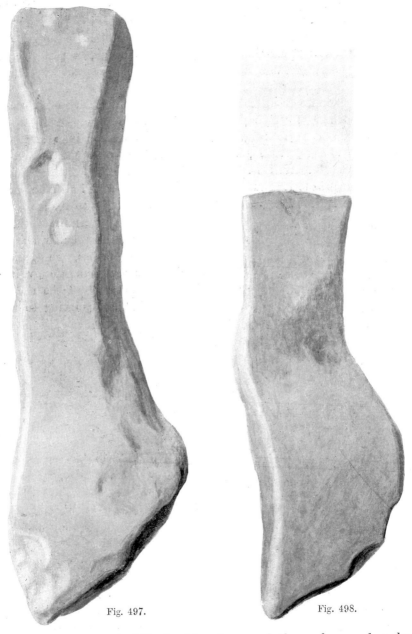

Fig. 497.   Fig. 498.

have seen, in the Dublin boulder-clay; and those also are largely formed of this characteristic limestone rock. This dolomite limestone must have been a favourite material in the elaboration of implements for illimitable ages.

As an illustration of the great range of form through which these limestone implements pass I have made drawings of two, which are duplicates of each other, and are, so far as my experience goes, unique

Fig. 499.   Fig. 500.

as to form. They are large specimens, the perfect one being 14 inches in length, and they could, I imagine, have been nothing else than a species of club. Their aspect suggests what effective weapons they must have been (Figs. 497 and 498).

A fine specimen of the skill of the ancient fabricator in dolomite limestone is shown in Figs. 499 and 500. Yet, when wet and lying among other stones upon the shore, it had so much the aspect of a naturally flaky, accidental fragment, that I, having turned it over with my foot, concluded it to be such ; the whole of the figure (499) presents a natural (cleavage) surface. But the work upon the " back " (to the right of Fig. 499) attracted notice, and that prevented the loss of so fine a specimen. That work is characteristically artificial. So is that of the whole of its other face (Fig. 500), a double bulb-of-percussion being perceptible to the left, midway between the handle and the point. The handle, though only the result of portions being broken out laterally, was very skilfully produced; indeed the whole form is fine. It was a knife or flayer, possibly both in turn.

Fig. 501 is interesting as having occurred at the same spot, though at another time, as the foregoing. They were both brought in from the deep sea. The handle in this is identical with Fig. 499 in form and in the manner in which it was produced. It was, I should say, a knife of unusual style, but still in work and intention distinctly related to Fig. 499. I might have given drawings of several other dolomite knives, more of the character of what we should style knifeblades, mainly small—from 2 to 3 or 4 inches in length, had space permitted. I have made drawings of two further

Fig. 501.

specimens, both of which might have been knives, while one of them may have been an effective chopper :—

Fig. 502 is a large rugged production, so rugged in style that among other stones it had apparently no more design or intention about it than a lump in our coal-scuttle; but I have learned to look twice at most stones upon any seashore, and the second look at this detected the intention of its form. In the drawing it will be clear to the reader that there is evidence of bold but equally clever flaking upon the side of the implement shown; while the handle and the dark facet to the right, which was bevelled to an excellent edge, with the general figure, to which I have appended tentatively a restored point end, form distinct evidences of intention.

If this implement be compared with the fine Egyptian knife or chopper (Fig. 228), it will be seen that the general design is the same, while the style of the work is very different. The Egyptian knife is of flint, and therein probably lies the difference in the expression of the work. As I have already pointed out, the dolomite lime-stone fabricator in Scotland felt at full liberty to elaborate with a bold free hand; the flint-worker had probably no material to be extravagant with, hence the dilettante work, which natur-ally conduced to better form, as well as more apparent design. Yet when done, the two were equally effective for their intended purposes. I there leave the argument.

I should, however, like to point to what seems to me another similarity in the characteristics of these dolomite things with the Egyptian forms. The common figure of the dolomite haches shown in the earlier part of this chapter is that of a triangle. The Egyptian weapons which accompany the knife-like tools of which Fig. 228 is a fine specimen, are very definitely triangular (Fig. 230). There is the further re-semblance in these Scottish things in their far more slender and thinner build than in the ordinary Palæolith, such slender form being also characteristic of those from Egypt; but there is the same difference in the style of the work of either, as in the case of the knife forms. As I believe I have sug-gested, these Egyptian haches may have been used at their broad ends, in which

Fig. 502.

case they would have been fine transitional forms, *i.e.* Palæo-Neo haches; it is an interesting question.

The other dolomite implement (Fig. 503) is decidedly a knife, *with* a handle and a notch or hold for the thumb. I need not more particularly describe it beyond stating that it is very fresh-looking, as are many dolomite examples from beneath the waves. This knife is 7 inches; Fig. 501 is, with the suggested restoration of the point, over 14, and the Egyptian knife 11 inches in length.

Figs. 504 to 507, which I have inserted with the foregoing knives, will convey an idea of what I mean by javelin or arrow heads. They are not nearly so like Neolithic as they are counterparts of javelin-heads and arrow-tips which I have found in the English and French Palæolithic gravels. That of Fig. 504, with side view, Fig. 505, is a beautiful specimen both in form and the skill with which it was flaked out. This was the characteristic method of the dolomite limestone worker, as it was in

Fig. 503.

the production of similar examples in the Palæolithic (flint) gravels, as against the laborious dilettanteism of Neolithic times. The elegance and the effectiveness of this (Fig. 504) was never surpassed in the more laboriously produced implements. Fig. 506 is another

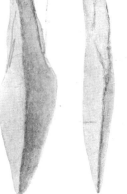

Fig. 504.   Fig. 505.   Fig. 506.   Fig. 507.

beautiful prod   on; both these last are from the Forth area.

In Fig. 507   ave attempted to reproduce the arrow-head referred to in the previous chapter as having been found *in situ* in the boulder-clay cliff of Killiney Bay, Dublin. It was highly rolled and battered before it found its last resting-place, but it still gives its whilom form and its intention. It is an excellent diamond in section, and is an exact duplicate of a number of finds from the English Palæolithic flints and also from Scotland. The projection from the line of the figure (Fig. 507) is a part of the cement-like matrix of Killiney Bay cliff.

Two knife forms of a different rock—ironstone—may here be suitably described. These (Figs. 508 and 509) were found together (most oddly) among seaweed after a storm, some years ago, a mile or two west of North Berwick. They are striking objects with deflected handles, which strongly recall the Egyptian examples before referred to. They are rotten, have lost their original surface by decomposition, and one is reduced in length. Yet they clearly indicate what they once were.

The *quartzite* series seems also to possess chopper forms *sui generis*, club-like weapons and

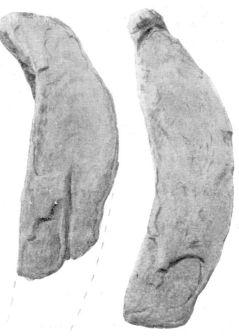

Fig. 508.   Fig. 509.

Palæolithic haches of heroic build, and they appear to indicate a peculiar time or fashion in the choice of material and style of elaboration. This is only what I judge should be looked for in this ancient man's relics. While we in the British Isles in two thousand years have passed through constant change in the form and use of weapons, from the polished stone axe and flint-tipped arrows to the now complicated firearms, who can imagine what changes of peoples, what fads and fashions and social evolutions fo   d each other during the well-nigh immeasurable periods o neir migratory movements in north-western Europe?

I have lately come upon a magnificent illustration of the capacity of the ancient quartzite fabricators. For actual skill in stone fracture I think I possess no illustration equal to it. It was, I believe, a wholly sculptured-out implement, a sword-like club almost suggestive of a Roman broad-blade. It might have been intended as a double-edged chopper for the cutting up of a large carcass, for which purpose nothing in stone could have been more serviceable. It is impossible to state definitely its intended purpose, but that does not detract from its fine features as a fabrication. I have made drawings of it (Figs. 510 and 511), giving a flat and an edgewise view. Here will be seen the marvellous power exerted over the intensely hard though brittle crystalline quartzite. It is now rotten and of a sandstone aspect. Its form is elegant, that of a willow-leaf, and gives a depressed diamond in section; the handle is deflected, doubtless for the purpose of the hand-grasp, which is perfect. It is 1 foot 5 inches in length, weighs a good many pounds, and was, if used in the hunting field, probably carried over the shoulder. With such a weapon, which a strong arm could wield with terrific force, a lion or bear or buffalo would have had a poor chance against a brave man; and he who made such implements was not only a man of fine physique, but also a daring hunter.

The "occurrence" of this relic is a puzzle. Although I found it on the shore of the Forth estuary, its position suggested that it was not a marine-derived specimen. Most of the estuary shore stones are washed in from the sea-floor; but some are derived from the breaking up of shore outcropping rocks or beds; while some are derived from the denudation of boulder-clay which, as I have said, dips down into the sea in many places in this area. Many from the deep sea are also certainly from the boulder-clay. Where it is not prevented by the use of blocks of stone or stone structures the sea is in places eating out shelves from the said boulder-clay; and these shelves may be traced along the Forth shore lands at several higher levels, pointing to ancient corresponding marine action. Our present specimen was found in the clay of such a shelf in the littoral zone not twenty feet from the line of a protective massive stone wall. That same boulder-clay shelf was being fashioned by denudation down to the present time, i.e. till the protecting wall was built. The implement was so far buried in the clay that only about one-third of its surface was seen, and I had some difficulty in ex-tracting it; and this difficulty would have been tenfold greater had

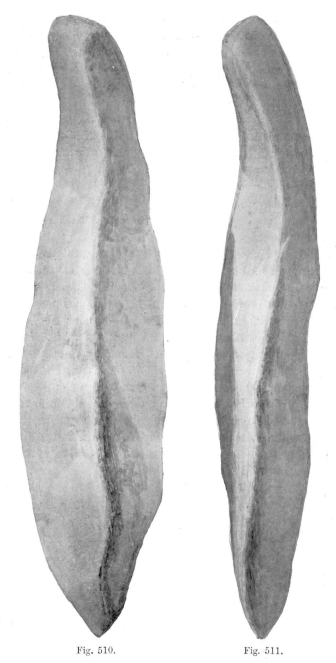

Fig. 510.   Fig. 511.

not its under-surface been so decayed that it left a distinct layer of itself in the clay and so had no hold. It must have been thus embedded an incalculable time in that clay—probably boulder-clay, whose present surface at that spot cannot, I think, have been exposed a great many years. Were it a less refined elaboration, and in a less perfect condition, I should have less hesitation in definitely associating it with the glacial deposit. But if such a form with so delicately designed a handle passed through a glaciation without a sign of such ordeal it seems to me to be well-nigh a miracle. Unless a stone is actually glaciated I have never claimed that any clay below high-water mark is necessarily boulder-clay except from other evidence, even though one may be morally certain about it; and in this instance I should prefer simply to call it a shore specimen. But what was not effected by possible glaciers, or other destructive agents, I had myself the misfortune to achieve. In making the drawings I dropped the implement end-wise, point downward; in its farther fall the handle so came into contact with one of my study-floor specimens as to break at about 3 inches from its end.

I have found various club-like objects, amongst which the immediately preceding might perhaps be included. In Fig. 512 and side view, Fig. 513, we have what I imagine was a club and nothing more. It is well-shaped as such, from a species of trap-rock. It is a shore specimen (Clyde), is in excellent condition, and it seems to indicate something which may be (for once) a piece of pure imagination, but it may also be evidence of a curious prehistoric event. In both drawings two unusual indentations are indicated in the surface of the broad end of the presumed weapon. These indentations seem to me possibly to indicate an encounter, say, with a man whose weapon was a pointed Palæolithic battle-axe. These scars are exactly what might have resulted from the clash of the two implements.

One of the most interesting phases of negative evidence, and one which has been consistently maintained throughout the whole forty-odd years of this investigation, is the entire absence of pottery among the relics of which this volume treats. I have never in any deposit in Britain, nor in association with the Scottish relics which come in from the sea-floor, nor even in a river-bed, found a piece of pottery that could be in any way associated with them. Such potsherds as I have occasionally found in river-beds or upon the shore have all been of comparatively modern aspect.

And this is the more remarkable, as the relics are so washed ashore in places as to suggest former submarine kitchen-middens or

repositories of relics which mark the prehistoric stations of these
ancient men; they even occur in the boulder-clay in such a way as
to suggest glacial invasions of Palæolithic refuse-heaps—ice-invaded

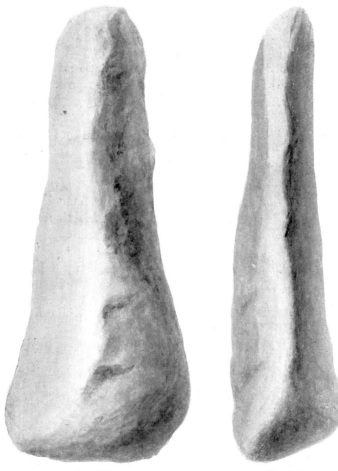

Fig. 512.   Fig. 513.

camps of the ancient fabricators. The fact remains that nothing
like pottery occurs with these relics.

Yet there is indication of the anticipation of pots and pans,
which we must just touch upon. In my boyish hunts among the
gravels of East Anglia, I was interested in the occurrence of natural
cups or pots, cavities in flint, from which what were once organic
forms (sponges?) had decayed out. I often wondered whether ancient

man ever had made use of them; beyond this question I never got, seeing that I left the flint area while the problem was being propounded. But several years ago my friend Mr. W. M. Newton, of Dartford, Kent, sent me a photo of about forty such hollow spheres, and he assured me that he often found that their openings or mouths had been artificially enlarged. In my later visits to the English flint areas I carefully sought out such objects, and now find that they had certainly been artificially treated, that some had actually been broken out from masses, so as to possess something very much approaching handles.

I have made drawings of four of these (Figs. 514 to 517), every one of which gives distinct evidence of artificial treatment of some sort. Fig. 514 is a hollow hemisphere, whose greatest diameter is $4\frac{1}{2}$ inches; it is therefore a fair-sized cup. Its mouth has, I believe, been greatly enlarged, but there is no decided evidence of this; there is, however, evidence that the edges of the cup have been artificially smoothed. It suggests to me that the cup was used much as the rubbing-stones were used in some domestic operation; it might of course have been deliberately smoothed with the intention of perfecting the cup itself. In any case it has certainly been artificially treated, and that is deeply interesting.

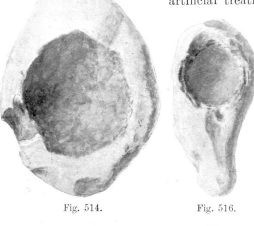

Fig. 514.

Fig. 516.

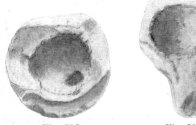

Fig. 515.

Fig. 517.

In Fig. 515, which is much smaller, its greatest diameter being $2\frac{1}{4}$ inches, we have evidence of the edges of the cup having been very skilfully flaked—four flakings completely encircling the cavity, the naturally jagged edges of which were rendered fairly smooth thereby, while the mouth was thus enlarged. That elaboration is evident in the drawing.

In Figs. 516 and 517 we have two actually "handled" specimens. The natural cavities have been so broken out from probably cumbersome nodules as now to possess handles. Among other hints, they actually suggest Roman lamps in form. And now, while my reader may smile at this, I propound the possibility of the man who made the weapons and domestic implements which we have discussed, having arrived at the achievement of a domestic light by the filling of such cavities with fat and a twist of moss. If this man knew the use of fire, he could not fail to know the effect of fat in the fire. All are from Croydon and Mitcham pits.

While I have not found any of these natural pots and pans among the Scottish relics, I have found artificial ones—not pottery, but pot-like cavities in stones, associated with these other relics. One or two I have thought may have been naturally produced, "pot-holes" broken out from the rocks in some river's course. I have found about half a dozen of these altogether, one of which I left upon a shore and never found again. One I illustrate in Fig. 518. It is a largish stone (over 6½ inches in its longest diameter), which has been highly marine-rolled, since it was either broken out from some stream's course, or deliberately ground or hammered out by the use of another stone. These Scottish "cups," associated as they are with relics that correspond so wonderfully with those of the flint gravels in which the natural cups occur, are exceedingly interesting, as being

Fig. 518.

possibly and even probably attempts to duplicate them. It is only of late years that I have recognised the existence of these pot-stones in

Scotland.   I have, however, doubtless unwittingly overlooked many
a similar relic, which some successor in this research will ere long
make more clear.   I can have hardly touched upon the wonderful
story ; resume it, you who have the years before you.

As a tail-piece, let me insert a drawing of the last Palæolithic axe
which has come to my hand (Fig. 519).   It is a shore specimen (1907)
of the Fife coast, of almost exquisite form, and in perfect preservation,
except that it was once upon a time highly (marine ?) rolled, and has
since become moulded and finely honeycombed beneath the waves ;
it is of a trappean rock.   In its fine conception, which is most cleverly
realised, it speaks volumes to me, volumes to which such a relic
unerringly points, and which yet remain to be opened and read.
Such a relic as this ought to be a lodestone strong enough to draw
our minds back to the remote ages that witnessed the rise and slow
evolution of man from rude beginnings to his present high position
as the "noblest work of God."

Fig. 519.

Appendix

NOTE I

"The Great Mammalia" in Scotland

IT became, some thirty years since, a question of the greatest interest to me as to whether representative remains of the "Great Mammalia" had been found in Scotland or no. I had then, as I conceived, found relics of Palæolithic man in Scotland. I had from certain "cave" and other data from England and the Continent associated that ancient man with the period of the "great," and now quasi-extinct, mammals of the Pliocene and Pleistocene epochs.

In order to satisfy myself on that head I made, so far as I could, an exhaustive hunt for records of finds of any remains of the great mammals north of the Border. The result was, so far as my memory serves me, distinct and undoubted records of such finds in at least six different localities. Five of these were elephant remains, generally described as of the *Mammoth*. There was also record of at least one rhinoceros, probably of more than one.

My notes of that inquiry of long ago ended in smoke, inasmuch as my papers having been found handy by a domestic for lighting fires, a large accumulation disappeared from mortal ken. In 1905 I was anxious to re-obtain information regarding the great mammals in relation to Scotland, and had made inquiries of certain scientists, whose positions in museums and otherwise one would have imagined a guarantee to such information; but no records seem anywhere to have been kept of the occurrence of mammal remains. While I was questioning the possibility of another hunt for records—a dreaded prospect, since my lost results had been obtained by wading through the *Statistical Account*, the *Edin. Phil. Journal*, *Journal of Science and Art*, *The Great Ice Age*, and similar works—an article upon "The Mammoth" appeared in the *Scotsman* (November 7, 1905), and this suggested a means of obtaining information on this head. The writer of the said article stated that, so far as he was aware, a relic of the mammoth had only once been found in Scotland (a tusk), and that was in so well-preserved a condition that an ivory-turner transformed it into billiard balls. According to this authority there was, therefore, by implication, no known relic of the mammoth in Scotland.

The *Scotsman* kindly inserted a letter from myself, in which I asked for information as to Scottish discoveries of relics of the mammoth

359

through its columns, or directly to myself. The result was that at least seventeen different finds of elephant remains are mentioned, and possibly twenty or so. Some accounts are mere memories or " traditions." Some are of actual events, with tangible data and place. Some are obscured by want of locality, etc.

In reply to my letter I received an anonymous post-card from " Elgin," on which was the definite statement that " there is a mammoth's tusk in the Anatomical Museum, University Buildings, head of Middle Meadow Walk [Edinburgh]. It was found in Forth Valley in digging a canal." As this could not be that which was converted into billiard balls, and which was also said to have been found in the Forth Valley, that is clearly two individual finds.

Following upon that was a surprising and valuable letter to the *Scotsman* (November 13, 1905) from Mr. Ludovic M'L. Mann, part of whose letter I quote *in extenso* : " As it does not seem to be generally known, I venture to mention the fact that in the parish of Kilmaurs, Ayrshire, in the old quarry at Woodhill, half a mile east of Crosshouse Station, the remains of at least eight mammoths have been discovered. All the remains were underneath thick boulder-drift. It is therefore clear that the mammoth was present in the area now called Scotland during one of the mild intervals of the great Glacial Period. While your correspondent laments that the Forth Valley ivory was turned into billiard balls, it is a matter for congratulation that much of the Kilmaurs ivory is still intact, as when found, and is in safe keeping in Scotland. As man was undoubtedly contemporary with the mammoth in England, it is not unreasonable to believe that when the mammoth was roaming over the plains of Midland Scotland, Palæolithic man was then present there also."

Kilmaurs and Kilmarnock were among the localities in my long-lost notes ; but, irrespective of this corroboration, Mr. L. M'L. Mann is a well-known enthusiast and authority in such matters of research. His state-ment, though it is the startling one of *eight* additional individual elephant discoveries, is thoroughly trustworthy, and thus we have *ten* different elephant finds definitely recorded.

Among my own books I have just turned to the following in Smith's (Jordanhill) *Newer Pliocene Geology*, p. 10: " Mr. Bald . . . found the tusk of an elephant in the excavation of the Union Canal ; but, unwilling to draw an important inference from a solitary fact, he supposed it might have been placed in the situation in which it was found [in the ' till ' or boulder-clay] from some accidental cause. Since that time, however, elephants' bones and tusks have been found near Kilmarnock, and at Kilmaurs in Ayrshire. I am assured by Dr. Scouler of the Royal Society of Dublin, and Dr. Couper of the University of Glasgow [predecessor in the Chair of the late Professor John Young], who visited these localities, that in both instances they were embedded in the *till*. At Kilmaurs they were associated with sea-shells."

The following occur as footnotes upon p. 42, *Newer Pliocene Geology* : " The elephant has been found in the *till* on the line of the Union Canal,

circumstances, the almost drast
give me a sense of and a tone c
And yet, as all through this volt
I have trusted to what Nature
be now: I am asserting only
writing of this world's physical
is startling to us it can only be

Five weeks' further search
only corroborated the results o
this year (1908) are still mor
glacial man and his attainment:
researches show, fully on a p
relics are the one main argum(
now brief, to my statements.

I have argued, for which I
that the fine "chopper" and o
domestic (?) forms which I hav
freely found are actually trace
to the glacial deposits; that is,
they at least have representa
which *are* glacial. I have f(
wonderful proof of this in thi
last Irish search. In the Kil
Bay Cliff—in the road-cuttin;
cavations before referred to, a:
the materal of which I founc
fine granite hache—I have 1
a chopper form of excellent d
and work *with a well-formed h*
This specimen readily verifi
self as to its "occurrence," b
facts of its being fretted
glaciated, and by the accreti
lime which newly obtained :
from the cliff usually show
which it clearly possesses.
an excellent specimen, 8 inc
length by $4\frac{1}{4}$, with a broad
and even now a good cutting
although it has been gl.
fretted, with which a (
could be cut up to-day. 1
made a drawing of it (Fig
which must suffice as tc
specimen.

I further found a magi
chopper blade of limeston
upon the shore (Killiney

Wern. Mem., vol. iv. p. 58; in the parish of Kilsyth, *Stat. Account*, vol. xxviii.
p. 233; at Kilmarnock, the remains of which are preserved in the
Andersonian Museum, Glasgow; and at Kilmaurs, associated with sea-
shells, and with the horns of the deer and fallow-deer, all apparently of
extinct species—they are preserved in the Hunterian Museum. Notices
of the rhinoceros in Scotland will be found in the *Wern. Mem.*, vol. iv.
p. 582, and vol. v. p. 573. Additional notices will be found in the
controversy between Drs. Fleming and Buckland respecting the animals
extirpated by man or destroyed by the deluge, *Edin. Phil. Journal*,
vols. xi. and xii. There is a head and horns of the elk from a marl-pit
in Perthshire preserved in the Hunterian Museum."

In the above we have not only further evidence of the occurrence of
elephant remains, but of other animals which were part and parcel of the
said "Great Mammalia." Let us keep to our text of the occurrence
of the Elephantidæ, the relics of other animals being accepted as
corroborations.

If we accept Mr. Bald's elephant tusk as possibly that in the
University Museum, Edinburgh, and do not count it again, we have still
to add the Kilmarnock and Kilsyth finds, which bring up the number of
definitely asserted individual elephant relics to *twelve*.

While the correspondence was going on in the *Scotsman* (1905),
Mr. Charles H. Alston reminded me, per letter, of a work by his brother,
Edward R. Alston, F.L.S., F.G.S., *The Fauna of Scotland (Mammalia)* (1880),
from which the following (p. 33) was sent as an extract: "*Elephas
PRIMIGENIUS* (Blumenbach), fossil elephant or mammoth.— Remains
of the mammoth have been found in Scotland, both under and in the
boulder-clay, the reindeer being the only other Scottish mammal whose
bones have yet been found in deposits of such antiquity. A tusk was
found between Edinburgh and Falkirk, and bones near Kilmaurs (Bald,
Mem. Wern. Soc. vol. iv. pp. 58-64), near Airdrie (Craig, *P. Geol. Soc. Glasg.*,
vol. iii. p. 415), and at Cliftonhall [on the Almond, near Edinburgh] (*Cat.
Western Scot. Fossils*, p. 152), and a molar tooth, now in the Hunterian
Museum of the University of Glasgow, near Bishopbriggs (Bryce, *Geol.
Arran and Clydesdale*). Besides these, Professor Boyd Dawkins informs
me that there are remains from Caithness-shire in the Kelvingrove
Museum in Glasgow; and Mr. J. Kirsop tells me that he has a well-
preserved molar found at Baillieston, near Glasgow."

This enlarges our list of occurrences, allowing again that between
Edinburgh and Falkirk to be Mr. Bald's, by no fewer than five localities,
viz. Airdrie, Cliftonhall, Bishopbriggs (of which these three were in my
lost list), Caithness-shire, and Baillieston. Thus seventeen occurrences
are tangibly verified.

But there are other references or traditions of elephant discoveries in
Scotland. My friend the Rev. A. T. Wilson, North Queensferry, wrote
to the effect that he remembered reading somewhere that in the digging
of the Forth and Clyde Canal two teeth of an elephant were found; and
that he also had an impression of similar teeth having been dredged up
somewhere on the East Coast. I have myself impressions of having read

of similar discoveri
of the find of an e
eight or nine years
eighteen different
with the indefinite
Mr. Milne-Hoi
tusk occurred nea
The occurrenc
Cervus megaceros ;
from Perthshire,
borative interest.
reindeer) was fou
specimen, in the I
tion, being worn
polished, ice-scrat
ice-worn stones o
Messrs. John Y(
p. 310).
The above ic
by the same Mr.
Hunterian Muse(
I had satisfie
remains of the Gi
late reinvestigat
was that of so fa
Thirty years ag
malian finds nor
myself as ocean
no doubt that :
Scotland, and n(
health and oppe
Continent and in
there human re
dream has been
Great Mammali
Scotland.

It is not wit
the closing line
nothing import
the momentou

These are instances where *occurrence* was everything and form of minor consequence, for they were all collected from this or that "pre-historic" midden, the "midden" being alone the voucher of their human origin and intention. On seashore or in ancient deposit, much more definite and illustrative examples are not only not seen, but, as I know from repeated experience in Scotland, are, if adduced, objected to as natural fragments.

One or two elaborations which I have very recently for the first time observed in that Museum, are, I think, of special interest; and these are forms which are best illustrated by the extraordinary boulder-clay find by Mr. Cotsworth on the Yorkshire coast-line (see Figs. 308 and 309, foregoing). One of these, somewhat more harpoon-like in form, is as large as the Yorkshire specimen—about 10 inches across, with the same species of handle—an almost perfect replica. This example is of a highly decayed coarse-grained basalt, or allied rock. A similar specimen alongside the foregoing suggests its having been fabricated from a once semi-polished stone; but I imagine it possible that it was sculptured out from a large surface-flake that was struck from a highly rolled, *i.e.* naturally semi-polished boulder of a compact "trap." No *occurrence* of these is given—they may be from Orkney, but I did not make that out definitely. They are described as "spade-like implements deposited by Sir H. Mitchell."

NOTE IV

"Flayer" and "Chopper" Forms from the English Gravels

It was deeply interesting to myself to have found in my visit this year (1908) to the National Museum, Dublin, several collections of Palæolithic implements which were not, I believe, in evidence there last year. One of these is a collection of typical English flint haches with this ticket— "Palæolithic implements from the river-drift gravels at Bedford, England, collected from the workmen in the gravel-pits at Biddenham and Kempston. Presented by W. G. Bligh, Esq." There were also other groups of English "river-drift" examples, all of which, with those of the above collection, were the characteristic weapons, or were presumed to be such.

But several features of these collections, *i.e.* features of certain of the specimens, were of peculiar interest from a comparative Scottish, and I may now add Irish, point of view. To one of these features I ought to point, inasmuch as it responds to and corroborates what I have already asserted from my own investigations in the English gravels. Not only are some of these presumed-to-be "haches" of our discussed "flayer" and "chopper-blade" forms, but several are distinctly chopper-blades minus a whilom handle, *i.e.* are chopper-blade ends broken off.

This is particularly interesting, since it parallels an error which I have in the preceding chapters confessed to have myself fallen into in my early finds of the Scottish fabrications. I collected some few specimens, years ago, as Palæo *haches*, which I now recognise as portions of whilom choppers, many more perfect examples of which I have since found that show what the broken portions are, but which the "collector" in England was never likely to see, inasmuch (it being clearly indicated by the descriptive ticket) as the "men in the pits" alone had the deciding of what was and was not representative of Palæolithic man.

I made drawings of several of these in my note-book, hoping to have given outline sketches of the same here; but that is not now possible: I will just refer to them.

Two of the flayer or chopper blade-like forms I sketched from the Biddenham and Kempston group—one of which is so chopper-like that its presumed operating end was never brought to anything approaching a point, while there is an excellent flaying or chopping lateral edge, and an equally apparent opposing hand-grasp.

Another, undoubtedly a chopper, and evidently minus the handle, is from the "Wye Valley, Farnham," where I last year (1907) found an excellent example of a chopper with a handle (see Fig. 297). But this present item was (in its perfect condition) of better form and of superior workmanship.

Another example is thoroughly, in form and style of elaboration, though it is of flint, representative of an extensive series of elaborations from Scotland and several from Ireland; and that is a broken-off blade, broken nearer the handle end.

Alongside the Scottish forms it would at once be apparent that these particular examples of English relics are replicas of many of the Scottish series, and are what I assert of them, viz. replicas of Scottish and now Irish domestic forms. The occurrence of these corroborative specimens in the English flint collections is most interesting when viewed from the aspect of the contents of this work.

NOTE V

"Tomahawks" *versus* "Domestic Forms"

Some two years ago (1906) Mr. James Cross, F.G.S., deposited an interesting collection of flints in the Museum, Chambers Street, Edinburgh, which I had the pleasure of inspecting. There are in the collection some finely shaped "orthodox" implements of elongated cone figure, with sharp and prolonged points and of excellent surface-flake workmanship. These are weapons proper, and if mounted, as I imagine they were, were highly effective for offence or defence. But the great interest of the every item. Here is, among other African explorers, one whose pre-conceived and personal views stand for nought in the presence of "form" and "elaboration", and "occurrence." These are with him, as they should be, the keys that will alone unlock the record of the wonderful past of our humanity. It is a delightfully refreshing record of ob-servation, because of this seeking at Nature's hands of what alone is evidential. One or two other features must be noticed.

1. On opening the volume my eyes lighted upon a plate of un-questionably *Eolithic* forms: forms so like those of the Kent plateau areas that they immediately brought to my mind the late Sir Joseph Prestwich and his efforts to show the verity as fabrications of Mr. B. Harrison's examples. Mr. Johnson gives several series of these Eoliths, in which he clearly exemplifies in my opinion a human intention and human work. He believes, as I do myself, that the Eolithic forms, inane though they be, with often a helpless kind of elaboration, are the natural and to-be-expected precursors of better form and enhanced workmanship. Some of his examples are undeniable as to a human origin, as he says: "It is incredible that a long tapering point [which some of his exhibit] could be hacked out by blind agencies" (p. 8). I add that it is in-conceivable. His evidence as to the Eoliths alone makes his volume of the greatest value.

2. It is doubly interesting to myself to find that Mr. Johnson has observed and made special note of the occurrence of the "Palæo-Neo" forms associated with undoubted Palæolithic haches, and which he unhesitatingly styles *Palæolithic*. He thus refers to them: "Associated with these implements [Palæo haches] which, though possessing the characteristic Palæolithic style and quality of workmanship, are of a type that is at least rare in, if not quite absent from, the typical assemblage [*i.e.* the orthodox collections]. They have been termed chisel-edged implements, and are true axe-heads. They present a great deal of variability, but two varieties stand out very prominently: namely (1) a form consisting of a broad rectangular blade, like that of the ordinary modern axe used for tree-felling; and (2) a form with a narrow blade and rounded top, similar to the common and well-known Neolithic type" (pp. 12 and 13).

The above quotation reads like and might be a description by myself of common Palæolithic forms from Scotland and Ireland. It is remark-able and corroborative of one of the most marked facies of the relics as they have come to my hand in the British Isles—most remarkable that the whole group of ancient relics as at present revealed, some 4000 miles south of Britain, should find a perfect reflection in the relics of this northern area. There are the barbarous and rough Palæolithic forms; there are the refined in form and work in the almond-shaped haches; there are, running through all the Palæolithic group, the forms which show the unbroken transition from Palæolithic into Neolithic times; in a word, that show that no such thing as an actual hiatus between any sets of people ever existed, as the universality of these *Palæo-Neo* forms clearly show—they originated in so remote a past that the whole world of humanity has possessed them in all its recorded history, so far at least as that history is shown to us by tangible evidence. There is no actual isolation of Palæo and Neo peoples one from the other.

It is remarkable that Mr. Johnson not only records finds of that ancient man's hatchet-shaped palæoliths, but the long and slender pseudo-Neolithic forms with the "*rounded* narrower end"—the characteristic feature of many from Scotland and Ireland, and which, if not hitherto denominated "*natural* forms," are described as Neolithic and as "ready for the grinding," and yet are, even in North Britain and Ireland and in southern England, common in ancient and even glacial and pre-glacial deposits. The whole world of humanity is at least akin in this one aspect of common forms and common methods of elaboration. Mr. Johnson has not apparently observed the " muller " forms nor any definitely "handled" implements. These, of a certainty, will be found associated with the already recognised forms in Africa as soon as they are looked for.

It is interesting to find quite a number of the names of explorers in this field of research in South Africa in Mr. Johnson's volume. I noticed those of Mr. Lamplugh, Mr. Balfour, Mr. Fielden, Mr. Mennell, Mr. Maciver, Mr. Rickard, Professor Young, and Mr. Cottell ; possibly I have missed other names.

NOTE VII

"Disc"-Stones

" Disc "-stones are recognised " pre-historic " relics even in Scotland. They have been found associated with the more modern man's relics—Neolithic, pre-historic, historic—in graves, in kitchen-middens, in caves, in and about ancient stone structures, in the soils. But I am not aware that they have ever been associated with a more ancient than Neolithic man. I have never heard nor seen that they have been recognised as occurring in a geologically ancient deposit.

That I had found several such elaborated and intentional disc-stones over thirty years ago, and a fine one in particular in the ancient delta-deposit at Forteviot (Scotland), had well-nigh passed from my mind, when, among the abnormally rich congeries of relics which in and about Killiney Bay (Ireland) presented itself to me in 1907 and 1908, I found exceptionally fine examples. I was then reminded of many similar items which I had for over thirty years seen upon seashore or in river-bed, and had failed to appraise at their full evidential value. From my Irish experience I am now aware of having in a sense wilfully discarded what would doubtless have been a fine and incontrovertible factor in the evidence of the more ancient man's being. The discovery of disc-stones in County Dublin is so pronounced both in the *facies* of the stones themselves